GOLD MINING IN THE 1980's

THE COMPLETE BOOK OF

MODERN PROCEDURE

by

DAVE MCCRACKEN

Cover artwork done by Floyd York of GRAPHICTECH WEST
Photos of Equipment courtesy of KEENE INDUSTRIES.
All other photos by author unless otherwise marked.
Technical artwork done by Leanne Lockhart McKay.
Gold Mining scenes by Jack A. McKay, Jr.
Copyright ©1982 David C. McCracken.
Copyright ©1985 David C. McCracken.

PUBLISHED BY   **KEENE INDUSTRIES**
                 9330 Corbin Avenue
                 Northridge, California 91324

                 (818) 993-0411

                 First Printing 1982
                 2nd Printing 1985

PRINTED AND BOUND IN THE UNITED STATES OF AMERICA.

ACKNOWLEDGMENTS

Individual acknowledgments are due to Joe Gibson, and to James Adams — who took the time away from their own special projects and helped me a great deal with this book. Both of them are experienced old timers in gold mining and their help has been very much appreciated. Another acknowledgment is due to Sam Davis — known as "The Pro" amongst some of the best miners in the business. Old Sam has been my greatest gold mining inspiration, and that's not likely to ever change. I am also grateful to Shelly Bosch, who has done a lot to help me get my books into final form, and to Alford and Frances Zoller — who have helped me more than they will ever know.

And finally, a special thanks is given to Mr. L. Ron Hubbard — as without his beautiful works in the field of the humanities, this book would probably never have been.

To Those Gold Miners — Past
Present and Future, Who Put
Their Hearts Into It.

TABLE OF CONTENTS

INTRODUCTION

ECONOMICS

GOLD is a medium of exchange which throughout the entirety of recorded history has maintained — or increased it's own trading value.

In a large civilization it is necessary to have some sort of exchange medium, because while it's nice to be able to trade three loaves of bread for a sack of potatoes, bartering becomes inefficient as a total means of exchange in a modern world. Without some kind of medium, the advancements of civilization would have been tremendously slowed — or might never have occurred at all. It takes a lot of time to haul your products all over the place in order to trade a small portion of them to each person who has something you need. In todays world you could spend more time running around trading your products, than in actually producing them. And what about the guy who makes electronic thigamageeks? Perhaps there are only two or three other parties on the entire planet who need such things. So it's necessary for them to be able to give him something of value, which he can then re-exchange for the things that he needs in order to get on with life.

Since the earliest days of civilization, gold has been considered to be valuable and so has been used as such a medium. Farmer Jones had a crop of corn. Some of the local people would come and trade gold for some of his corn. He needed a cow and so traded some of his gold to a cattle rancher for one. The cattle rancher needed wire to keep his stock on the range, so he took some of his gold over to the nearest trading post and traded for wire, and so, on it went.

It doesn't really matter why gold is considered valuable. It's enough to know that it has been considered valuable to mankind for as long as written history tells, and it is likely to be considered as valuable for a long time to come. The reason for this falls under the heading of *ECONOMICS.*

Thorndike Barnharts advanced dictionary defines economics as *"science of the production, distribution and consumption of goods and services."* A basic fundamental of economics is that in order to survive, any group or individual must produce some kind of goods or services which can be exchanged with others for more than they cost to produce. The key word is exchange. In todays free world — and in tomorrows, exchange is necessary.

Money by itself has no true value of it's own. It's paper. All the value that a paper currency has is that which is attached to it by the agreement of the people who use it, and their trust in that government which prints it.

Originally, the purpose of paper currency was a substitute for the use of gold and silver. Gold is heavy to carry around in any large amounts. It also takes time to weigh it out each time that it passes hands, and you can never be certain of its purity without an assay by a competent technician. Some ruling body probably came up with the idea of paper currency being used in place of gold. Basically a good idea — as long as paper was directly backed by the real thing. A dollar was worth one pinch of gold; the fellow traded in some of his gold for dollars, because they were easier to deal with. This was fine as long as he could trade the dollars back for gold if he wanted to. There was never any worry about the gold's exchange value because it had always been safe, and so there was no need to worry worry about the exchange value of paper currency as long as it was backed up by gold (or silver) and could be traded back for the same amount of gold or silver at any time.

Over the years, for one reason or another, the system of "having so many dollars represent so many units of gold, which was held safe by the government" dropped out; and a new system was set up in which paper currency was printed up with nothing at all to back it up and hold it stable — other than the authority of the government.

With the new system, a loaf of bread could be traded for a dollar, but why? The dollar has no value of its own. The answer is that the dollar can be traded for a loaf of bread because that authority which makes the currency says that it can. So it takes a lot more trust in the government in this new system, because you are using a medium of exchange that has no intrinsic value, and which has no actual valuable commodity backing it.

The thing about a paper currency which is not backed by anything of value, is that there is nothing really to hold it stable as a currency. Such currencies can inflate (become worthless in its trading value) because of a number of reasons, the main one being that the world at large becomes less trustful of that government which is standing behind the currency. Therefore as an exchange medium, it becomes less trustworthy, and thereafter will become worth less as a bargaining commodity.

If a person has all of his assets in paper money form, as in a bank or in bonds, and the government which puts out that currency folds up or is overrun, or goes suddenly unstable for some reason, that person's assets can become a lot smaller — or disappear all together.

Another way for a currency to inflate, meaning to become worth less in its trading value, is for the government to print up a bunch of it and just give it away without demanding in return a fair exchange of what it is supposed to be worth. In this case, you have on the one hand, the government printing up money and saying that it is   worthy of being used as an exchange medium; and on the other hand, the government is just giving it away and demanding nothing in return. This activity lessens the currency's exchange value, and is a reason why the currency of any welfare state is guaranteed to inflate.

One way to watch the rate of inflation of currency over an extended period of time is to watch the exchange market value of gold for that currency. Once in the USA, gold sold for $17 per troy ounce. Today, it sells in excess of 26 times as many more dollars ($450). The appearance of this is that gold has increased its value 26 times more than it was worth during the mid—1800's. Actually, this is not the case. While today gold may be a touch more valuable than it once was - because it's in such great demand as a stable investment during such unstable economic times — the truth of the matter is that the dollar has depreciated in its exchange value to the point where it takes 26 times (or more) as many of them to equal the same amount of exchange value it once had. To further show this point, there was once a time in the U.S. when you could buy a loaf of bread for a nickel. Today, a good loaf of bread on the average store is selling for $1.30. Is bread worth 26 times more than it used to be? No! Bread is bread; and if anything, it should take less to buy a loaf — because there is no scarcity whatsoever.

A gold miner today can cash in an ounce of gold and go out and buy about the same amount of goods and supplies as an oldtimer could by cashing in an ounce and shopping in a large town during the mid—1800's. You have to remember that a guy could get a haircut for a nickel and a steak dinner with all the trimmings for a quarter in those days.

If that same oldtimer were using his dollars on today's market, he would need in excess of 26 times as many of them to buy the same amount of goods; and that was only about 120 years ago. That's a lot of inflation! Yet if that miner brought his own gold to the present, he'd be able to buy the same amount of goods — or more — as he could back in the 1800's.

So why the lesson in economics? Just to show that gold is very stable as an exchange commodity, is likely to be considered as valuable for a long time to come, and to show how the inflation of paper currencies has adversely affected the gold mining industry, until recently. . .

GOLD MINING

There seems to be a prevalent idea in modern society that during the gold rush days the oldtimers mined out most or all of the gold. This is simply not the case. While the early birds probably did get most of the exceptionally easy to find and recover bonanzas, they did not come anywhere near to finding all of — or even most of the gold.

This idea that most of the gold has already been found and recovered probably stems from the fact of an almost total lack of gold mining activity since the early 1940's — that is, until recently. The reason is as follows:

During the early rush days, it was made mandatory — by law — in the USA, to sell all gold that was mined in the USA to the government at a set price, which was arbitrarily fixed by law. This fixed price was probably OK during the early days; but over the years, inflation caused the dollar to rapidly decline in its exchange value — yet the fixed exchange rate for gold required it to be bought by the same amount of dollars. As inflation caused the costs of operating a gold mine to become more in dollars, and the fixed rate of exchange for gold remained the same in dollars, it became necessary to find and recover more and more gold in order to keep an operation running without a loss. Many mines which were once run at good profit eventually had to be shut down due to the effects of inflation, and the fixed exchange rate of gold. Even when they were producing the same amount of gold — or more — than they once were producing at a profit.

In 1934, the fixed rate was raised from $20.67 to $35 per troy ounce of pure gold, and this started a minor gold rush! Many old mines were re-opened and worked at a profit using newer mining techniques and modern equipment. But the fixed rate remained the same; inflation continued; and eventually all but the richest of producing gold mines had to be shut down.

In 1941, most of the mines that were still in operation were shut down due to the war effort. After the war was over, very few gold mines were re-opened because of the increase in minimum wages and the many jobs that were available elsewhere. Plus, inflation had continued and the fixed rate remained at $35/ounce.

Since that time and until recently, very little actual gold mining has occurred. For the reasons laid out above, there was little interest in it. After all, who would want to mine gold — which had depreciated in its exchange value at a rate of 26 times in the last 120 years? And that was the case as long as the gold exchange value remained arbitrarily fixed and inflation rates continued to soar. This is probably the reason for the idea that "all the gold has already been mined up," because nobody was mining!

In 1974, a bill was passed through congress which made it legal for individuals to own gold again, and to buy and sell it on the open market. With the arbitrarily fixed exchange finally being taken off gold, the currency exchange value for gold sky rocketed. Consequently, a great many mines that were shut down years and years ago are presently being re-opened at a good profit. Many areas which could not be worked viably at an earlier time can now be mined by the individual and give excellent returns.

A tremendous amount of progress has been made in earth moving equipment and gold recovery methods over the past hundred years — especially within the past 40 years, while the field has been dormant. Today, it's possible for the individual to process tens — or even hundreds of cubic yards of gold bearing materials; whereas in the same or similiar areas, he may have been able to move just a few yards during the early days.

Today, supplies and equipment are readily available to the modern day prospector at relatively low cost, compared to what the oldtimer had to pay for tools and supplies on the early frontier — if he could get them at all.

One thing about the old days is that it was often necessary for the early miner to drag, haul and hoist his equipment over some rather inaccessible terrain. He also had to hunt much of his food and fight off the Indians — all while trying to find and recover acceptable paying quantities of gold. Today there are highways, roads and trails which have been made all over gold country that pass through or at least nearby the same spots in which it took the earlybirds weeks or even months to get into, along with their gear.

A great amount of natural (and man caused) erosion has taken place within the last hundred years or so; which has placed a remarkable amount of new gold into the present rivers and streams. This is evidenced by the many valuable deposits that are being regularly turned up out of the same streams and rivers which were supposed to have been thoroughly mined by the 49er's or those who followed them.

Yes, the 49er's got most of the easiest rich deposits, and they were some rich deposits indeed! How could they help it when they were tripping over the nuggets lying on the streambanks! However, most of the deposits that were taken by the earlybirds were those that were easily exposed and mined during their time. But by no means did they find all of the easy deposits, because new ones are being found at this writing.

Present day geologists say that not one percent of all the gold on or inside the earth's crust has yet to be mined. Actually this varies, some experts say that not twenty percent has yet to be mined. However, they all seem to agree that most of it still remains to be found and recovered. True, much of this gold is down beneath tons and tons of sediment or down into the earths hardrock surface and is all but inaccessible to us without the most sophisticated (and expensive) mining equipment available today. Yet, there is still a magnificent amount of gold that is accessible to the small time operator, and a good many bonanzas are yet to be had.

With the steadily increasing market exchange value for gold, and with experts in the economic field agreeing that it will see the $1000./ounce mark — and higher, within the next few years, and with runaway inflation rates occurring at this very moment, and with the working mans wages being taxed more and more all the time; a successful gold mining venture is a very comfortable activity to be involved with today. And so more and more people are turning to gold mining as a profession or hobby activity.

An ounce a week — untaxed, would be acceptable wages today, and with the modern equipment which is readily available at relatively low costs — namely the sluicing device and the suction dredge (both covered later — in detail), and a little bit of hard work and experience; and ounce a week average — over top of expenses (and taxes) are not too difficult to attain. As a matter of fact, if you are willing to put in the time study and effort to gain some experience and a greater understanding, much higher averages can be — and are being attained by the small time operator.

There is a gold rush occurring today, in the 1980's, which is of a size that is comparable to the rush which occurred during the 1800's. Today's gold rush is not nearly as dramatic, because in those early days if one was going to go gold mining, it had to be a total commitment. Those were some rough times on the early frontier and survival was at stake.

Today the modern prospector can go out on the weekend and sample out various locations, using his modern day methods, and cover ground that might have taken weeks to prospect by the methods used during the early days — or might have been impossible to work at all.

Some tremendous discoveries were made during the earlier rushes, and some miners became wealthy as a result. Yet, for the most part, those who went to mine gold were unable to find enough to even make wages. The reason for this was that the equipment and methods being used in the early days enabled the small time operator (the one or two man operation) to process only a minute amount of earth, which made it necessary to find the richest deposits of gold — that had to be easy to mine, because of their limitations. These deposits were few, and finding them meant a considerable amount of prospecting and hard work, and when a hot spot was found, it was very exciting and a good deal of drama resulted.

Conditions are different today. Routes have opened up, recovery methods have been improved, and processing equipment is available to the individual that will allow him to do far far more than the earlier prospectors could, and as a result the success rate amongst miners in finding paying quantities of gold today is a great deal higher than it ever was during the earlier rushes.

Perhaps there are not as many prospectors running around in the hills as there once were, but it's a fact that a much greater percentage of today's prospectors do far better than the early guys did — and with much less investment too.

Take it from me, I've been out in them thar hills and streams and have taken a fair amount of gold myself — and plan to get lots more for that matter! There's plenty to be had.

I'm not saying it's all roses and whipped cream. It takes hard work, study and persistence to learn the hows and the wheres of it, and to be continuously successful — whether as a hobby or as a profession. But it's being done, and on a broader scale every day.

Oh, don't worry, there's still plenty left for you, and there will be for some time to come.

I don't claim that the data, equipment and procedures which are covered in this manual are the best that have been developed — ever. A lot of mining has gone on over the years, and with the almost total lack of it during the past half century or so, much of the data has been lost. A lot of it was never written down. I only state that the material which I cover in this volume is the best that I personally have run across

— and that IT WORKS! It works for me, my various partners have done well with it, and it has worked for many others whom I have been associated with in the gold mining field that are successful. My purpose here is not to set myself up as an authority on the best procedures and equipment, etc. It's to give you something to go on that WORKS, so that you too can get started and do well at it. After you have been into it for awhile, you'll get your own ideas of the best methods and equipment for the job — which is good. If you run across something in the field that seems to work better than the way I have outlined it in this volume, by all means write me a letter and tell me about it. I'll be doing a revision on this manual every once in awhile; and if you point out something to me which is better, I'll add it in so that everyone can benefit.

This book has been designed to give you a no-nonsense account of gold mining basics, in which I have attempted to cover everything possible that you will need and want to know about the successful procedures being used to find and recover gold in the 80's.

If you are interested in mining gold and want to succeed at it, if you are willing to stick with it — and keep at it, no matter how tough the going gets, I'd like to see you succeed too — and this book was written for you.

So here's the data. Have at it.

I'll see ya out there.

Good Luck

Dave Mac

 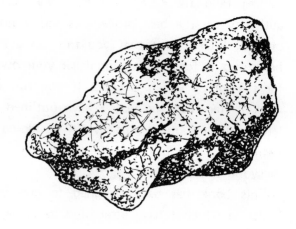

CHAPTER 1

GOLD — WHAT IT IS

All things of the physical universe which can be sensed by man are made up of one or more chemical elements. An "element" is a basic simple substance which cannot be further broken down by chemical means. Elements are the basic building blocks of the material universe in which we live. Scientists have discovered over 100 basic elements, and have laid them out in order on the "periodic table of elements" according to their atomic structures.

Gold is one of the 92 naturally occurring elements found on earth. There is no known natural substance that can destroy gold. It can be dissolved by chemical means, but even then it remains as gold — only in a more widely dispersed state.

For eons, man has dwelled on where gold might originally have come from — that is, its native source. Scientists have recently discovered that gold can be artifically produced by the atomic bombardment of lead, which is another basic element. However, the process is very expensive, more so than the actual monetary value of the resulting gold. So it is not artifically produced on a commercial scale. However, this discovery has brought on the theory that the gold being found on our earth might originally have been manufactured in the nuclear furnaces of stars which have long since vanished, our planet being part of the remaining debris.

The scientific symbol for gold is AU. It is number 79 on the periodic table of elements. Gold is not magnetic, but it is an excellent conductor of electricity. Its melting point is about 1945° F. Gold is not corroded or tarnished by moisture, or oxidized (rust) by the effects of oxygen and water, or affected by ordinary acids such as most other metals are. Deposits of gold that have laid inside a mountain or under a streambed or even on the ocean's bottom will remain there and be rather unaffected until moved by the natural forces of the earth — or taken by man.

Gold is a very soft metal, being 2.3 on a hardness scale of 10, which is one of the factors giving gold its tremendous malleability — meaning that it can be pounded, twisted, rolled and or squeezed into all kinds of different shapes without breaking apart. In fact, the yellow metal can be pounded so thin that it can be looked through, and yet still remain intact as a solid sheet of gold. It has been said that such sheets of gold can be produced so thin that it would take about a quarter of a million of them stacked one on top of the other, to make a pile which would stand one inch tall! Thin sheets of gold such as these have the distinctive quality of allowing sunlight to pass through, yet they will reflect off a large portion of the sun's infrared rays (heat). For this reason, thin layers of gold are being used in the window glass employed in many of today's modern skyscrapers, to help save on the tremendous costs of energy necessary to keep the interior of such buildings cool during the hot summer months. Similar films of gold have also been used in the face shields of astronaut helmets to reflect off much of the increased bombardment of infrared rays which occurs out in space.

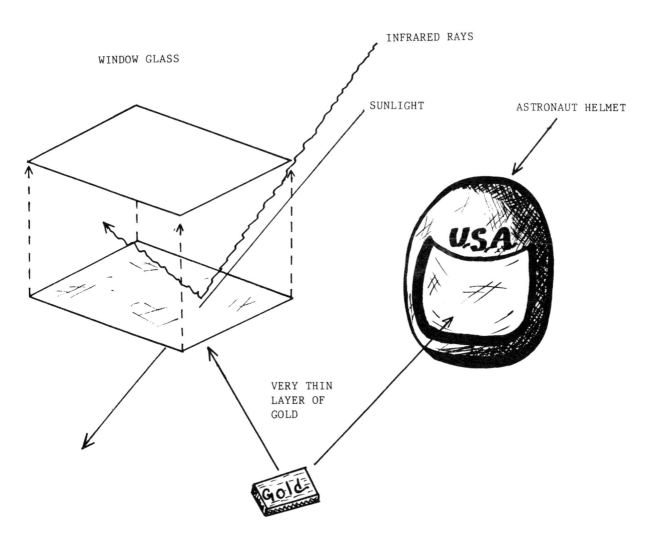

Fig. 1—1. Gold has many uses — one of which is that in very thin sheets, it will reflect off a large portion of the sun's infrared rays, but allows sunlight to pass through.

Gold is also extremely ductile — meaning that it can be drawn out into wire or threadlike forms without becoming brittle and breaking. It is said that gold can be drawn out so thin that a single ounce could be made to stretch a continous length of 35 miles. That would make the thread very thin indeed, but that's exactly what is needed in todays electronics industry where entire circuits are being placed in chips the size of a pinhead. Because of it's high electrical conductivity, it's extraordinary resistance to deteriorization and its ductile qualities, gold is in great demand by the electronics industry and so it's not uncommon to find it being used in the circuits of many of today's common everyday electronic devices — like TV's and calculators etc., not to mention it being used in some of the more sophisticated electronics of today's modern world.

Gold is also commonly used by dentists and is widely used to make jewelry.

Gold's use in the making of coins has greatly increased within the past few years as an effort on the part of some nations to stabilize their rapidly inflating economies.

Gold has another distinctive quality, which is perhaps most important to the prospector — other than it's value, and that is of its weight. Gold is extremely dense, which makes it one of the heaviest of all metals. The specific gravity of gold is 19.3, meaning that it weighs 19.3 times more than an equal volume or mass of pure water. Iridium (one of the platinum metals) is the only metal that has a higher specific gravity than that of gold, it being 22.6. Gold is 2-1/2 times heavier than silver and over 8 times heavier than the quartz rock which it is commonly associated with when found in hardrock form. A single cubic foot of gold will weigh approximately 1187 pounds. It is this quality — of gold having a superior weight factor over that of the other materials which are usually found along with it, that is used in gold recovery methods, as will be covered in detail within the following chapters.

Gold is not the most valuable metal, but it is extremly valuable and probably the most sought after of all the valuable metals found on earth. At today's market exchange value of gold, that same cubic foot of pure gold would be worth in the neighborhood of 6-1/2 million dollars. A cubic inch of pure gold would value at about 4 thousand dollars at today's market prices. So gold is valuable, very valuable indeed, and it does not take very much of it to accumulate a considerable amount of wealth.

There is one other of golds' distinctive qualities that is worthy of mention, which is that in it's natural form, gold is a very rich and beautiful substance to look at. In fact, this is so much the case that there is a saying amongst experienced miners — and those individuals who handle a great deal of the yellow metal, that it is not a good idea to look at any substantial amount of raw gold for very long at any given period of time, because it has a tendency to bring on a condition referred to as "gold fever." It's true!

"Gold Fever" affects different people in different ways, and while it might make one person want to buy the gold at almost any price, it could just as easily make another want to steal it — at any price. However, the "fever" tends to always make an individual want to have the gold for oneself, and more of it if possible, with the means of getting it depending on the character of the individual. This condition, (gold fever) is something to take note of for anyone who is planning to get involved with mining or dealing with gold. It's nothing to laugh off, for this condition has been the cause of a great many deaths, failures, wars, enslavements, loss of friendships, and basically, has altered the course of a significant amount of history — much of it being the worse for the others involved. It's true that for many, gold is the thing of which dreams can be materialized, and therefore gold has a tendency to strike below the social behavior in a person and bring out some of the stronger passions which lie underneath. It is well to keep this strongly in mind during the stage in which you are considering who to take on as a partner (or as employees) in a gold mining venture of any size.

One common characteristic of a person who has been touched, just mildly, with a case of gold fever is that he tends to throw all good business sense to the wind and dive in head over heels, much as a young child might do if he found a tub full of his favorite candy or ice cream. It is this very same factor that the con-man stirs up and plays off of, and if you don't think that there aren't a few good ones out there in the field — think again. The vast majority of failures in gold mining ventures are the result of this same loss of good judgment which sometimes occurs when dealing with the valuable metal.

Perhaps the most successful precaution against being struck to any harmful degree with the "fever" is in honestly taking on the viewpoint that "anything worthwhile is worth lots of time and energy." It's the guys who intend to get rich quickly without any amount of energy output on their own parts who most often fail in the business of gold mining. If upon examining your own intentions, you find that you are interested in getting rich quickly — without having to work for it, it's almost a certainty that you've caught at least a touch of the fever. On the other hand, if you're interested in going out into Gods country to see if you can find some of the yellow metal as an adventure, and or perhaps to see if it can be done as a viable business venture, you're probably on the right track and you are more likely to succeed — and who knows, maybe you will strike a big one; it happens all the time! Just remember that the finding and recovering of gold is similar to any other business venture. It takes a bit of time and work to get consistently good at it. Take it on as such and you will have no trouble — and no losses.

SOURCE OF GOLD

When considering the source of gold on this planet alone, it is necessary to study the earth and to take a look at some of it's more recent geological history.

Scientists believe that the earth is an extremely solid mass, which grows more and more dense towards it's center.

It is believed that the gold which is found on the earth's surface and in it's outer crust was once deep down inside the earth's molten mass and was carried up to the surface by the effects of volcanic activity.

GROWS MORE DENSE TOWARDS
CENTER

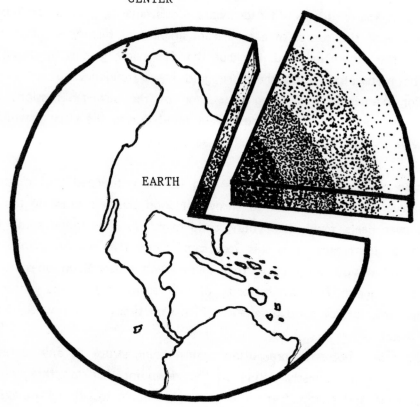

EARTH

Fig. 1—2. Scientists believe that the earth is solid, and becomes more and more dense towards it's center.

In hardrock form, gold is generally found associated with quartz in the form of veins, which protrude through the general mountainous rock — referred to as "country rock" by the geologists. In the early days of gold mining, it was generally believed that these quartz/gold veins were once pushed up out of the lower bowels of the earth as volcanic magma. Upon this principal it was thought that a vein should become richer as one followed it deeper into the earth. However this was not always the case.

More recently it has been found out that quartz veins were not formed during the same time period as the country rock that surrounds them, but later. The cooling of the earth's outer crust (country rock) apparently caused many cracks and fissures from which the gasses and superheated steam could escape out of the earth's molten interior. These water vapors also carried minerals with them through these avenues of escape, one of the predominant minerals being silica — which forms quartz. The water vapors carried other minerals upward too, of which gold, silver, iron and platinum are just a few. Silica has distinctive characteristics of it's own, one of which is that it tends to trap heavier elements when they are passed over and through it in a dissolved form. So while the water vapors pushed the heavier minerals upward towards the earth's surface through cracks and fissures, they often combined with silica and formed vein like structures. (See figure 1-3.)

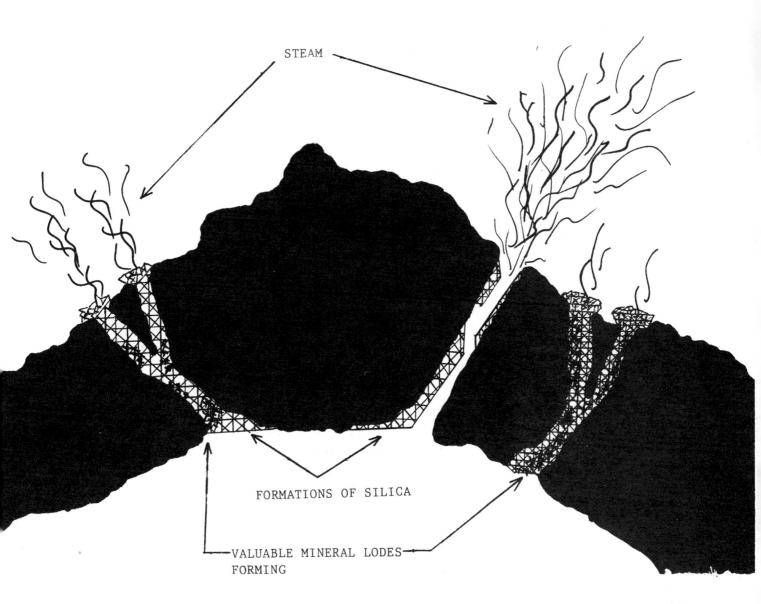

STEAM

FORMATIONS OF SILICA

VALUABLE MINERAL LODES
FORMING

Fig. 1–3. Formation of mineral lodes.

Generally, gold is associated with quartz. However quartz is not always associated with gold, in that there are many many thousands of quartz veins that have no gold — or at least not enough gold in evidence to make the mining of the vein profitable. Veins which contain valuable minerals are referred to as "lodes."

"Ore" has been defined as any deposit of rock from which a valuable metal or mineral can be profitably extracted.

When a valuable lode is found, in order to mine it, the ore is usually blasted out of the vein and is crushed down into a very fine powder from which the gold, silver and other valuable minerals can be extracted by any number of chemical or mechanical procedures. This entire process is called "lode mining" or "hardrock mining" and is covered more in detail within Chapter 9 of this volume.

Millions of years passed after the rich mineral lodes were formed, during which time a large amount of wear and tear was caused by heat and cold, animals and vegetation, rain and wind, snow and ice, glaciers — and their resulting runoffs, earthquakes, and ocean tidal changes as great as 800 feet in elevation for each tide — due to the moon revolving closer to the earth during an earlier period. So after the rich veins were formed, a tremendous amount of erosion took place, which washed most of the exposed rich mineral lodes out of the mountainous rock and into the stream and river systems which flowed during that time period.

The steady flow of water over a streambed causes a continous movement of the streambed materials, which causes a natural sorting of the various minerals as to their different sizes, shapes and weights. Gold, being extremely heavy in relationship to most of the other materials that end up in a streambed, tends to be deposited in the various common locations where heavier materials can become trapped because of their superior weight. Deposits of gold and other valuable minerals which have been washed away from their original lodes and redeposited in streambeds are called "placer deposits." (Pronounced "Plaster" — without the t.)

The activity of finding and recovering placer gold deposits entails an understanding of where heavy sediments will collect while being transported by the forces of nature, of which much of the remainder of this manual will outline for you.

Gold, directly from a lode is crystaline in structure, (see figure 1-4) and is usually referred to as "rough gold" because of the coarseness of it's surface. Once having been washed from it's original lode and having been swept away by the forces of nature, gold tends to become pounded flat and rubbed smooth.

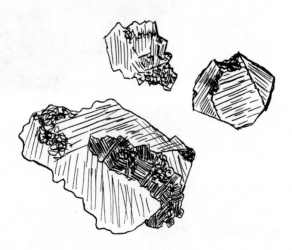

GOLD DIRECTLY OUT OF A LODE IS
CRYSTALINE IN STRUCTURE

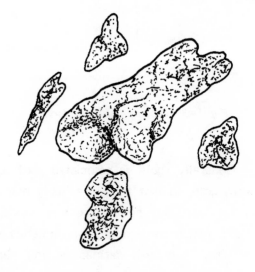

GOLD TENDS TO GET POUNDED SMOOTH
AS IT IS BEING WASHED FURTHER
FROM IT'S ORIGINAL LODE

Fig. 1—4.

Often an experienced prospector can get a pretty good idea of how far that a piece of gold has traveled from it's lode by the degree of roughness on it's outer surface.

PURENESS OF NATIVE GOLD

In it's native state out of a lode, gold is usually not 100 percent pure, but almost always has a percentage of other metals along with it. These other metals contained with gold — whether of value or not, are called "impurities." The impurities with gold most often consist of silver, copper and a little bit of iron, platinum and cadmium in differing amounts. The proportions of these other minerals change from lode to lode, which gives the gold coming from one location different colors, qualities and value than the gold extracted from another location.

When someone finds gold — either in placer or lode form, it is not uncommon to have the gold tested (assayed) to find out what percentage of impurities are present, and exactly what they are. The actual gold content in the native gold just out of a lode or placer deposit ranges in different amounts from location to location, but a reasonably safe average (at least in California) would be to say that 80% is gold and 15% is silver or copper.

Gold which contains 20% or more of silver in it's content is called "electrum."

Pieces of placer gold — and those pieces that have eroded from a lode, come in a wide variety of sizes and shape, ranging from large pieces (nuggets) as great as 200 pounds in weight (very rare) to "flakes," and smaller "grains," and even smaller "dust," down to pieces so microscopic in size that it would take — perhaps 8 million particles combined in order to accumulate enough gold to value one dollar.

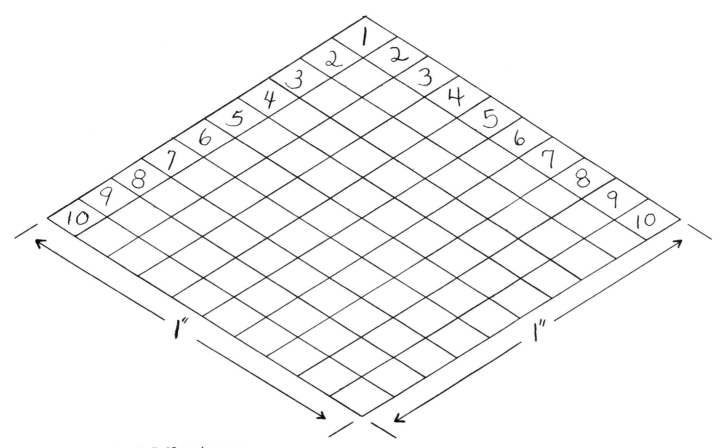

Fig. 1—5. 10 mesh screen

The general breakdown that is commonly used to classify the size differences of gold is done with the use of mesh screen. "Mesh" signifies the number of openings contained in a lineal inch of screen or wire cloth. For example, a screen labeled "10 mesh" would contain 10 openings per lineal inch, or 100 openings per square inch. "20 mesh" would have 20 openings per lineal inch, or 400 openings per square inch, and so on. (See figure 1-5.)

Those pieces of gold which will pass through 10 mesh (1/16" size openings), yet will not pass through 20 mesh (1/32" sized openings) are classified as "10-20 mesh." Gold passing through 20 mesh which will not pass through 40 mesh (1/64" sized openings) is classified as "20-40 mesh," and so on. (See figure 1-6.)

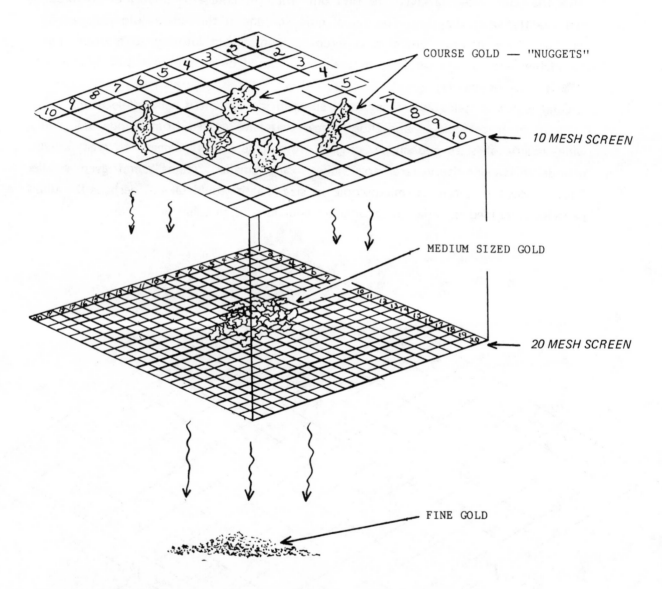

Fig. 1–6. Gold is classified and labeled as to it's size.

Amongst some miners, the various sized pieces of gold are labeled as to their different mesh sizes. "Coarse gold" or "nuggets" are agreed to be any pieces of gold of a size greater than 10 mesh. Medium sized pieces of gold — flakes and so forth are of the 10 - 20 mesh range, of which it would take an average of 2,200 separate pieces (colors) to make up a troy ounce. "Fine gold" is of the 20-40 mesh size, of which it would take an average of 12,000 separate colors to make a troy ounce. "Flour gold" or "dust" includes all pieces which are smaller than 40 mesh, including the microscopic sized particles.

Because gold is so malleable, as it is pounded, rubbed, and pushed along by the forces of nature, the gold will tend to hold together, whereas some of its impurities will be pounded and washed free. So generally, pieces of gold become more pure as they are pounded and worked by the different forces of nature — especially in a streambed where it can be heavily pounded by rocks, boulders and such, along with the steady flow of water to help wash away the impurities. This pounding also has the effect of breaking much of the gold down into smaller pieces, from which more impurities can be washed free. And so it is generally found to be the case that smaller pieces of gold are of richer gold content than the larger sized pieces. For example, the fine and flour gold recovered out of many goldbearing streams in the Western U.S. will be found to have a gold content greater than 90%; whereas the nuggets recovered out of the very same deposits are often found to have a gold content of less than 80%. At first glance, this might seem to indicate that fine gold has a greater value than the course gold does, and this is true as far as the actual gold value is concerned. However, the larger pieces have "jewelry specimen" value, due to their own unique and natural characteristics, and so can bring in a far greater monetary exchange than their actual gold value. Fine gold is usually sold to a smelter, who melts it down and refines it into pure bullion form, to be eventually sold on the world gold market.

INDICATION OF GOLD CONTENT

There are two ways of labeling the gold content of raw and unprocessed gold which are commonly being used in the field today. The "fineness," or "percentage system," is used most often amongst miners and refiners. This system breaks down the purity into thousandths in order to label the "fineness" (purity) of the gold sample. For example, a specimen that contains 90% gold and 10% impurities would be labeled .900 fine; 88% gold content would be labeled .880 fine; 75% gold content would be indicated as .750 fine, and so on. In this system, .999 fine is used to indicate pure gold. The fineness system is often used amongst assayers to indicate the gold content in the samples which they test.

The other system sometimes used to indicate the gold content in your samples or specimens is the "carat system." This method is most commonly used within the jewelry business, and is based on a 24-point system with 100% gold content being 24 carats, 50% gold being 12 carats, 75% gold being 18 carats, and so on.

MEASURING GOLD BY WEIGHT

There are also two separate measuring systems being used to weigh gold. The most commonly used is the "troy system" which is as follows:

$$24 \text{ grains} \ldots \ldots \ldots \ldots = 1 \text{ penny weight}$$
$$20 \text{ pennyweight} \ldots \ldots \ldots = 1 \text{ troy ounce}$$
$$12 \text{ troy ounces} \ldots \ldots \ldots = 1 \text{ troy pound}$$

Scales having these kind of measuring increments are usually available wherever gold mining equipment is sold. The troy system, as laid out above is most commonly used in the field and when gold is sold on the open market.

A troy pound is equal to .3732 kilograms, whereas a standard pound (avoirdupois) is equal to .4536 kilograms, so you see that they are not the same — a standard pound weighing considerably more than that of a troy pound. Also take note that there are only 12 troy ounces to a troy pound, as opposed to the 16 ounces that it takes to make up a standard pound, the result of this being that a troy ounce weighs slightly more than a standard ounce.

The other system of measuring gold is by grams. Most triple beam balance scales measure in terms of grams instead of troy increments, and so it is not uncommon to find a gram scale being used to measure gold too. In this case the conversion scale is as follows:

TROY — GRAM CONVERSION TABLE

$$1 \text{ troy pound} \ldots \ldots \ldots \ldots = 373.241 \text{ grams}$$
$$1 \text{ troy ounce} \ldots \ldots \ldots \ldots = 31.104 \text{ grams}$$
$$1 \text{ pennyweight} \ldots \ldots \ldots \ldots = 1.552 \text{ grams}$$
$$1 \text{ grain} \ldots \ldots \ldots \ldots \ldots = 64.8 \text{ milligrams}$$

FOOLS GOLD

It is not unusual for a beginner to wonder about the difference between gold and the other materials found in a streambed or lode deposit. Sometimes a beginner will puzzle over shiny rocks, and quite often iron pyrites (fools gold) are mistaken for the real thing. In fact, this is so much the case that there is a story of an entire shipload of iron pyrites having been shipped over to England during the 1500's — the yellow stuff having been mistaken for gold. So you can understand where it gets the term "fools gold."

Gold is a brassy yellow metal, and once you have seen a bit of it in it's natural form a few times, you will no longer have any difficulty in distinguishing it from the other materials that are commonly associated with it. Gold does not look anything like rock. It looks like metal — gold metal. If you are just starting and have not yet had the opportunity to see much gold in it's natural form, there are three easy tests which will validate your discoveries one way or the other.

Glitter Test: Gold does not glitter. It shines — sometimes it's bright, sometimes it's dull; but very seldom does it glitter. The thing about fool's gold (pyrites), is that because of its crystaline structure, it tends to always be glittery. Take the sample and turn it in your hand in the sunlight. If it is gold, the metal will continue to shine regularly as the specimen is turned. A piece of fool's gold will glitter as the different sides of its crystal-like structure reflect light differently, due to it being turned in the sun.

Hardness Test: Gold is soft metal — like lead — and will dent or bend when a small amount of force is applied to it. Pyrites and shiny rocks are generally hard and brittle, and just a little amount of pounding will shatter them. Gold never shatters!

It is said that the oldtimer used to put a specimen in his mouth and bite on it to test to see if it was gold. This is another way of testing the larger sized specimens. However, keep in mind that a larger sized piece of gold is worth a great deal and the resulting tooth marks could lessen its value. If you find a piece of gold that is big enough for you to bite on, I can assure you that you will have no doubt that it is the real thing, simply because of its nature — and its weight; but if you are still uncertain of your find, you might try using the sharp edge of a knife and gently press in on the specimen in a place which is less likely to be noticed. If it's gold, an indentation can easily be made into the metal with the blade of your knife. If it is a rock or iron pyrites, you will not dent its surface.

Acid Test: Nitric acid will not affect gold (other than to clean it); whereas, it will dissolve many of the other materials which are found in a streambed — including iron pyrites. Nitric acid can be purchased from most any drug store or prescription counter, and is also usually found wherever gold mining equipment is sold. If in question whether your specimen is fool's gold or some metal other than gold, immerse it in a solution of nictic acid. If your specimen is gold, it will remain rather unaffected; whereas, if it is fool's gold or most any other kind of metal, it will dissolve in the acid.

CAUTION: Nitric acid can be very dangerous to work with, and certain precautions must be taken to prevent harm to yourself and your equipment when working with it. These, and mixing instructions, are covered in Chapter 7 of this volume.

PLATINUM

Platinum is an industrial metal, having a family of 6 separate metals — being platinum, palladium, iridium, osmium, rhadium, and ruthenium. These metals are always naturally alloyed amongst each other so that not any one of them is ever found alone.

Platinum is a valuable metal — its value ranging in the same neighborhood as that of gold. It also has a high specific gravity, sometimes even heavier than gold — depending on how much iridium is present.

Often, platinum will be present along with placer gold deposits, and so will become trapped in the same recovery systems that are used to recover gold. Sometimes platinum will be present in enough quantity that it could be worth a great deal of money to you to know what it looks like — so you don't discard it along with the waste materials.

Platinum is usually a dull silvery colored metal, much like that of steel — only different, in that it is non-magnetic and is not affected by nitric acid like steel is; and platinum does not rust. Platinum usually comes in the form of large and small flakes — just like gold, and sometimes in the form of nuggets.

Platinum does not have as great an affinity for mercury (quick silver) as do most shiny metals. However, it can be made to have affinity for mercury by the use of certain involved chemical processes.

Russia has been the world's number one producer of the platinum metals for the last hundred years or so.

If at first you should have difficulty in telling the difference between platinum and lead, remember that platinum usually takes on a dull shiny color, whereas lead does not shine at all — unless it is covered with a coat of mercury. Lead (and mercury) are also easily dissolved by nitric acid, whereas platinum remains unaffected. Most other shiny, silvery colored metals which will be found in the recovery system will be magnetic. Platinum is not.

SILVER

Most silver mining is done by the hardrock method of extracting ore out of a lode and processing out the silver by chemical and mechanical procedures. The silver which is recovered out of most placer deposits is that silver which is still alloyed with the gold, and the black sands, that are being taken out of the deposit.

Native silver has a specific gravity of about 10 or 11 (it's heavy), and so will be trapped in most recovery systems, if present as itself in a placer deposit — which is uncommon. Generally, silver in its native form does not look like shiny silver — like in silverware. It looks more like a silverish rock which is uncommonly heavy. Sometimes, silver is so tarnished that it can not be distinguished by color at all.

CHAPTER II

PLACER GEOLOGY

Thorndike/Barnhart's **Advanced Dictionary** defines "placer" as "A deposit of sand, gravel or earth in the bed of a stream containing particles of gold or other valuable minerals." The word "geology" in the same dictionary is defined as "The features of the earth's crust in a place or region, rocks or rock formations of a particular area." So in putting these two words together we have "placer geology" as the nature and features of the formation of deposits of gold and other valuable minerals within a streambed.

The main factor which causes gold to become deposited in the locations where it does is that of it's superior weight over the majority of other materials which end up in a streambed. By superior weight, I mean that a piece of gold will be found to be heavier than most any other material which displaces an equal amount of space or volume. For example, a large boulder will weigh more than a half ounce gold nugget, but if you chip off a piece of the boulder which is of the exact same size as the gold nugget, the nugget will be found to weigh about 6 or 7 times more than the chip of rock.

31

As gold is eroded from its original lode, gravity, wind, water, and the other natural forces of nature will wash it away and downwards until it eventually arrives in a streambed. (See figure 2-1.)

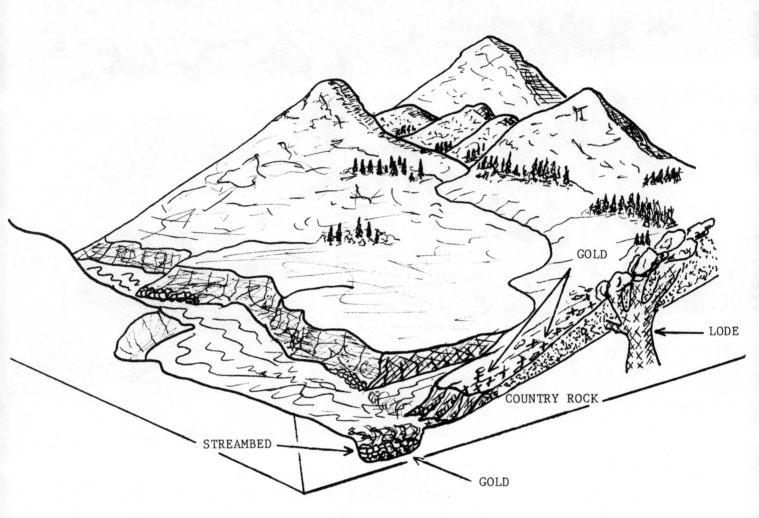

Fig. 2—1. Gold erodes from its natural lode and eventually is washed into a river or streambed.

There are several different types of gold deposits which a prospector should know about, because they have different characteristics and are dealt with in different ways. They are as follows:

LODE: Any valuable mineral deposit, still in hardrock form, that fills a crack or fissure which expands through the general country rock is referred to as a "lode." Lodes are the original source of placer deposits.

RESIDUAL DEPOSIT: A "residual deposit" consists of the pieces of the lode that have broken away from the outcropping of the vein by the erosive effects of nature, but which have not yet been washed away from the near vicinity of the lode. A residual deposit usually lies directly beneath its lode, as shown in figure 2-2.

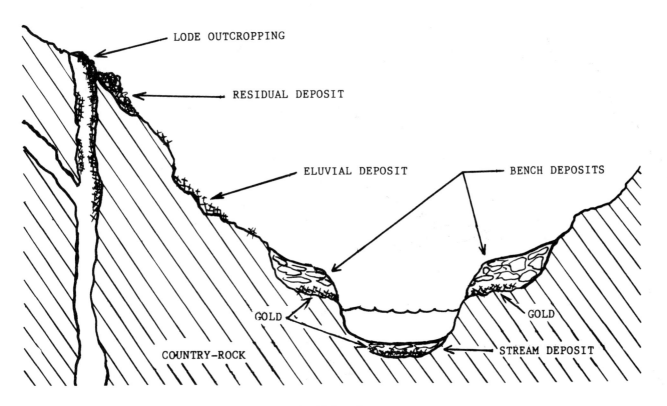

Fig. 2—2. The five main different types of gold deposits.

ELUVIAL DEPOSIT: "An eluvial deposit" is composed of those pieces of ore and free gold which have eroded from a lode and have been swept away by the forces of nature, but which have not yet been washed into a streambed. (See figure 2-2.) The fragments of an eluvial deposit are often spread out thinly down along the mountainside below where the original lode is located. Usually the various forces of nature cause an eluvial deposit to spread out more widely as it's segments are washed further away from the lode deposit, as shown in figure 2-3. (Next page)

BENCH DEPOSIT: (Also "terrace deposit.") Once gold reaches a streambed, it will be deposited in different standard ways by the effects of running water — of which most of the remainder of this chapter will cover. During the years and years of running, a stream of water tends to cut deeper and deeper into the earth. This leaves many of the older sections of streambed high and dry. Old streambeds which now rest above the present streams of water are referred to as "benches." The accumulations of gold and other valuable minerals which are contained in an old, high streambed as such are called "bench deposits." Figure 2-2 shows bench deposits as they are, however the diagram can be misleading in that at first it might appear that the gold out of an eluvial deposit can drop directly down to become the gold in the bench deposit. This is not the case. In actuality, an eluvial deposit might be swept down to rest on top of an old streambed (bench), but it will still remain as an eluvial deposit until it is washed into a stream of water. A bench placer deposit contains the gold that was deposited in that streambed before it was left high and dry.

Many benches are lying close to the present streams of water, and are actually the remains of the present stream as it ran years and years ago, as shown in figure 2-4.

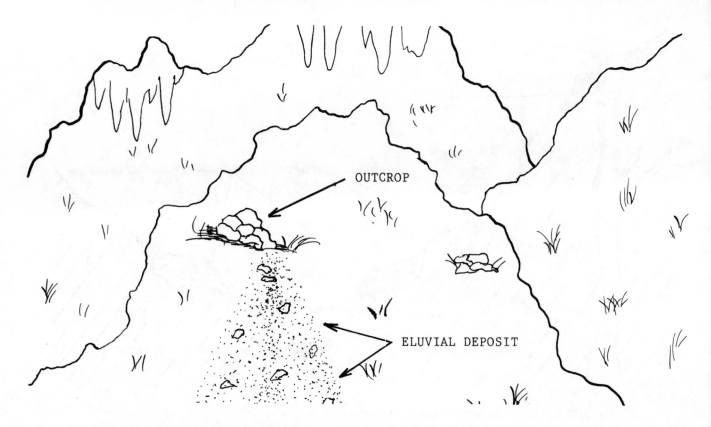

Fig. 2–3. An eluvial deposit contains those pieces of ore that have been swept away from the lode which have not reached a steambed.

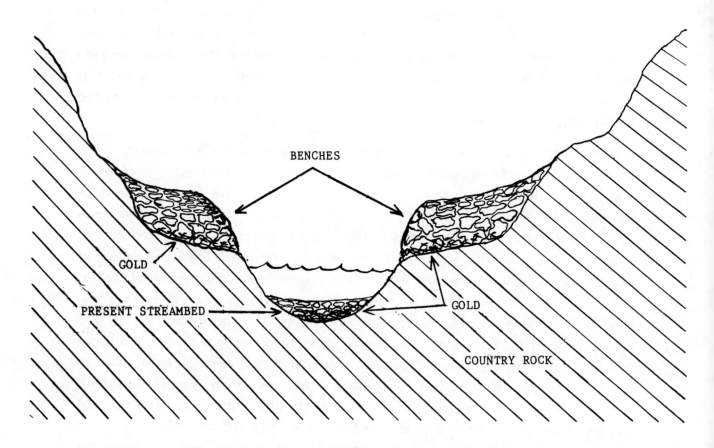

Fig. 2–4. Benches are the remains of older streambeds which once ran in that location.

Some dry streambeads (benches) are situated far away from any present stream of water. These are usually the remains of the ancient rivers, which ran before the present river systems were formed. Ancient stream benches can be found on top of mountains, far out into the deserts, or can be found near some of today's streams and rivers. The ancient streambeds — wherever found — are known for their rich deposits of gold.

Most surface gold mining operations today direct their activities at bench deposits. The reason for this is that the presence of an old streambed is evidence that it has never been mined before, and any gold which was once deposited there will still be in place.

STREAM PLACER: In order to discuss what happens to gold when it enters a stream of water, it is first necessary to understand the two terms: "bedrock" and "sediments." Billions of years ago, when the outer perimeter of the earth cooled, it hardened into a solid rock surface — called "bedrock." All of the loose dirt, rocks, sand, gravel and boulders which lie on top of the earth's outer hardrock surface (bedrock) are called "sediments." In some areas, the sedimentary material lies hundreds of feet deep. In other areas, especially in mountainous country and at the seashore, the earth's outer crust (bedrock) is completely exposed. Bedrock can be observed usually by driving down any highway and looking at where cuts have been made through the hardrock in order to make the highway straight and level.

Streambeds are composed of rocks, sand, gravel, clay and boulders (sediments) and always lie on top of the bedrock foundation. (See figure 2-5.) Bedrock and country rock are the same thing.

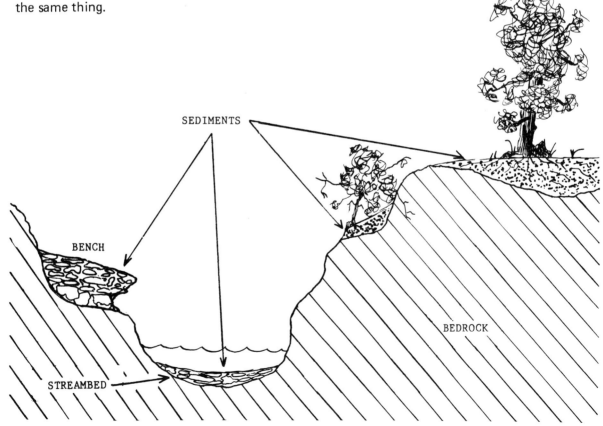

Fig. 2—5. Streambeds are composed of sediments which lie on top of bedrock.

A large storm in mountainous country will usually cause the streams and rivers within the area to run deeper and faster than they normally do. This additional volume of water increases the amount of force that flows over top of the streambeds which lie at the bottom of these water-ways. Sometimes in a very large storm the increased force of water is enough to sweep the entire streambed down the surface of it's underlying bedrock foundation. It is this action, which causes a streambed to cut deeper into the earth over an extended period of time. A storm of this size will also erode a significant amount of new gold into the streambeds where it will mix with the other materials.

Gold — being heavier than the other materials which are being swept down stream during a large storm, will work it's way quickly to the bottom of these materials. The reason for this is because gold has a much higher specific gravity than the other streambed materials and so will exert a downward force against them. As the streambed is being vibrated and tossed around and pushed along by the tremendous torrent of water caused by the storm, gold will be vibrated downward through the other materials until it reaches something which will stop its descent — like bedrock.

With exception of the finer sized pieces, it takes a lot of force to move gold. Being that gold is about 6 or 7 times heavier than the average of other materials which commonly make up a streambed, it takes a lot more force to move gold down along the bedrock than it does to move the other streambed materials.

So there is the possibility of having enough force in a section of river, because of a storm, to sweep part of the streambed away; yet perhaps not enough force to move much of the gold which is lying on bedrock.

When there is enough force to move gold along the bottom of a riverbed, that gold can then become deposited in a new location wherever the force of the flow is lessened.

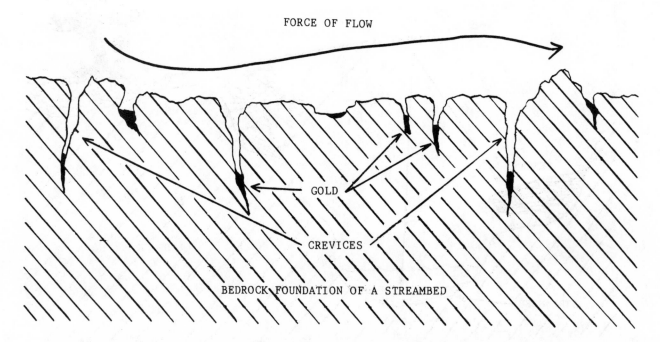

Fig. 2—6. Crevices in the bedrock are natural places where gold can drop out of the main force of the stream and become trapped.

Bedrock irregularities at the bottom of a streambed play a large role in determining where gold will become trapped. One good example of a bedrock gold trap is in the case of a crack or crevice in the bedrock surface, as shown in figure 2-6.

Many bedrock gold traps are situated so that the main force of water — being enough to move gold, will sweep the traps clean of lighter streambed materials. This leaves a hole for the gold to drop into and become shielded from the main force of water and material which is moving across the bedrock. And there the gold will remain, until some fluke of turbulence boils it out of the hole and back into the main force of water again, where it can then become trapped in some other such hole, and so on.

Some types of bedrock are very rough and irregular, which allows for many many gold traps along it's surface, as shown in figure 2-7.

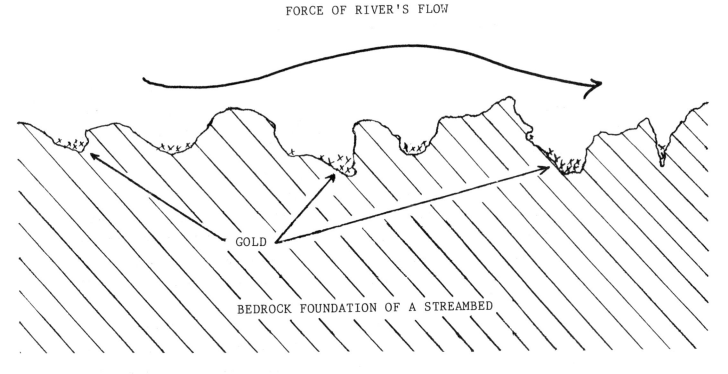

Fig. 2—7. Some bedrock surfaces are very rough and irregular — which allows for many gold traps.

How well a crevice will trap gold greatly depends on the shape of the crevice itself, and it's direction in relation to the flow of water. Crevices which extend out horizontally into a riverbed are often very effective gold catchers, because the force of water is usually enough to keep the upper part of the crevice clean of material, yet the shape and depth of the crevice will prevent gold from being swept or boiled out once it's inside, as shown in figure 2-8.

37

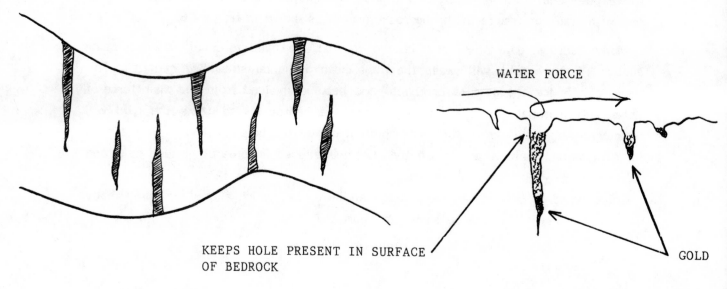

TOPVIEW   SIDEVIEW

WATER FORCE

KEEPS HOLE PRESENT IN SURFACE
OF BEDROCK

GOLD

Fig. 2—8. Horizontal type crevices often make excellent gold traps.

Crevices which run lengthwise with the flow of the stream or in a diagonal direction across the bed, can be good gold traps or poor ones, depending on the shape of the crevice and the individual set of circumstances covering each separate situation. For the most part, water force can get into a lengthwise type crevice and prevent a great deal of gold from being trapped inside. However, this greatly depends on the characteristics of the bedrock surface and there are so many possible variables that it is no use in attempting to cover them all — such as the possibility of a large rock becoming lodged inside of a lengthwise crevice making it's entire length of a gold trap of bonanza dimensions. There's really no need to say much more about lengthwise type crevices because if you are mining along and uncover one, you're going to clean it out to see what lies inside anyway.

Potholes in the bedrock foundation of a streambed have a tendency to trap gold very well. These usually occur where the bedrock surface is deteriorating and some portions are coming apart faster than others, which leaves holes that gold can drop into and be protected from the main force of water. (See figure 2-9. Next page)

Bedrock dikes (upcroppings of a harder type of hardrock) which protrude up through the floor of a streambed can make excellent gold traps in different ways, depending on the direction of the dike. For example, if a dike protrudes up through the floor of a streambed and is slanted in a down stream direction, (see part A of figure 2-10) gold will generally become trapped behind the dike where it can become shielded from the main force of the flow. A dike which is slanted in an upstream direction is likely to trap gold in a little pocket just up in front, as shown in part B of figure 2-10. (Next page)

38

WATER'S FLOW

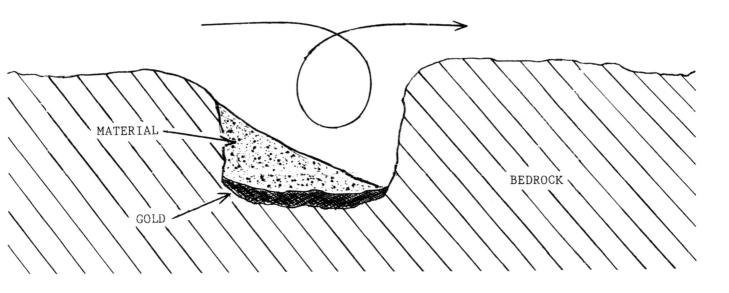

Fig. 2—9. Potholes in deteriorating type bedrock surfaces often make for good gold traps.

WATER FORCE

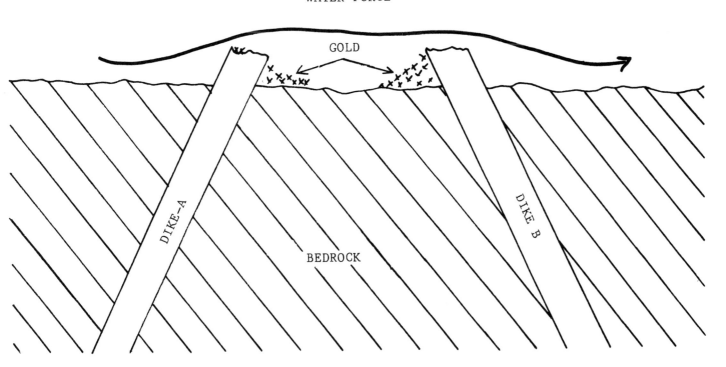

Fig. 2—10. Bedrock dikes trap gold in different ways depending on their direction to the stream's flow.

Hairline cracks in the bedrock surface of a streambed often contain surprising amounts of gold. Sometimes you can take out pieces of gold that seem to be too large for the cracks which you find them inside of, and it leaves you wondering how they got there. Once in awhile a hairline crack will open up into a space which holds a nice little pocket of gold, as shown in figure 2-11.

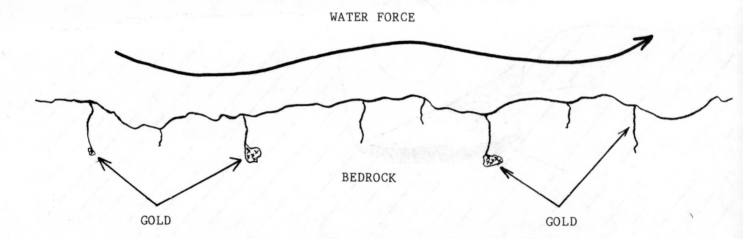

Fig. 2—11. Hairline cracks often hold plenty of gold, and sometimes open up into small pockets.

How smooth that the bedrock surface is, has a great deal to do with how well that it's various irregularities will catch gold. Some types of bedrock — like granite for example, are extremely hard and tend to become pounded into a smooth and polished surface. (See figure 2-12.)

Fig. 2—12. Smooth and polished bedrock surfaces do not retain gold very well.

Polished bedrock surfaces like this do not trap particles of gold nearly as well as the rough types of bedrock surfaces do. Also, polished bedrock — which sometimes contains large and deep "boil holes" (holes which have been bored into the bedrock by incredible amounts of water turbulence), is often an indication of too much enturbulated water force to allow very much gold to settle there at all.

Rougher types of bedrock, as shown in figure 2-13, often being full of irregularities — both large and small, have the kind of surface where most acceptable paying placer deposits are found. This kind of bedrock can be either very hard — and still contain it's roughness, or can be semi-decomposed, either way, and it will still trap gold very well.

Fig. 2—13. Rough types of bedrock surfaces tend to trap gold very well.

Basically, anywhere that rough bedrock is situated so that it's irregularities can slacken the force of water in a location where gold will travel is a likely place to find gold trapped.

Obstructions in a streambed can also cause the flow of water to slow down and can be the cause of a gold deposit, sometimes in front and sometimes to the rear of the obstruction. An outcropping of bedrock which juts out into a stream or river from one side can trap gold in various ways, depending on the shape of the outcropping and the direction which it protrudes out into the stream. An outcropping which extends out into the river in an upstream direction is most likely to trap gold in front of the outcropping, where there is a lull in the water force, as shown in part A of figure 2-14. Part B of the same diagram shows that the gold deposit is most likely to be found on the down stream side of an outcropping which juts out into the river in a downstream direction, because that's where the force of the flow lets up.

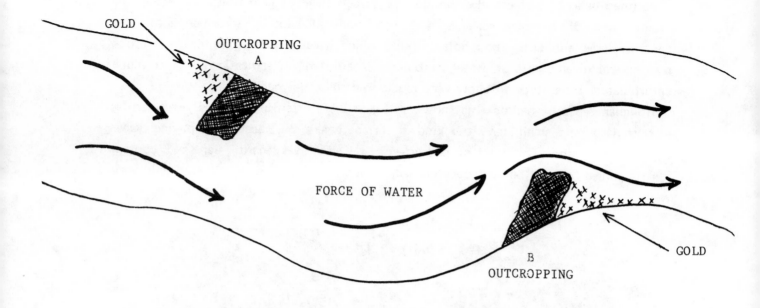

Fig. 2—14. An outcropping can be the source of a gold deposit in various ways — depending on the direction which it juts out into the streambed.

One of the most common locations in a stream or river to find a gold deposit is where the bedrock drops off suddenly to form a deep water pool. Any place where a fixed volume of water suddenly flows into a much larger volume of water is a place where the flow will slow down. Wherever the flow of water in a streambed slows down is a good place for gold to be dropped, and so it's not uncommon to find a good sized gold deposit in a streambed where there is a sudden drop-off into deeper water, as shown in figure 2-15.

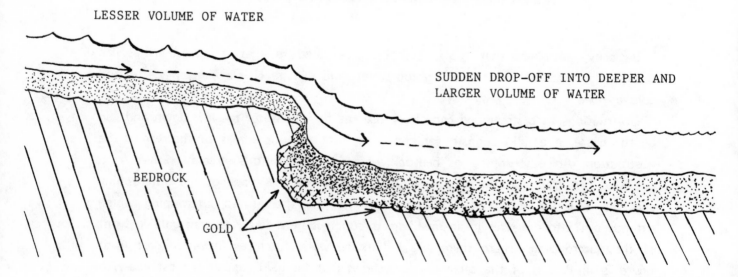

Fig. 2—15. Any sudden drop-off into a deeper and larger volume of water is a good spot to look for a depsoit of gold.

A waterfall is the extreme case of a sudden bedrock dropoff and can sometimes have a large deposit of gold at it's base — but not always. Sometimes the water will plunge down into the hole of the falls and create so much turbulence that any gold which is dropped into the hole during a storm will become ground up or boiled out. (See figure 2-16.)

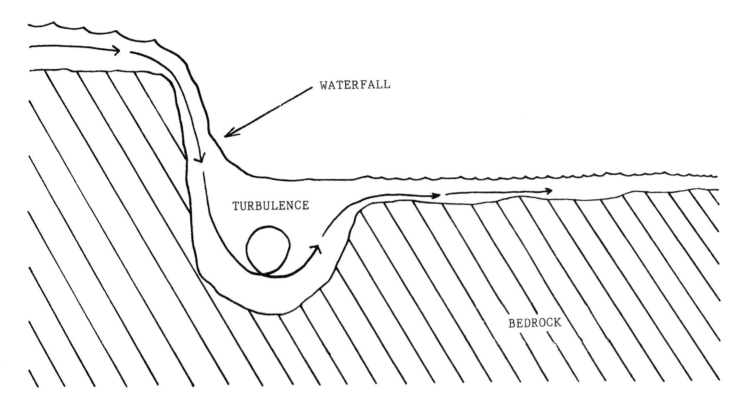

Fig. 2—16. Sometimes the amount of turbulence at the base of a waterfall is so great that everything is boiled out during high water.

On the other hand, sometimes large boulders can become trapped at the base of a falls and protect the gold from becoming ground up or boiled out by the turbulence. In this case the falls can become a bonanza as shown in figure 2-17. (Next page)

In some waterfalls the gold which has been boiled out will drop just outside of the hole, where the current has not yet had enough runway to pick up speed again — at least not enough to carry off much of the gold which arrives there, as shown in figure 2-18. (Next page)

Waterfalls are often the territory of the suction dredger, because this type of gold trap usually deposits the gold underwater, yet this is not always the case. Sometimes during the low water periods of the season, some of the ground below a falls is exposed and often there is very little streambed to move in order to reach bedrock — where most of the gold is likely to be. The only dependable way to determine if gold will be present below a falls is to sample around and find out. Usually this is rather easy (unless you run into huge boulders), because if the area has been boiled out and swept clean of gold, much of the time the bedrock will be exposed or have a layer of

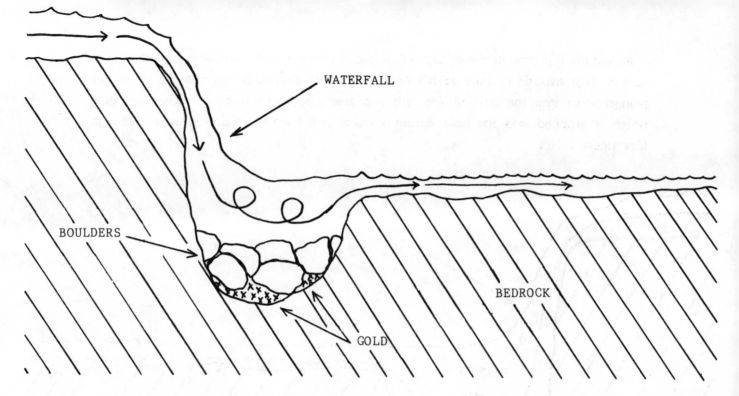

WATERFALL

BOULDERS

BEDROCK

GOLD

Fig. 2—17. Sometimes boulders at the base of a waterfall will protect gold from being boiled out of the hole.

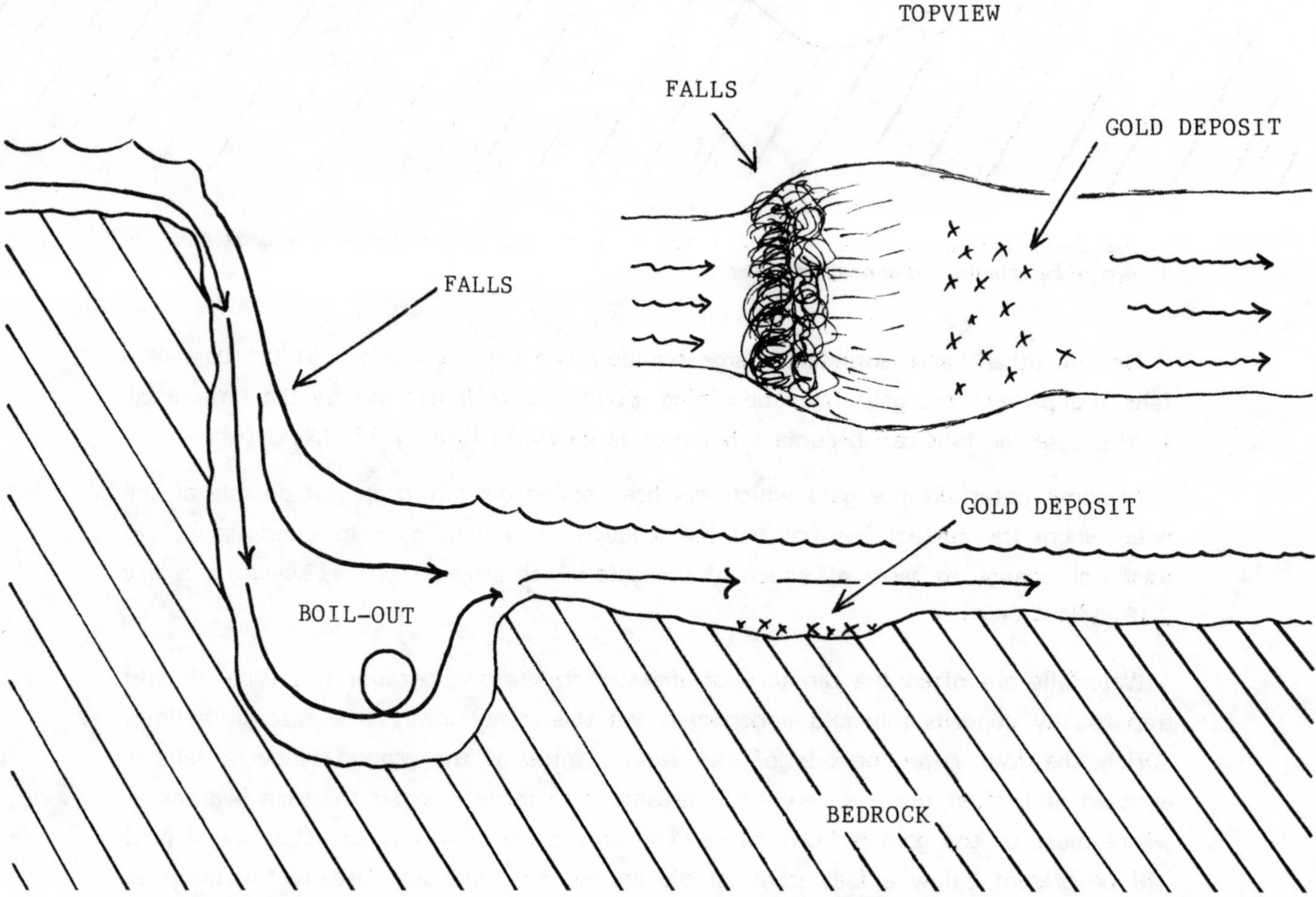

TOPVIEW

FALLS

GOLD DEPOSIT

FALLS

GOLD DEPOSIT

BOIL-OUT

BEDROCK

Fig. 2—18. Sometimes gold will deposit just beyond the boil-out caused by a waterfall.

light sand and gravel on top. Again, this is not always true, with each falls having it's own individual set of circumstances.

Another common location where a good sized gold deposit is likely to be found is where the lay-out of the country side causes the stream to run downhill at a rather steep grade for some distance and then suddenly it levels off. It's just below where the slope of the streambed levels off that the water flow will suddenly slow down, and that's where you are likely to find gold. (See figure 2-19.) Areas like this are known for their very large deposits.

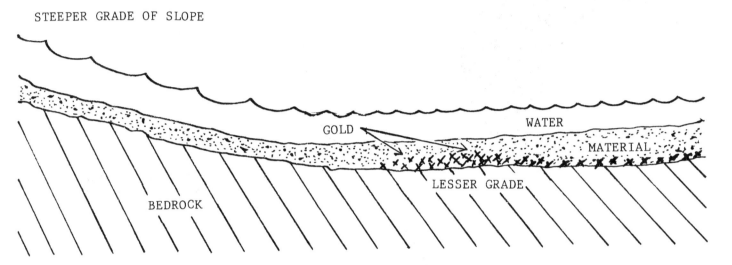

STEEPER GRADE OF SLOPE

GOLD

WATER

MATERIAL

LESSER GRADE

BEDROCK

Fig. 2–19. The area just below where a streambed's slope lessens, often contains a good sized gold deposit.

Boulders are another type of obstruction that can be in a riverbed and cause gold to drop out of a fast flow of water. Boulders are similar to gold in that the larger they are, the more water force it takes to move them. Sometimes in a storm the force of water can pick up enough to sweep large amounts of streambed material and gold down across the bedrock. When this happens, the force may or may not be great enough to move the large boulders. A large boulder which is at rest in a stream, while a torrent of water and material is being swept past it during a large storm, will slow down the flow of the stream just in front, below, and just behind the boulder. This being the case, if the storm's torrent happens to sweep gold near the boulder, some of the gold is likely to drop where the slackening of current is, as shown in figure 2-20.

One thing to know about boulders is that they do not always have gold trapped around them. Whether or not a specific boulder will have a deposit of gold along with it depends greatly on whether or not that boulder is in the direct path which the gold would have taken when it traveled down that section of streambed during earlier highwater periods.

Because of it's weight, gold tends to travel down along a streambed taking the path of least resistance. For the most part this route seems to be the shortest route possible between any major bends in the stream. (See figure 2-21. On following page.)

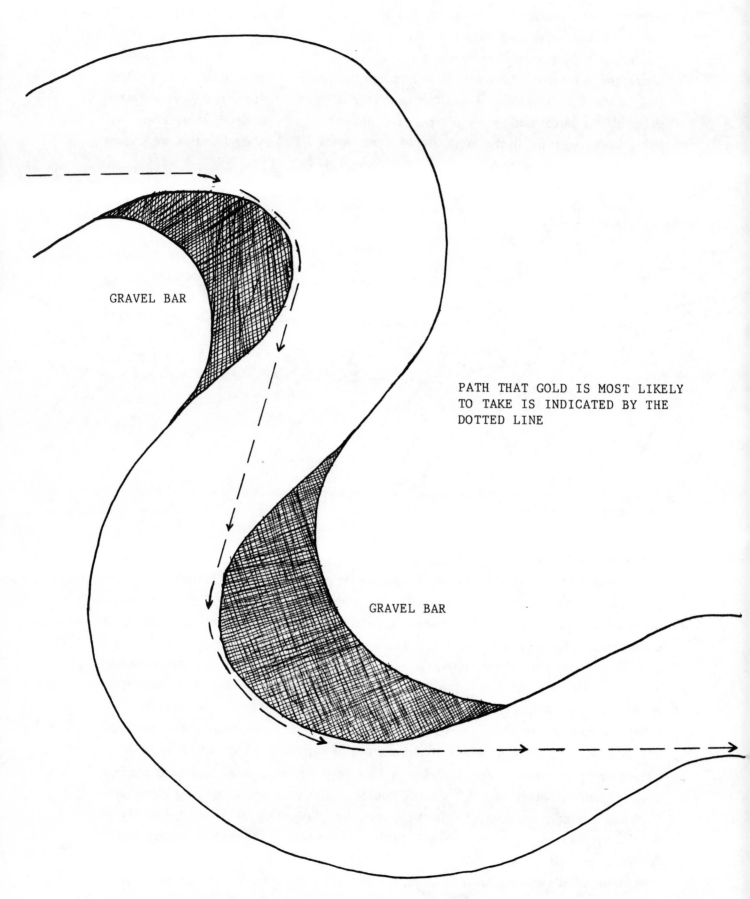

GRAVEL BAR

PATH THAT GOLD IS MOST LIKELY
TO TAKE IS INDICATED BY THE
DOTTED LINE

GRAVEL BAR

Fig. 2–21. Gold tends usually to follow the shortest route possible between any major changes in the direction of the stream or river.

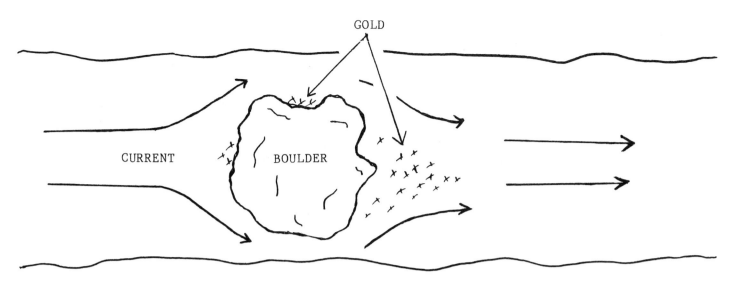

GOLD

CURRENT   BOULDER

Fig. 2—20. A boulder at rest in a streambed during a large storm might trap gold wherever it slows down the water force.

Take note in figure 2-21 that the route which the gold is taking rounds each curve towards the inside of the bend. While this might not be the route which gold always takes in a streambed, it's true that when it comes to curves, the vast majority of gold deposits are found towards the inside of bends and very few are found towards the outside in comparison. Perhaps the reason for this is because the centrifugal force causes a much greater energy of flow to the outside of the bend. This creates less force towards the inside — which allows for gold to drop there.

It's important for you as a prospector to grasp the concept that under most conditions, gold tends to travel the shortest distance between the bends of a stream or river, and that it also seems to follow the inside of the bends, because your best bet in prospecting is to direct your sampling activities towards areas which lie in the path that gold would most likely follow in it's route down stream. This entails an understanding of what effects that the various changes in bedrock and the numerous obstructions will have on changing and directing the path of gold as it is pushed down stream during extreme high water periods. For example, if you are looking for concentrations of gold around and behind boulders, you are much better off to check out the boulders which lie in the path that gold should, in theory, take; rather than to just sample boulders randomly in the streambed, no matter where they are located. (See figure 2-22. on the following page.)

Another situation in a stream or river where there is likely to be a large deposit of gold is where the stream runs narrow or at a certain general width for a distance and then suddenly opens up into a wider portion of streambed. Where the streambed widens, the water flow will usually slow down because the streambed allows for a larger volume of water in such a location — especially during extreme high water periods. Where water force slows down, gold will usually drop, as shown in figure 2-23.

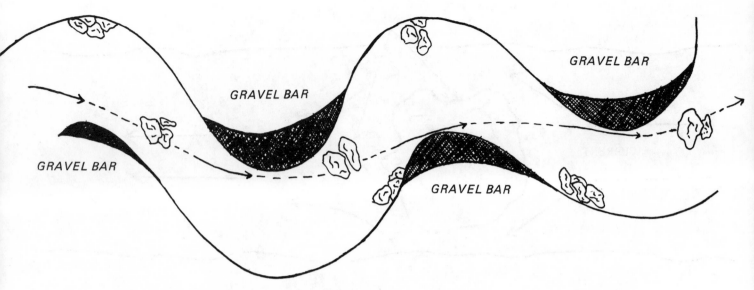

Fig. 2—22. The general path that gold should follow is indicated by the dotted line. Which boulders would most likely to have gold concentrations along with them?

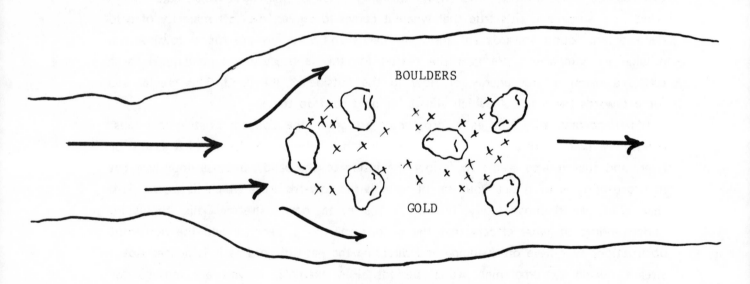

STREAMBED SUDDENLY
WIDENS

BOULDERS

GOLD

CAUSES WATER TO SUDDENLY SLOW DOWN
AND DROP BOULDERS AND GOLD

Fig. 2—23. Anywhere that a streambed suddenly widens enough to slow the force of the stream during highwater periods is a likely place to find a deposit of gold.

Notice in figure 2-23 that some boulders have also dropped where the water force is suddenly slowed down. Boulders are similar to gold in that it takes a tremendous amount of force to push them along, and wherever that force lets up enough, the boulders will drop. So boulders are often found in the same areas where large amounts of gold are deposited. But, gold is not always found where boulders are dropped, because there are so many boulders and the vast majority of them do not follow the same route that gold generally takes. Nevertheless, it's well to take note that those places where boulders do get hung up, which are on the same route that gold should follow, are generally good places to direct some of your sampling activities.

ANCIENT RIVERS

About two million years ago, towards the end of the Tertiary geological time period, the mountain systems in the Western United States underwent a tremendous amount of faulting and twisting, which changed the character of the mountains into much of what they look like today. It was during that period that the present drainage system of streams, creeks and rivers were formed, which run pretty much in the westerly direction.

Prior to that, there was a vastly different river system, that generally ran in a southerly direction. These were the old streambeds which ran throughout much of the Tertiary period, and so are called "tertiary channels" or "ancient rivers." The ancient rivers ran for millions of years, during which time an enormous amount of erosion took place which washed the majority of gold from the exposed rich lode deposits into the rivers.

The major changes that occurred towards the end of that period, which rearranged the mountains and formed the present drainage systems, left portions of the ancient channels strewn about, with some portions being placed on top of the present mountains, some being left out in the desert areas, and some portions being close to and crossed by the present drainage system.

Geologists have determined that the majority of gold in today's river system is not gold that has eroded more recently from lode deposits, but gold that was eroded out of the old ancient riverbeds where they have been crossed by the present river system.

The ancient channels, where they have been discovered and mined, have repeatedly proven to be extremely rich in gold deposits. In fact, many of the richest bonanzas that have been found in today's river system, were discovered directly beneath where it has crossed the old ancient streambed gravels. Other areas which have proven to be very rich in today's river system have been found to be close to the old channels, where a few million years worth of erosion has caused much of the channel — and its gold-to be deposited into the present streambeds.

The ancient channels (benches) are notorious for their very rich bottom strata. This strata is usually of a deep blue color; and indeed the rich blue color, when encountered, is one of the most certain indicators that ancient gravels are present. This bottom strata of the ancient gravels was referred to by the oldtimers as the "blue lead," probably because they followed its path all over the west whereever it led them, because it always paid so well.

Ancient blue gravels usually oxidize and turn a rusty reddish brown color after being dug up and exposed to the atmosphere. Often the ancient blue gravels are very hard and compacted — but not always.

Running into blue gravel at the bottom of a streambed does not necessarily mean that you have located an ancient channel, but it's possible that you have located some ancient gravels, which might have a rich pay streak along with them.

Most of the high benches that you will find up alongside of todays rivers and streams, and sometimes a fair distance away — but which travel generally in the same direction, are not Tertiary channels, but more likely to be the earlier remnants of the present rivers and streams. These old streambeds are sometimes referred to as the "Pleistocine channels," because they were formed and ran during the earlier part of the present "Qualernary period" (geological time), which is called the "Pliestocine epoch" by the geologists.

Some high benches that rest alongside of the present streams and rivers were formed since the passing of the Pliestocine epoch. These are referred to as "Recent benches," having been formed during the "Recent epoch" (present epoch).

Some of these benches — either Pliestocine or Recent, are quite extensive in size. Dry streambeds as such are scattered about all over gold country, some which have already been mined, most of which are still untouched.

Usually, all that is left of a bench after it has been mined are rock piles, as shown in figure 2-24. Notice in the picture that part of the unmined streambed is in the background, behind the trees.

Fig. 2—24. Usually all that is left of a high bench after it's been mined are piles of the larger sized streambed rocks and boulders.

Most of the hydraulic mining operations that operated during the early to mid 1900's were directed at high benches. "Hydraulic mining" was done by directing a large volume of water, under great pressure, at a streambed in an effort to erode its gravels out of the bed and through recovery systems, where the gold would be trapped. (See figure 2-25.)

Fig. 2—25. A hydraulic mining operation. Photo courtesy of Trinity County Historical Museum.

So some bench gravels have been mined, but most of them still remain intact; and while most of the Pliestocine and Recent benches are not as rich in gold content as were the Tertiaries, it still remains true that an enormous amount of gold washed down into these old channels when they were running. So they are pretty darn rich in some areas, and pay rather consistantly in others. Also, any gold that ever washed down into any old bench which has yet to be mined, still remains there today. It's for this reason that the majority of successful surface gold mining operations today direct their attention towards bench gravels.

FLOOD GOLD

A large percentage of the gold which is found in today's creeks and rivers has been washed down into them out of the higher bench deposits by the erosive effects of storms and time. A certain amount of gold is being washed downstream in any river located in gold country at all times — even if only microscopic in size.

The larger in size that a piece of gold is, the more water force that it takes to move it downstream in a riverbed. The amount of water force that it takes to move a significant amount of gold in a riverbed is usually enough force to also move the streambed too. This would allow the gold to work its way quickly down to the bedrock, where it can become trapped in the various irregularities.

Some streambeds contain a high degree of mineral content, and grow very hard after having been in place for a number of years.

Sometimes a storm will have enough force to move large amounts of gold, but will only move a portion of the entire streambed, leaving a lower strata in place in some locations. When this happens, the gold which is moving along at the bottom of the flooding layer can become trapped by the irregularities of the unmoving streambed layer that lies underneath. The rocks in a stable lower strata as such can act as natural gold traps, as shown in firure 2-26.

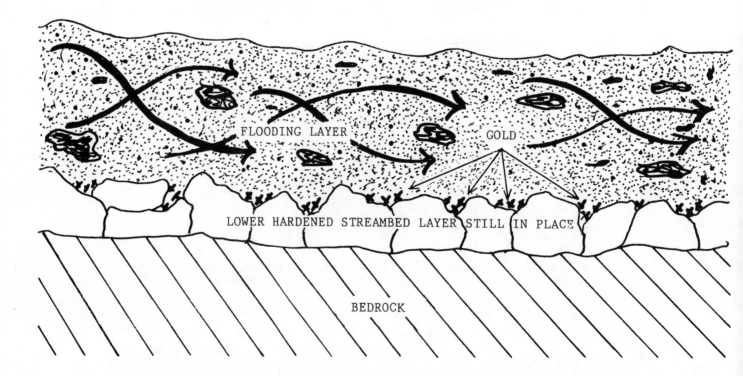

Fig. 2—26. Flood gold is that gold which rests inside and at the bottom of a flooding layer.

Different streamed layers, caused by flooding storms, are referred to as "flood layers." The flood layers within a streambed — if present, can be easily distinguished because they are usually of a different color, material consistancy, and hardness than the other layers of material within the streambed. That gold which is found at the bottom of — or throughout a flood layer is called "flood gold." Sometimes the bottom of a flood layer will contain far more gold than is present on bedrock. Sometimes, when more than one flood layer is present in a streambed, there will be more than one layer of flood gold present too.

The larger a piece of gold is, the faster that it will work it's way down towards the bottom of a flooding layer of material as it's being washed downstream during a storm. Finer sized pieces of gold might not work their way down through a flooding layer at all, but might remain up in the material.

So you can run across a flood layer which has a line of the heavier sized pieces of gold along it's bottom edge, or a flood layer which contains a large amount of fine gold dispersed throughout the entire layer, and you can also run across a flood layer which contains a high degree of fine gold dispersed throughout, and a line of heavier gold along the bottom edge.

Not all flood layers contain gold in paying quantities for the small sized mining operation, but in gold country all flood layers do seem to contain gold in some quantity — even if only microscopic is size.

Some of the best areas in which to test for paying quantities of flood gold are where the stream or river widens out, or levels out, or changes the direction of its flow, as in such places the flow of water in a storm will slow up and possibly allow concentrations of flood gold to collect.

GRAVEL BAR PLACERS

Gravel bars located in streambeds that flow through gold country — especially the ones located towards the inside of bends, tend to collect a lot of flood gold, and sometimes in paying quantities even for the smaller sized operations. The flood gold in bar placers is usually consistantly distributed throughout the entire gravel bar. Often the lower end of a gravel bar is not as rich as the head of the bar, but the gold there is usually more uniformly dispersed throughout the material.

FALSE BEDROCK

Once in awhile a prospector will uncover an extremely hard layer of material located just above the bedrock and mistake the layer for being bedrock because of it's hardness. A hard layer as such is often called "false bedrock." Such a layer can consist of streambed material, or of volcanic flows which have laid down and hardened on top of bedrock, or it can consist of any kind of mineral deposit which has hardened on top of the true bedrock.

Sometimes there will be a good paying gold deposit underneath a false bedrock layer, but when there is, it's usually rather difficult to get at it.

CHAPTER III

WHERE TO FIND GOLD

The 1872 Mining Law says that any citizen of the United States (or person who has declared his intention of becoming one) can claim sections of land in his own name for the purpose of developing the mineral resources on that land. This is generally true of any lands owned by the federal government which have not already been set aside for some other purpose.

The bulk of National Forestry land falls under the catagory of land which can be used for the purpose of mineral development. Most of the gold bearing country within the Western United States is located in National Forests and so is open for the gold prospector to do his thing — whether as a hobby, adventure, or as a profession.

Some of the specific areas which are closed to mineral entry — meaning that you cannot file a mining claim on the land, are as follows: National park land, military land, Indian reservations, resevoirs, permanent lake beds, city owned land, state owned land, private land, state monuments, some sections of forestry lands which are set aside by the Department of Fish and Game for study or development reasons. Wilderness and primitive areas are also withdrawn.

Just because a section of land is withdrawn from mineral entry, does not always mean that you cannot prospect in the area. It does mean that you cannot claim the mineral rights within that section of land for yourself. In some of these places — like Fish and Game Department withdrawals, it's possible that prospecting can be done on the land, and it's just a matter of contacting whoever is in charge to find out. This is also true of private and Indian owned lands.

There are maps available which outline the areas that are primitive, National Parks, Indian reservations and private land, as well as the areas that are just plain National Forestry land and open to mineral development by the individual. These maps can usually be obtained by contacting the Forestry Department that has jurisdiction over the area which you are interested in.

Some rivers within the National Forests have been entirely withdrawn from mineral entry, yet are left open to be prospected by anyone who is interested. Some Forestry Departments have withdrawn sections of river for recreational purposes; so that outsiders can have a place to mine recreationally, without having to worry about filing claims and such. Information on places that are wide open to the public, along with data concerning the local rules and regulations, can also be obtained by contacting the Forestry Departments within the areas of your general interest.

Actually, there are just a few rules and regulations that the small time operator has to worry about. He usually does not affect enough environmental change to warrant the necessity to have an approved plan of operation with the Forestry Department, at least not during the time of this writing.

In the state of California, it's necessary to apply to the Fish and Game Department for a permit before running a dredge in any stream, creek or river. At the time of this writing, the permit costs $5.00 and is just a matter of filling out a paper at any Fish and Game Department within the state. The permit lasts until the beginning of the new year — at which time a new permit needs to be filled out and paid for — just like a fishing license. The Fish and Game Department in California has certain dredge size limitations for some of its rivers and streams, and also has time limits for dredging operations in some of the water ways. Their stated reason for this is to prevent any damaging effects to the fish movements. When you fill out and pay for your yearly permit, the Fish and Game Department will also give you a list of the various dredge size limitations and the dredging periods which apply to the streams, rivers and creeks that they are interested in protecting. If you should want to use a dredge of a larger size, or operate during the off-time period in such a waterway, it is necessary to apply for a special permit with the Department of Fish and Game. Sometimes the permit will be directly approved; and at other times, the department will want to send a person out to the spot and have him do a study. In this case, the special permit will cost you $75 — at least that's what it costs during the time of this writting.

One other rule, which is strictly enforced, is that a U.S. Forestry Service approved spark arrester is required on any internal combustion type engine which is operated inside of forestry land. This is true of chainsaws, motorcycles, and also of the small engines that are used to pump water to the various types of mining equipment. These spark arresters are almost always available wherever gold mining equipment is sold.

The vast majority of land contained inside the boundries of National Forest is open to mineral entry. It's not uncommon to go into an area which has all the signs of being a good gold bearing location and find that much of that specific sight appears to be already claimed up by the individuals who got there first. In this case, if you are interested in finding an open spot to file on, it's necessary to go to the County Clerk's office and learn how to research out the area that you want to file on. This is usually not hard to do; but it takes time and patience — how much, depending entirely upon how many claims have been filed in the area that you are interested in. The County Clerk will help you around and show you what you need to go about your research.

You do not need to file a mining claim in order to mine or prospect in an area. The purpose of a mining claim is to secure the rights to mine the minerals on that section of land for yourself.

Mining law at present is a very large and technical subject that just a few of today's miners are aware of in its totality. This is really too bad, because every player in a game should be aware of the rules which govern the game. Otherwise, the rules can be changed easily, unbeknown to most of the players!

The California Division of Mines used to put out a publication which covered the subject rather well. Presently, it seems to be out of print — or very hard to come by.

Actually, I don't believe that there is any volume written and available today which covers all of the different parts of present day mining law that affects the modern day miner, in an easy to read and understand form.

The subject is probably not nearly as complicated as it looks at first glance, once you get through all of the legal hodge podge of terminology and put it into layman's terms. A manual put together as such would be extremely valuable to the entire field at this time; and if one does not come about within the next few months or so after this printing, I believe that I'll get together with one of my more legally informed friends and put such a volume together. So watch for some kind of legal manual to be available soon. If I do it, it will be called **Mining Law In The 1980's,** or something on that order.

If the mineral rights on the section of ground which you would like to mine are already legally claimed by someone else, you can almost always work out some kind of a deal with the owner. Some claim owners will allow you to prospect on a small scale for no other commitment, other than to let them know how much gold you find and where. After all, a 20-acre claim covers a lot of ground, and any smart owner wants it sampled thoroughly to get an idea of its value and where the gold lies.

Sometimes the owner of a mining claim will agree to a percentage deal. Ten percent to the owner is the most widely accepted deal at this writing, unless the ground that the claim owner is going to allow you to mine is already tested and has proven to be rich paying ground, at which time his percentage can be more — how much more usually depending on the highest bidder that is present.

Some claim owners prefer to not have anyone else mining on their claims. It's not uncommon in gold country to see claims which are paying medium sized dredges (one man operation) one to two ounces of gold per day, consistantly. Some claims are paying far better amounts.   So it's understandable that the owner of the claim — and the miners - do not want a bunch of bystanders hanging around. The main thing to remember is that the owner of a valid mining claim does have the total rights over the minerals on that section of ground; and if he says ''No!'' , you might as well go find another piece of ground; because he does have that right, as will you, if and when you claim a section of mineral rights for yourself.

LOCATING GOLD BEARING GROUND

Deposits of gold have been located in all 50 states. Gold can often be found in many plants, animals, in sea water, and even in your own back yard. If you are seriously interested in mining gold, the thing that you will want to do is to locate it in large enough amounts to make it worthwhile to expend the energy needed in order to recover it.

When starting out in gold prospecting, your best bet is to begin in a location which is an already proven gold producing area. It's a proven fact that a geological location which has trapped gold in the past is likely to do so again. It's easy to get the idea that an area which has already been heavily mined is all played out (no more gold left); and for the most part, this would probably be so if it were not for the many large winter storms that have occurred since earlier mining activity was done. In our case, we have about 120 years of erosion that has taken place since most of the rivers and streams were mined, and some very large storms have occured during this period. So, many of the river and streambeds which once produced well are producing well again; and if you are just beginning and are trying to figure out where to start your operation, one of your best bets is to locate already proven gold bearing ground and start there.

GEOLOGICAL REPORTS AND MAPS

As already mentioned, during the earlier days of mining, it was mandatory — by law, for a miner to sell his gold to the government. The government, in turn, kept records of how much gold was bought from the various mines within the various counties. These records are open to public scrunity.   As a result, books have been published which give an account of how much recorded gold has been mined out of the various rivers, streams, creeks, and other locations within the various gold producing areas. These books are usually available in places where gold mining equipment is sold, and can be valuable to the prospector who wants to place himself in an already proven gold producing area. For example, in looking over one such book, I found that Trinity County in Northern California produced better than 2½ million ounces of recorded gold. That makes it a high   producer when compared to Modoc County, which has produced no more than 15 thousand ounces according to the same book. In looking this over, we can determine that of the two counties, Trinity County would probably be the better direction to go in an effort to search out paying quantities of gold. The book goes on to mention that the Trinity River, which flows through Trinity County, has produced over a million ounces of recorded gold. This data is valuable, because it tells us that the Trinity River has been a good gold producing river in the past and so is likely to be a good gold producer at the present.

There are specific county reports available from the Bureau of Mines, which give a wealth of data about the different kinds of minerals which have been located within the various counties, and where they have been found. These reports often include several maps, including a geological type map that shows the many different geological rock formations within the county, and sometimes also the placement of the Tertiary gravels. There is also usually a map included which shows the locations of the mines and mineral resources within the specified county. The report usually includes a large section that gives a listing of all or most of the mines which were selling gold to the government prior to or during the time when the report was being written. This listing usually includes data concerning each separate mine, such as: it's name, location, name of owners at the time, geology concerning the deposit, how it was being mined, and sometimes how rich the material was and how much recorded gold was produced out of the mine. (See figure 3-1 on following page.)

There is probably no need to go into how valuable such a report can be to a prospector. Basically, it gives him an individual break down of a specific county showing where gold has already been located in paying quantities and the specific geological information concerning those areas.

In California, for information concerning where to buy specific county geological reports write to:

California Division of Mines
P.O. Box 2980
Sacramento, CA 95812

Sometimes a specific county report will be out of print and so cannot be purchased, in which case the Division of Mines should be able to tell you where to locate one for study purposes. Usually the larger sized libraries and museums within a county have copies of the specific county geological reports which have been published about their own areas.

If you are seriously considering the idea of prospecting out paying quantities of gold and do not already have a good general location picked out, or you are looking for a better location, you should consider the idea of looking over the available **Where To Find Gold** books, and then the geological reports which lay out the counties that interest you. Perhaps this is not the only way of locating good ground, but it is a very highly workable method, because in following this procedure you are utilizing the accumulated data from most of the mining which has already occurred. If you do a good job of it, you are almost certain to place yourself into good gold bearing country.

GOLD, PLACER—Continued

Map no.	Name of claim, mine, or group	Location	Owner (Name, address)	Geology	Remarks and references
	Trinity Gold and Mining Company				See La Grange, herein.
	Trinity Gold Mining Company				See Lower Buckeye.
	Trinity Gold Placer Mining Syndicate, Ltd.				See Blythe.
	Trinity River Hydraulic Mine				See Hawkins Bar.
	Trinity River Mining Company				See English Tom.
	Turney (Wickline)	Sec. 30, T 35 N, R 10 W, MDB&M		10-ft. gravel bank.	Small-scale operation at Dedrick on Canyon Creek. In 1946 L. L. Turney and Joe Wickline mined with bulldozer. Gold recovered in sluice box 20 ft. long. Small producer.
	Two Sisters and Wonder	Sec. 25, T 35 N, R 8 W, MDB&M	Undetermined		Placer claim about 3½ mi. NE of Minersville. No published description. Idle. (Averill 41:88.)
	Tyson	Sec. 30, T 35 N, R 10 W, MDB&M	Undetermined		Placer claim S of Dedrick. No published description. Idle. (Averill 41:88.)
	Union Gulch Placer	Sec. 9, T 33 N, R 9 W, MDB&M	Undetermined		About 2 mi. E of Weaverville. No published description. Idle. (Averill 41:88.)
164	Union Hill	Sec. 6, T 32 N, 9 W, MDB&M		River terrace gravel.	175 ft. above Trinity River about 1 mi. NE of Douglas City. First worked 1862, again 1906-14. Leased during early 1920's. Idle. See McMurry and Hupp also. (Crawford 94:314; 96: 465; Brown 16:915; Tucker 22: 97, 207; 23:58; Haley 23:94; Logan 26:49.)
	Unity				See Nugget Bar.
165	Up Grade (Bonus, Good Enough)	Sec. 18, T 6 N, R 7 E, HB&M			Placer deposit about 3 mi. SW of Denny at confluence of New River and Panther Creek. Sampling by open cuts, adits, and shafts in 1939 said to have indicated large deposit of gravel suitable for hydraulicking. (Averill 41:64.)
166	Upham (Pine Tree)	Sec. 29, 30, T 32 N, R 8 W, MDB&M		Terrace gravel 15 to 50 ft. higher than present bed of North Fork Indian Creek; gravel about 24 ft. deep above hard hornblende schist bedrock.	Hydraulic mine 8 mi. SE of Douglas City. Water brought from Indian Creek through 3,800-ft. flume. (Averill 33: 72; 41:64.)
167	Uphill Mining Company (Hornet Bar)	Sec. 5, 8, T 32 N, R 9 W, MDB&M. Sec. 1, T 34 N, R 11 W, MDB&M. Sec. 29, T 34 N, R 10 W, MDB&M		Gravel over greenstone bedrock.	Short-lived dredge operation. Gold averaged 4½ cents per cubic yard. See also Indian Creek (Bennett) dredge, herein.

Fig. 3—1. Example of a single page in a geological report, under the "Tabulation of Mines" section.
Note: Monetary figures based on $35.00 an ounce.

Another thing to keep an eye out for when looking for good present day placer ground, is the presence of high benches in the vicinity — especially near the stream or river that you are interested in, if working such. Mainly, it's these benches that are eroded away and washed into the present streams during storms that put new deposits of gold into the streams and rivers. One hundred and twenty years of natural erosion and storms has been enough to deposit a large amount of gold into some of the present rivers and streams. Perhaps they are not all as rich as they once were, but some of them pay pretty good and consistently to those who know how to find the deposits. Rivers in California, which were supposedly mined by the 49er's, are paying regularly in 15, 30 and 40-ounce concentrated deposits, with 80-ounce deposits being turned up here and there. It's also not uncommon to hear about a 100, 200 or even 400-ounce catch being turned up by a small to medium sized dredging operation and being mined out during the course of the season — but this is more rare. It's the 5 - 20-ounce concentrations that are rather consistent and not too difficult to find, if you are willing to do the work of sampling to locate them. By concentrations, I don't mean finding all of the gold in a single crevice or hole. The concentrations are usually spread out over a small area — say 15 feet wide by 30 or 40 feet long. They can be smaller — or larger - depending on each individual situation. The gold can be found to be inside the bedrock traps, or up in the material itself, or maybe found in both areas. These concentrations are usually found in a position in a stream or river where the water force is made to slow up because of a sudden major change in the bedrock, a group of obstructions in the stream flow, where the river makes a turn, or other such places as covered earlier. In concentrations such as these, you usually don't get all of the gold in a single day, but instead are more likely to be into excellent wages for a week or a month or two or mabye more, depending on the size of the deposit and how long that it takes for you to mine it out once you have found it.

Deposits such as these are being turned up rather consistently in the already proven gold country, which was gone through by the earlier miners, and being rich when they went through it, too.

Sometimes, these present day deposits are discovered directly below where an old high bench is bleeding off (eroding) into the present stream or river. I know of one case where an 80-ounce deposit was taken in about 6 days out of a small concentrated area just below where a bench had been bleeding into the river. The gold was all laying on top of hard packed streambed layer, under about 6 inches of loose sand and gravel — and all right up alongside of the stream bank. Not all concentrations are found just below old benches, not by a long shot; but it's not too uncommon to hear of concentrations being located just below high benches, and so it's worth a bit of your sampling energy to test such areas out.

The maps that show the locations of mines and mineral resources, which often come along with a county geological report, can be very helpful in telling you where good paying high bench deposits are or were located in relationship to the streams or rivers that you might be interested in. The location of placer mines are shown on such maps; and when these are indicated some distance away from the present body of water, you know that the mine was processing high bench gravels. (See figure 3-2.) On many of these maps, as shown in this figure, each mine is numbered. To be sure that the mine was processing old bench gravels, you can look up its number within the "tabulation of mines," contained in the geological report, and read the information concerning that individual mine, as shown earlier in figure 3-1.

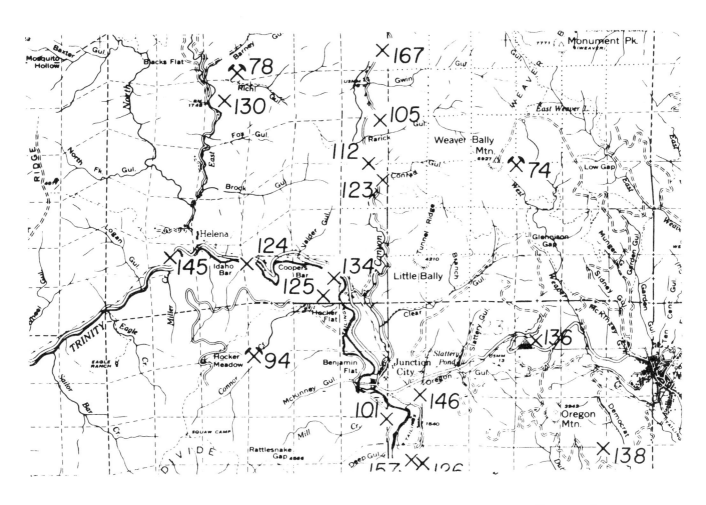

Fig. 3-2. The criss-crosses show where earlier placer mining operations occurred. The crossed picks show where earlier lode mining took place. Each mine is numbered.

The indication of high bench mining, having once occurred near a stream or river, is an indication of potential rich paying gravels which may still be present to some extent within that area; and the last 120 years of erosion just might have redeposited a large amount of gold out of the high deposits and into the present stream or river. This is not a sure thing; it's just a possibility; but when researching where gold is likely to be, it's good procedure to put as many possibilities in your favor as you can. If there are high bench deposits which contain paying quantities of gold near a stream or river, or the remnants of the bleedoffs of old such beds are still present, it's almost a certainty that the last 120 years of erosion has washed some of its gold into the present stream — how much, remains to be seen. The indication of an old mine being present shows that the deposits were there and that they were probably relatively rich too.

USING TOPOGRAPHIC MAPS

Topographic-type maps are put out by the Geological Survey of the Department of Interior, and can usually be purchased at most any sports equipment shop within the area that you are interested in. The purpose of the Topographic map (topo) is to show the surface features of the area that it covers, including the mountains, valleys, hills, lakes, rivers and streams, bridges, roads and trails, etc. This is accomplished with the use of "contour lines," which show the elevations in feet above or below sea level. All points on a single contour line have the same elevation. To make the elevations easy to follow on a "Topo," usually every 5th line is made more boldly than the other lines,   with its elevation numbered, as shown in figure 3-3. On most such maps, each separate contour line indicates a change of 50 feet in altitude.

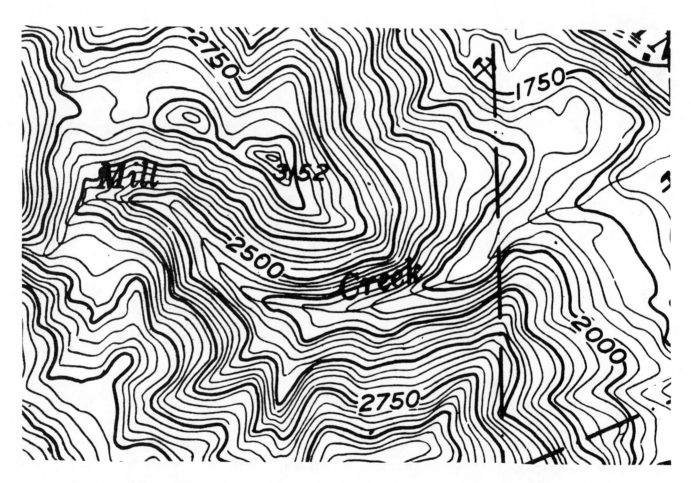

Fig. 3—3. Contour layers.

In looking over a topo, you can see the different grades of slope on the various hills, mountains, streams and rivers, etc., within the areas that you are interested in. Where the contour lines are closer together, it indicates that the grade of drop in that location is more steep than in an area where the contour lines are further apart. So, in this way, a topo can give you a top view of the general lay of the land.

Topo's also include the various roads and trails within the area; and by looking these over and the elevation changes, you can get a good idea of the accessibility of a location.

Topo maps also show where the large tailings piles lay from the earlier large scale mining operations. These are an index of where very large scale operations were mining — such as the old bucket line dredges — which processed thousands of yards of material per day. (See figure 3-4.)

Fig. 3—4. Tailings are sometimes shown on topographical maps, also.

There are two specific geological situations which often cause large concentrations of gold to deposit — both of which are easily spotted on topographical-type maps. The first of these is where a gold bearing stream, river or creek drops off steadily at a rather steep and steady grade, and then suddenly levels off to a degree for some distance. As mentioned earlier, the reason why locations like this pay so well is because where the grade of slope in a waterway is lessened, the water force of the entire stream of water lets up — which can be the cause of a major dropping area for gold. This can be true of any major change of slope in any gold bearing waterway. It doesn't have to be from steep slope to level. It can be a steady dropping off to just a little bit less dropping off. Anywhere on a map where the slope of grade in a stream or river is lessened in any amount, the water force is likely to be less in that general area, and a deposit of gold might be present. On a topographical map, the grade of a river or stream can be accurately observed by following the contour lines and noting their distance apart. Where the contour lines along the streambed become closer together, it indicates that the downward grade of slope in that location is more steep, and the water will generally be moving faster there. Where the contour lines in the stream suddenly become further apart, it indicates that the slope of the stream is less steep in that area, and the water force is likely to slow down there (See figure 3-5.). The best areas for finding gold are where the grade lets up and remains that way for some distance.

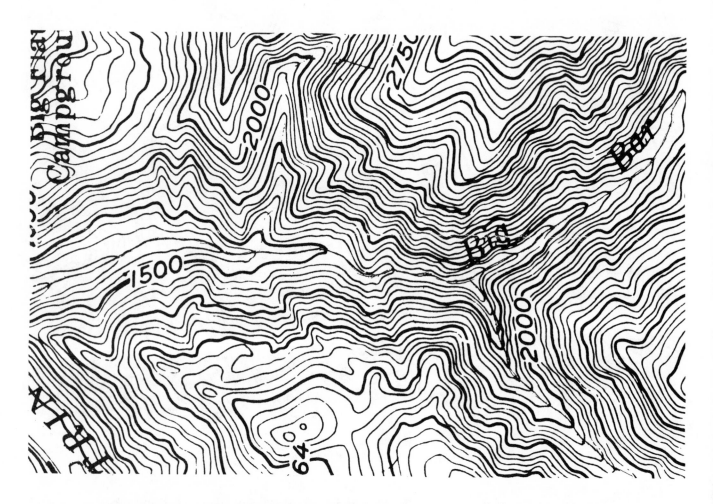

Fig. 3—5. Follow Big Bar Creek from right to left, and notice how the contour lines are further and further apart. This indicates a gradual lessening of slope.

The other geological situation which pays rather consistently, and is easily found on a topo, is where the channel of a riverbed remains rather narrow or at a certain width for a distance, and then suddenly opens up into a larger and wider sized streambed. During extreme high water periods, the larger volume of area in such locations will cause the water force of the river to slow up. Figure 3-6 shows an example of this happening and how it looks on a topo.

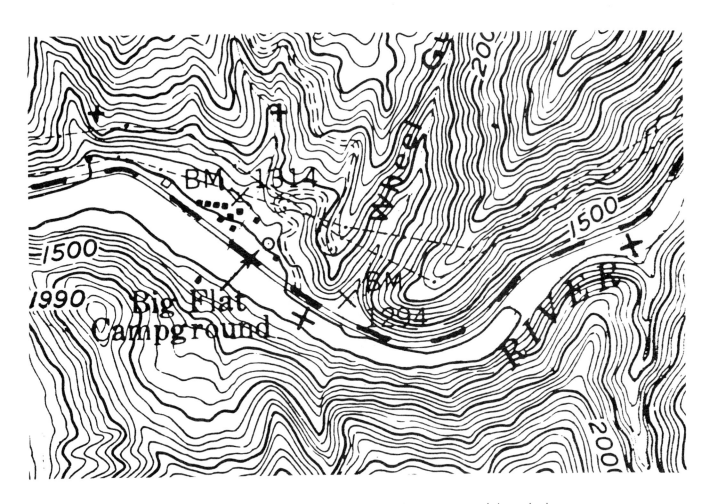

Fig. 3—6. Notice where the basic riverbed suddenly opens up much larger in size.

The best gold deposits in this sort of situation are found where the riverbed opens up and remains open for some distance. Sometimes the deposit is found a ways downstream from where the bed first opens up, because it might take some distance for the stream of water to slow down enough to drop gold. This is also true of major changes in slope as covered earlier. Sometimes more than one deposit can be found in situations like this, depending on the size of the change. In one case I know of, where the river remained rather narrow for some miles and then opened up (see figure 3-6) and remained opened up for some miles, hundreds of deposits have been turned up — with thousands of ounces of gold being taken out within the last few years. The whole area was rich, and by all reports on it's history, the whole area was thoroughly mined during the late 1800's, with it being very rich then too.

APPLICATION OF GOLD FINDING INFORMATION

It's not uncommon to be sampling out a location, which by all visible indications should have a gold deposit present, and yet not be able to find one. There are numerous reasons why a gold deposit might not be where it should be — the main reason being that someone else got to it first. Once in awhile gold deposits are located

65

in places where all the visible signs show that they should not be. Geological conditions do change over an extended period of time. Bleedoffs from ancient gravels and other high bench deposits can sometimes lay gold in places where the present geological conditions might not warrant investigation. It is for these reasons — all the discrepancies which can occur — that there is a common saying amongst miners that the "Gold is Where you Find it," and no statement more true about the yellow metal has ever been made. However, there is always a reason for gold to be in the location in which it is found, as well as a reason for it not being there when the present signs indicate that it should be. The multitude of environmental and man-made factors which have come into play over the years that have placed gold in deposits are not all open to investigation at the present. An incident or two of not finding gold where it appears that it ought to be, and perhaps an incident of someone finding gold where is appears that it ought not be can sometimes leave an inexperienced person believing that "GOLD is where you fine it, and it doesn't really matter where you look!" This is not a healthy viewpoint from the standpoint of the author; because in my experience, the most successful prospectors have been the ones who have learned to look for gold where it ought to be and understand that sometimes it won't be there for reasons which cannot be presently seen. It's also true that the really experienced prospector can almost always see the reasons why it is or isn't there.

While it's true that gold is going to be where you find it, there are a certain set of factors about gold which are also invariably true. You can use them to determine where to look for it. As mentioned earlier, gold is about 6 or 7 times heavier than the average of other materials contained in a streambed. It generally works its way quickly down to the bottom of the other materials that it is moving along with in a large storm. It takes much more force to push gold along than it does to move normal streambed materials. Wherever that force is lessened, gold can become deposited — whether that change is because of irregularities in the bedrock, a major change in the size or slope of the streambed, a bend in the river, or obstructions in the path of the water's flow. Gold tends to follow a common path down a streambed — that path usually being the shortest possible route between the major changes. Places where boulders tend to get hung up in the river, along the line of travel which the gold should follow, are places where gold is likely to get hung up, too. All these factors are true — they follow the natural laws which make up our physical universe; and it's the experienced and successful prospector who uses them in his search, putting as many of them in his favor as possible in his effort to find gold deposits.

One example of the use of the data, as laid out in this Chapter, is as follows. . . . In looking for a place to dredge large quantities of gold, we open up a **Where To Find Gold** book and pick out Trinity County as a good gold producing area. There are many other good gold producing areas — some of them much better than Trinity County in the book; but for our purposes, we choose Trinity County because it's nearby. Plus, the book mentions the million ounces taken out of the river — which interests us, because we are going to dredge. We break out our Fish and Game Department permit lists and find out that the Trinity River is open year round for dredging from the confluence of the North Fork of the Trinity on downward until it pours into the Kalamath River. Again, this interests us because we don't want to be limited on time when we get into a large deposit. We look over the forestry map and see that the entire upper stretch of river runs through National Forest, with just a few scattered pieces of private property here and there — which is good. So we get hold of the Trinity County geological report, break out the maps and look over that section of river to see where the various successful placer mining activities took place. In doing so, we find out that the large bucket line dredges operated down to just above the confluence of the North Fork and that several successful high bench operations worked just above and below the confluence of the North Fork. (See no. 124 and no. 145 in figure 3-2.) In tracing down river from the North Fork on our topographic map, we see that the highway follows the river for it's entire length from this point — which we are impressed with, because it gives us excellent accessibility; and we also see that the river drops off at more or less a steady grade and runs rather narrow for some miles until the streambed suddenly opens up into about twice that width in the small town of Big Flat. (See figure 3-6 for exact location of example.) The topo shows us that the river runs wide for some miles afterwards. We know that many of the small towns in gold country were settled by mining communities during the early days where large deposits of gold were located, and we take the presence of the small town of Big Flat in that location as a positive sign. All signs so far indicate that this general area should be pretty good, so we drive there to have a closer look. In doing so, we notice that the exposed bedrock in the area all seems to be rough and semi-decomposed. We also notice lots of old tailings on the banks where the old benches used to lie, and we notice some bench still in place. An obvious good sign is that there seems to be a lot of dredging activity in the area. One short trip to the local Forestry Department and we find out that there is a long stretch of river in that same location which has been withdrawn from mineral entry so that anyone — including us, can mine there. The rangers show us the boundries of the free dredging area and give us a permit to dredge there — all in about 10 minutes time. We go down to the sight to look it over and run into the local gold buyer who lets us know that the area is hot hot hot and swears up and down that he's bought over 300 ounces of gold out of that one section of free dredging ground within the past two seasons alone, and mentions that most of the gold taken out of the area was not sold to him. Some inquiries about the other claims within the area show that they too are paying very well and that percentage deals can be worked out with the owners.

"Big Flat" is a legitimate location and this story is true. Gold is still being taken out in paying quantities at the time of this writing, but much of the area has been worked out during the last few seasons. (At least until the next big storm.)

The purpose of the story is not to start a major gold rush towards Big Flat, but to show how the **Where To Find Gold** books, geological reports, topos, forestry maps and a general knowledge of placer geology can be used to pinpoint locations which are likely to have large paying placer deposits.

Granted, you don't have all these maps and reports on hand. However they are not hard to come by and the **Where To Find Gold** book is really all that you need in order to get started. There are many such books available. Once you have one in your possession, you can study through it and decide which county or counties you are interested in and write to the various agencies for the proper reports and maps. Another way is to go to the county itself and get the maps and reports and have a look at the area first hand while you study them. A few phone calls will almost always find you the geological reports of a county within any of it's larger sized towns.

The idea is to put yourself into a geological location which has as many factors in your favor as you possibly can. Finding rough bedrock is good. Locating it on the inside of a bend in the stream is better. If there are boulders present, in the right places, the chances of a gold deposit being there are increased. If there is a steeper grade which flattens out not too far up stream, and if there are signs of lots of earlier mining activity — such as rockpiles upon the streambanks, all the better for a good gold deposit to be present. Get the idea? And finally, if there is a road or trail present, it will make it much easier for you to get in and sample that section of ground quickly, but we'll get into sampling in a later chapter.

ACCESSIBILITY

It has been said that the more difficult it is to get into an area, the less likely it is that it has been mined earlier. This is true only to a degree. You have to remember that during the early rush days, most of the Western United States was rather inaccessible, but that didn't stop the 49er's. Today, highways, roads and trails go through a lot of ground that has not been touched since the late 1800's, and some which was never touched at all. So it's not uncommon to see good sized paying quantities of gold being recovered directly off the roadside. You also hear of tremendous finds being made up in the more inaccessible areas too. At the time of this writing it doesn't seem necessary to HAVE to get up into the remote locations in order to locate good gold finds (even though they are there) because there seems to be a lot of acceptable paying accessible ground which has yet to be thoroughly mined. So accessibility is not necessarily a factor as to where you will find gold today, although it is a factor as to where you will be able to haul your equipment without a good deal of additional effort, and is something to take into consideration during the planning stages. Topo's can be a big help in this.

BELOW OLD HYDRAULIC MINES

Some of the larger sized hydraulic mining operations moved so much material, that entire mountainsides were washed away in the process. Experts have agreed that as much as a third to one half of the gold which was moved by many of the hydraulic operations was lost because of the tremendous volumes of material that were washed through their recovery systems all at once. The lost gold would have been washed away along with the tailings. Locations where hydraulic tailings were washed into a present day stream or river are always good places to do some sampling, because these areas have proven to be rich time and time again. A third or half of all the gold from an operation which moved hundreds of thousands — or even millions of cubic yards of gold bearing material could cause quite a large deposit, or series of deposits downstream.

In one known area, two personal friends of mine were prospecting around in a wash below the old dumping ground of a medium sized hydraulic operation that ran sometime during the early 1900's. One of the fellows happened to notice that the culvert passing underneath the highway was made of corrugated steel, which seemed to him would act much the same as the riffles in a sluice box. There were also railroad ties placed along the bottom edge of the culvert to protect it from the tremendous pounding of rocks and materials that would wash through during large storms. Since he was sampling the area anyway, he decided to test out some of the material laying in the bottom of the culvert. I guess the combination of railroad irons and corrugated steel acted as a good gold trap. They ended up taking better than 13 ounces out of the culvert within the next two days!

There's a similiar story about a professional dredger I know. He owns a claim located on a river where a medium sized hydraulic operation (operated in the 1930's) dumped its tailings into the river. For some time, it has been rumored that this guy's claim is so rich that he consistently pulls about a pound of gold each day that he dredges, and has been doing so for years. Now one thing about gold mining is that the stories tend to grow as they are passed along from one person to the next. I do OK myself when I am into a good deposit, but a pound a day — consistently — for a matter of years, seems a bit much to swallow. So, one day I happened to be present on the scene while he was doing his final clean-up after a full day of running. By my conservative estimation, he had no less than 6 ounces of gold in his pan — with probably 60% of it being of jewelry grade. And for whatever it's worth, he was obviously disappointed with his production for the day!

There are many other such confirmed stories — some of them even better — about the gold deposits which have been located below where the trailings of an old hydraulic operation dumped into a present day stream, creek or river. So keep this in mind when you are searching out likely spots.

CONSTRUCTION CUTS

Wherever construction operations have cut into or through old dry streambeds and exposed the bedrock and/or the lower strata of gravels, is a good place to sample for deposits of gold. It is only in the most recent past that many of the present roads and highways were built through gold country. Many of these cut directly through old Recent and Pleistocene benches in places, and sometimes you will run across the ancient Tertiary gravels in this way, too. Usually, these construction cuts are made directly through the channel, leaving the bottom strata and bedrock entirely exposed to the scrutiny of any prospector who happens along. (See figure 3-7.)

Fig. 3—7.

While the Highway Department is not likely to be happy about you starting up a gold mining operation along side of the road (it's probably against the law), you can easily get away with taking a few samples of the exposed lower stratas of such cuts to see if the ground is rich enough to pursue further action. If the ground proves to be rich, perhaps the streambed can be traced to a point further away from the road and an operation can be started up there.

Foundations for houses and buildings are often dug into an old streambed, and sampling could be done before the concrete is poured. It might be worth your while — many very rich deposits have been found in just this way. The same thing holds true when digging pools and wells. Did you ever hear the story about the lady who found gold in her back yard when she decided to take samples out of her well? It turned out that her house was built upon a very rich section of riverbed and the gold that she recovered was worth in excess of the value of her property — house and all.

NATURAL EROSIVE CUTS

Anywhere that natural erosion has cut a path through an old streambed, is a place worth doing a bit of sampling. This is especially true when the streambed is cut into all the way down to bedrock or the lower strata of material, because in this case the erosion has already done the hardest part of the job in uncovering the lower strata for you — where the pay dirt is most likely to be found. Sampling out locations such as this is usually rather quick and easy, and sometimes very rewarding.

LAKEBED DEPOSITS

Sometimes the spot where an old river or stream reached a lake was a major dumping ground for gold, because that was where the force of the river dissipated to nothing. This is true of old dried up lakes and of the present ones — man made or otherwise. The mouth of the stream, and sometimes out into the lake itself, can be found to be very, very rich, and is a good place to sample. In the case of the present lakes, I recommend that you check with the local authorities before starting, to make sure that it's alright — it might be against the law to mine in some lakes.

BEACH DEPOSITS

Millions of years of erosive activity has caused an enormous amount of gold to wash down through the rivers and into the ocean. Experts have said that the vast majority of eroded gold has washed into the oceans and has yet to be recovered. Much of this gold is of microscopic size and remains in a state of suspension in the seawater itself. So far, no means of recovering this ultra fine gold has yet been developed which has proven to be viable in a large scale operation.

Also, much of the gold which has washed down into the ocean is of a larger size and can be recovered by the standard recovery methods. This gold can often be found on the beaches nearby the gold bearing rivers, where the fine particles have been washed up by the tides.

Northern California, Oregon, Washington State and Alaska are all well known for their gold beaches. These are usually covered in the various **Where To Find Gold** books.

Occationally, certain tidal changes cause entire beaches to be covered with a layer of exposed fine gold, which causes many of the locals and tourists to rush down and try to recover it. Often the next change in the tide will wash it all away, or cover it up. The main point here is that the gold beaches should not be discounted as possible locations in which to prospect for and recover gold.

ANCIENT BEACHES

If you have spent much time traveling near the sea shores, you might have noticed what appears to be lots of old dry streambeds scattered about, sometimes located close to the ocean, and in other cases, miles and miles away. Some of these are quite massive and it's hard to believe that they were once streambeds because they are so large. Yet they are laid out just like a streambed. . . It's ancient oceanbed; and in some places, as in Northern California, Oregon, Washington State and in Alaska, they are very rich in fine gold.

Some major operations were run on ancient ocean beds during the early 1900's with good results.

Sometimes these old beds are quite extensive in height and size, and so are out of the range of the small time operator. However it's not uncommon to find streams and creeks which cut directly through old ocean bed, and these might be found to be rich — along with any other places where the natural erosion could cause a concentration of gold to take place.

CHAPTER IV

PANNING FOR GOLD

Processing streambed material with the use of a gold pan is probably the oldest method of recovering placer gold in existence. Some of the first gold pans consisted of Indian woven baskets and wooden bowls — called "beteas." In the 1800's, gold pans made out of tin were developed by the Americans — which have evolved into todays ultra modern space age plastic and steel spun gold pans.

The gold pan still remains as one of the most valuable tools used by today's modern prospector, whether he is running a small time operation or one of large scale. Most often, the recovery systems on the larger pieces of mining equipment — like dredges, are cleaned up with the use of a gold pan. "Clean-up" is the procedure of separating the gold from the other heavy materials which get trapped in a gold recovery system.

The basic principle upon which most of today's recovery systems operate is that if you have a device which will catch (trap) the heavier materials out of the streambed material that is being processed, then you will catch the gold — because gold is the heaviest of all. These recovery systems very seldom catch only gold. They also trap other heavy materials out of the streambed, such as pieces of lead and iron, old nails and coins, and the heavier iron rocks and sand — called "hematite" and "magnatite." All these heavy materials which collect in a recovery system — gold included — are called "concentrates."

Towards the end of the day — or operating period, when it's time to collect the gold which has been trapped in a recovery system, it is done by cleaning all of the concentrated materials out of the system, and then separating the gold from the other heavy materials. This process is often done with the use of a gold pan.

At first, if you are rather new to the subject, this might strike you with the consideration that gold mining is still in the dark ages. Not true! There simply is no quicker and more effective way of separating gold from the other heavily concentrated material that comes out of a recovery system — that is, unless you want to put out thousands for a specialized machine to do it for you. And even then, you have to haul the machine around with you and set it up, etc. So many clean-ups are done with the use of a gold pan — and with good reason.

One of the other main uses of a gold pan by today's modern prospector is in that of sampling out different locations. This is done in an effort to find new and better deposits to mine.

One reason why the gold pan is such an asset as a sampling tool is because it is light and so can be carried anywhere with little additional effort. It's also very accurate and effective as a gold recovering device. The gold pan is quick and easy to use. It takes no time at all to set one up for operation, and it only takes a little water to work one properly. To put it simply, the gold pan is one of the most effective gold recovery tools ever developed, and has a wider range of operational ability than any other gold recovering device.

On an amateur basis, the gold pan can be profitable to play with and provide hours on end of recreational enjoyment.

By using a gold pan, a beginner can learn the basics of gold recovery and of mining in general. For when one has learned how to use a gold pan effectively, he or she understands the basics of mining gold — whether it is realized or not.

The gold pan is very simple to learn how to use, and recovers gold so well that even a beginner would have difficulty losing a piece of gold the size of a small pellet — even on the first few attempts.

TYPES OF PANS

There are a host of different kinds of gold pans on today's market. Rather than go into each one of them individually, I'll go over the main characteristics and their advantages and disadvantages, and let you decide which pan you will be most comfortable in using.

Plastic pans are moulded from space age plastics, and for the most part are unbreakable — although there are a few on the market which break rather easily. The way to tell if a plastic pan is unbreakable is by taking it in both hands and putting a strain on it, as shown if figure 4-1. In doing so, and by watching and feeling, you'll get the idea if the pan will continue to bend or will break when additional force is applied. Be careful not to apply so much pressure that you break a breakable one. I hereby refuse to accept financial responsibility for all the gold pans which are going to be destroyed by this. (The shop owners are going to love me.)

Fig. 4—1. Gold pans tend to take a lot of banging around out in the field. It's well to have an unbreakable one.

Steel pans will bend, but it takes a tremendous amount of force to bend one, like dropping it over a cliff or running it over with your car or something on that order. For the most part, with everyday normal use, there is no need to worry about the durability of either the unbreakable plastic pan or the steel one.

Plastic pans are lighter than the steel ones. If you are planning on an extra long and difficult hike for sampling purposes it could make a difference, although those who prefer the use of the steel pan over that of the plastic kind say that the difference in the weight factor is not enough to make them change over.

Plastic gold pans generally float, whereas a steel one will quickly sink to the bottom — unless it's dropped into the water in such a position that it floats like a boat. These factors can either be an advantage or disadvantage, depending on the circumstances in which you are using the gold pan. For example, if you are prospecting near deep water and your steel pan slips off the streambank and sinks, it means that you will probably have to go underwater in order to retrieve it — or abandon it there. Most of the plastic type pans will float and you can fish them out with a stick or wade out a bit and grab them. Yet, in the case of shallower water which is running fast — like in a set of rapids, if you drop your plastic floater, you have got to be very fast indeed in order to catch it, the steel gold pan will usually sink and anchor itself to the bottom.

Plastic type pans will not rust, while steel ones will — especially if a set of wet concentrates out of a recovery system are allowed to sit in one for an extended period of time. Yet, some miners insist that the rust in their gold pan helps them to recover the fine gold. Other prospectors like a smooth edge at the bottom of their gold pans. It's all a matter of preference. By the way, the best way to prevent a steel pan from rusting is to empty it out and place it upside down when not in use.

One advantage to a plastic pan is that nitric acid can be used to clean gold directly in the pan if you should decide to do so during the final clean-up procedure (Chapter 7). Nitric acid will attack steel, and so a steel pan cannot be used in conjunction with the acid during the final clean-up stages.

Another advantage to the plastic pan is that you can use a magnet to separate the magnetic black sands (iron) out of the final concentrates directly in the pan during clean-up (Chapter 7), whereas a steel type gold pan will react to the magnet and interfere with this process.

During the final clean-up steps back at camp (Chapter7), there is always a need for a metal container to put your gold into, to heat it up and dry it out. A steel gold pan can come in handy when doing this part of the clean-up.

It's a good idea to have a plastic gold pan on hand if you are planning to use an electronic metal detector in your prospecting activities. In this way, you can shovel the ground where you are getting a signal into the pan and then scan the pan to see if you have recovered the target which is causing the signal. A steel gold pan cannot be effectively used in this procedure, because it will cause the detector to read out falsely.

Many plastic gold pans are moulded with a small set of riffles in one part of the pan. Different manufacturers have designed different types of riffles — each with their own unique way of assisting in the recovery of gold. Some of these riffles — when utilized correctly, do help in the recovery of gold, and are referred to as "cheater riffles"; because sometimes with the use of them, a novice can quickly learn to pan nearly as fast and as well as an old pro who has had years of experience.

One disadvantage that a plastic pan has, is that it will melt with very little provocation. So keep yours well out of range of the campfire and also out of the rear window area of the car on a hot, sunny day.

Plastic pans are made in black, green and other dark colors so that the small particles of gold will stand out better. This gives you more control over the fine particles of gold while working them in the pan.

It has been said that the steel gold pan has an advantage over the plastic one in that it can be used to cook with. While this is probably true, it's not recommended that you use your steel pan to cook with, because the cooking greases and oils are absorbed into the pan and can thereafter effect how well that the pan will recover gold. Oil has a tendency to attach itself to pieces of gold — which are then susceptible to attaching themselves to air bubbles, and floating out of your pan while you are working it.

Steel pans usually come new with a thin layer of protective oil on them to prevent them from rusting before they are sold. It is generally recommended that this oil be cleaned out of a new steel gold pan before it is used out in the field.

There are several ways of cleaning the oil out of a steel pan. One is to rub it out with a rag which has been dampened with paint thinner. Perhaps the best and most often used method of cleaning the oil from a steel pan, is by heating it slowly over a stove or an open fire until it reaches a dull red glow and then dropping it into clean cool water. This process leaves the pan with a dark blue hue, which gives a good dark background to make the fine particles of gold stand out better. Care must be taken when cleaning a steel gold pan in this manner to prevent using excessive heat — which can cause the pan to warp.

Any gold pan that is used regularly has a tendency to collect a certain amount of body oils. Body oils can affect your gold pan in the same manner of lost gold particles. So it's good practice to clean your gold pan periodically, whether it is steel or the plastic type.

A plastic pan can be effectively cleaned by rubbing it with a clean rag which has been dipped in isopropyl alchol.

One of the main differences between gold pans is the difference between the "drop center" type pan and the "straight angle bottom" pan. The difference is in the shape of the angle between the sides and the bottom of the pan (See figure 4-2). "Drop Center"

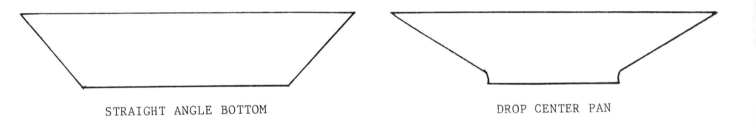

STRAIGHT ANGLE BOTTOM   DROP CENTER PAN

Fig. 4—2.

gold pans are most commonly found in plastic, although some steel versions of this are available. The dropped center acts as a protective trap for gold which has worked its way to the pan's bottom, and prevents it from sliding forward when the pan is tilted forward and worked (See figure 4-3 on next page.).

Straight angle bottom gold pans can be located either in steel or in plastic. Some prospectors prefer this type of pan because it allows them to separate ALL of the heavy black sands from the gold out in the field while panning, so that it doesn't have to be done later during the final clean-up steps (Chapter 7). The trap in the drop center-type pan has a tendency to hold onto some of the black sands too, along with the gold, which makes final separation more time consuming.

When out in the field, it's not uncommon to hear arguments as to which pan is better. These arguments are silly, because the different pans — whether steel or plastic,

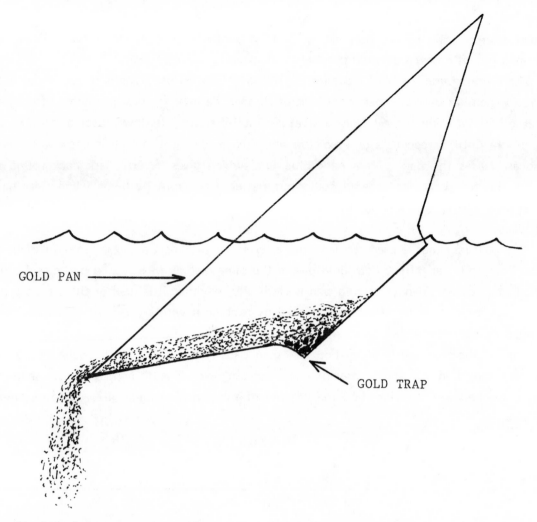

GOLD PAN

GOLD TRAP

Fig. 4—3. A drop center-type gold pan tends to keep gold from sliding forward while the pan is tilted forward when it's being worked.

drop center or straight angle bottom, each have advantages for different uses. For this reason, many prospectors have serveral different kinds of gold pans, and use the one that is most suited to their needs.

The main pan which a prospector decides to use in his everyday panning is a matter of personal preference. If you are just beginning and don't feel qualified to choose the "best one" for you, don't worry about it too much. It's my opinion that once you understand the basics of panning gold, you can make any of these pans work well — and develop more skills as you do so. After all, some of the earliest miners made woven baskets work!

Gold pans come in a multitude of different sizes, ranging from 6 inches in diameter, to 18 inches in diameter, and possibly even larger (See figure 4-4.). The average size usually seen in use out in the field is about 14 to 16 inches in diameter.

THE GOLD PAN AS A PRODUCTION TOOL

The main thing to remember about the use of a gold pan is that while it is effective as a gold catching device, it can only process a limited amount of streambed material. For this reason, the gold pan is normally not used as a production tool in

Fig. 4—4. Gold pans are available in different sizes.

professional use — other than in the most remote locations where it would be very difficult to haul larger pieces of equipment, and where there is only a limited amount of ground present which is paying well enough to make the panning worthwhile.

The gold pan is most commonly used to locate richer paying ground (sampling), so that the larger production equipment can be brought in to that spot in order to work the ground at greater profit.

There are stories — comfired I hope — in the old mining records, about ground being so rich during the days of the 1849 gold rush, that as much as 96 ounces of gold were recovered from a single pan. That's 43,200 dollars at today's rate of exchange, and must have been some very rich ground indeed! Stories like that are rare, and ground like that is not run across very often. However, it's not too uncommon to hear of prospectors today who are able to consistently produce better than an ounce per week with a gold pan in the high country, and have the gold to show for it. Some do much better, but these guys have been at it for awhile and have located hot spots. I personally know of two guys who support themselves with a gold pan, and one of them lives pretty darn good. As mentioned earlier, the gold pan has unlimited accessibility, and these guys concentrate on the pockets in the exposed bedrock along the edges of the creek beds in their areas, picking up a few pieces here, a few there, and a little pocket once in awhile. It adds up, and to them it's better than punching a time clock.

There is still plenty of rich ground to be found in gold country if you are willing to do the work involved in finding it.

GOLD PANNING PROCEDURE

Panning gold is basically simple, once you realize that you are doing the exact same thing that the river does when it caused gold to concentrate and deposit in various locations.

The process basically consists of placing the material that you want to process into your pan, and shaking it in a left to right motion underwater in order to cause the gold — which is heavy — to work its way down towards the bottom of the pan, while the lighter materials — which are worthless — are worked up to the surface where they can be swept off. The process of shaking and sweeping is done until only the heaviest of materials are left — namely the gold, silver and platinum, if present.

Once you are out in the field, you will notice that no two people pan gold exactly alike; and after you have been at it awhile, you will develop your own little twists and shakes to accomplish the proper result.

Here is a basic gold panning procedure to start off with which works well and is easy to learn.

STEP 1: Once you have located some gravel that you want to sample, place it in your gold pan — filling it about 3/4 of the way to the top. After you've been at it awhile, you can fill your pan to the top without losing any gold. While placing material in your pan, pick out the larger sized rocks, so that you can get more of the smaller material — and gold — into the pan (See figure 4-5).

Fig. 4—5. Panning step 1: Fill pan about 3/4 full of material.

STEP 2: Choose a spot where to do your panning. It's best to pick a location where the water is at least 6 inches deep, and is preferably moving slightly — just enough to sweep away the mud and silty water as it is washed from your pan, so that you can see what you are doing better. You don't want the water moving so swiftly that it will upset your panning actions. A mild current will do — if available.

It's always best to try to find a spot where there is a rock or log or streambank or something that you can sit down on while panning. You can pan effectively while squatting, kneeling or while bending over; but it does get tiresome, and if you are planning to process more than just one or two pans, sitting down will make the job much, much more pleasant.

STEP 3: Carry the pan over to your determined spot and submerge it underwater (See figure 4-6).

Fig. 4—6. Panning step 3: Submerge pan fully under water.

STEP 4: Use your fingers to knead the contents of the pan in order to break it up fully and cause all of the material to become saturated with water. This is the time to work apart all the clay, dirt, roots, moss and such with your fingers to ensure that all of the materials are fully broken up and in a liquid state of suspension in the pan.

The pan is underwater while doing this. Mud and silt will be seen to float up and out. Do not concern yourself about losing any gold when this happens. Remember: Gold is heavy and will tend to sink deeper in your pan while these lighter materials are floating out (See figure 4-7).

Fig. 4—7. Panning step 4; use fingers to fully break up material in the pan.

STEP 5: After the entire contents of the pan have been thoroughly broken up, take the pan in your hands (with cheater riffles on the far side of the pan) and shake it — using a vigorous left and right motion just under the surface of the water. This action will help to break up the contents of the pan even more and will also start to work the heavier materials downwards in the pan while the lighter materials will start to surface.

Be careful not to get so vigorous in your shaking that you slosh any material out of the pan during this step. (See figure 4-8.)

Fig. 4—8. Panning step 5; shake pan just underwater in a vigorous left and right motion.

Depending on the consistency of the material that you are working, it may be necessary to alternate doing steps 4 and 5 over again a few times to get the entirety of the pans contents into a liquid state of suspension. It is this same liquid state of suspension that allows the heavier materials to sink in the pan while the lighter materials emerge to the surface.

STEP 6: As the shaking action causes rocks to rise up to the surface, sweep them out of the pan using your fingers or the side of your hand. Just sweep off the top layer of rocks which have worked their way up to the pan's surface. (See figure 4-9.)

Fig. 4—9. Panning step 6; sweep the larger sized rocks over the side as they emerge to the surface of the pan.

Do not worry about losing any gold while doing this, because the same action which has brought the rocks to the surface will have worked the gold deeper down towards the bottom of the gold pan.

Rotating your pan in a circular motion underwater will help to bring more rocks to the surface where they can be swept off in the same way.

When picking the larger rocks out of the pan, make sure that they are clean of clay and other particles before you toss them out. Clay sometimes contains pieces of gold and also has a tendency to grab onto the gold in your pan, so look before tossing.

STEP 7: Continue to do steps 5 and 6, shaking the pan and sweeping out the rocks and pebbles, until most of the medium sized material is out of your pan.

STEP 8: Tilt the forward edge of your pan downward slightly to bring the forward bottom edge of the pan to the lowest position, as shown in figure 4-10. With the pan tilted forward, shake it back and forth using the same left and right motion. Be careful not to tilt the pan forward so much that any material is spilled over the forward edge while shaking.

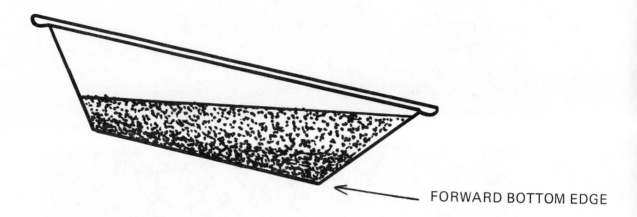

PANNER IS OVER THERE

FORWARD BOTTOM EDGE

Fig. 4—10. Panning step 8: Tilt the pan forward slightly and shake.

This tilted shaking action causes the gold to start working it s way down to the pan's forward bottom edge, and continues to work the lighter materials to the surface where they will be swept off.

STEP 9: Carefully, by using a forward and backward movement — or a slight circular motion, just below the surface of the water, allow the water to sweep the top layer of worthless, lighter materials out of your pan. Only allow the water to sweep out a little at a time, while watching closely for the heavier materials to be uncovered as the lighter materials are swept out (See figure 4-11.).

Fig. 4—11. Panning step 11: Move the pan back and forth to get the water to sweep the top layer of lighter material out of the pan.

It takes some judgment in this step to determine just how much material to sweep off before having to shake again so that no gold is lost.* It will just take a little practice in panning gold before you will begin to see the difference between the lighter materials and the heavier materials in your pan, and get a feel for knowing exactly how much material that can be safely swept out before re-shaking is necessary. When you are first starting, it's best to re-shake as often as you feel that it's needed to prevent losing any gold. *When in doubt — shake!* There are a few factors which can be pointed out to help you with this. Heavier materials are usually darker in color than the lighter materials are. You will notice while shaking the pan that it's the lighter colored materials which are vibrated to the surface. You will also notice that as the lighter materials are swept out of the pan, the darker colored materials are uncovered. Materials tend to get darker (and heavier) as you work your way down towards the bottom of the pan, where the darkest and heaviest materials will be found — they being the purple and black sands, which are minerals of the iron family. The exception to this is gold — which is heaviest of all, and usually is of a bright and shiny metalic color, and so shows out well in contrast to the other heavier materials at the bottom of the gold pan.

One other factor to keep in mind, is that the lighter materials sweep out of your pan easier than do the heavier materials. So as the heavier materials are uncovered, they are increasingly more resistant to being swept out of the pan, and will give you an indication of when it's time to re-shake.

Gold is very shiny — and heavy, in contrast to the darker and heavier concentrates in the gold pan. As you work your way down through your pan, sometimes gold particles will show themselves as you get down to the heavier materials; and in seeing them, you will know that it's time to shake again.

There is another popular method of sweeping the lighter materials out of the top of your pan which you might prefer to use. It is done by dipping your pan under the water and lifting it up, while allowing the water to run off the forward edge of the pan, taking the top layer of material along with it (See figure 4-12).

Fig. 4–12. Washing the top layer of material out of the pan by the dipping method.
*For a visual demonstration of gold panning procedures, see Dave McCracken's video (Page 1).

STEP 10: Once the top layer of lighter materials are washed out of your pan, re-shake to bring more lighter materials to the top. By "lighter materials," I mean in comparison to the other materials within the pan. If you continue to shake the "lighter materials" to the top and sweep them off, eventually you will be left with the heaviest materials of all, which is the gold. It doesn't take much shaking to bring a new layer of lighter stuff to the surface. Maybe 8 or 10 seconds worth of shaking will do it, maybe less — all depending on the consistency of the material and how much gold is present.

Continue to pluck out the larger sized rocks and pebbles as they show themselves during the process.

STEP 11: Every few cycles of sweeping and re-shaking, tilt your pan back to the level position and re-shake. This keeps any gold from being allowed to work its way up the forward edge of your pan.

STEP 12: Continue the above steps of sweeping and re-shaking until you are down to the heaviest materials in your pan. These usually consist of old pieces of lead and other metal, coins, BB's, old bullets, buckshot, nails, garnets, small purple and black iron rocks, and the heavy black sand concentrates — which consist mainly or in part of the following: magnetite (magnetic black sands), hematite (non—magnetic black sands), titanium, zircan, rotite, manazite, tungsten materials, and sometimes pyrites (fools gold), plus any other items which might be present in that location which have a high specific gravity — like gold, silver and platinum.

BLACK SANDS

Heavy black sands — the kind that end up at the bottom of your gold pan, are usually present to some degree anywhere in a streambed. When panning the lower strata of streambed, just above bedrock, you will usually end up with at least some black sand at the bottom of your gold pan.

The presence of a large amount of heavy black sands in a particular streambed location is not a sure fire index of the presence of gold being nearby, only that some heavier materials have traveled over and concentrated to some degree in that particular location. There is a greater quantity of black sand in a streambed than of gold; and they, being much lighter than gold, do not necessarily follow the same path that gold does. Heavy black sands tend to concentrate in a much wider range of locations than gold does. However, heavy black sands tend to always concentrate in the same location that gold does; so if there no black sands present in a particular streambed location, it's less likely that you will find gold there. In this way, the presence of heavy black sands — or the lack of them, tells a story of its own. You will want to watch for them while prospecting out new ground.

Gold has about 4 times the weight of the heaviest black sands. It's about 6 or 7 times heavier than the average of other materials generally found in a streambed. So, as you are panning, the materials become more and more heavy as you work towards the bottom of the pan. It is a bit more difficult to seperate gold down through heavier material than it is to vibrate it down through lighter material while panning. This doesn't really amount to a problem when streambed materials are being panned, because usually there are not enough heavy black sands in a single pan to amount to much. When panning off a set of concentrates that have been taken out of a sluice box or some other type of recovery system, much more black sand will be present and it becomes slightly more difficult to work the gold down through the heavier materials as one gets towards the bottom of the pan. Even still, the gold is much heavier than the heavy black sands, and the process of shaking and sweeping remains basically the same as before, with it necessary to be a little more careful so as to prevent losing any gold out of your pan during the process. (See figure 4-13.)

Fig. 4—13. It's necessary to be a little more careful when sweeping out the black sands so as to to prevent loss of gold.

Once down to the heaviest of the black sands in your pan, you can get a quick look at the concentrates to see how much gold is present by allowing about a half cup of water into the pan, tilting the pan forward as before, and shaking from left to right so as to place the concentrates in the forward bottom lip of your pan. Then level the pan off and swirl the water around in slow circles. This action will gradually uncover the concentrates and in this way you can get a look at them — and at any gold which is present. The amount of gold in your pan will give you an idea of how rich the ground is that you are sampling. (See figure 4-14 on next page.)

Many beginners like to stop panning at this point and pick out all the pieces of gold (colors) with a pair of tweezers. This is one way of recovering the gold from your pan, but it is a very slow method.

Fig. 4—14. The final concentrates can be swirled away to see how much gold is present.

Most prospectors who have been at it for awhile will pan down through the black sands as far as they feel that they can go without losing any gold. Then they check the pan for any colors by swirling it, and pick out any of the larger sized flakes and nuggets to place them in a gold sample bottle, which has been brought along for that purpose. Then the remaining concentrates are poured into a small coffee can and allowed to accumulate there until the end of the day, or week, or whenever enough concentrates have been collected to make it worthwhile to process them with mercury in order to recover all of the gold out of them. (Covered in chapter 7.) This is really the better method if you are interested in recovering more gold, because it allows one to get on with the job of panning and sampling without getting deeply involved with a pair of tweezers. Otherwise you can end up spending 25% of your time panning and 75% of your time picking.

It is possible to pan all the way down to the gold — with no black sands, lead, or other foreign materials left in the pan. This is often done amongst prospectors when cleaning up a set of concentrates which have been taken from the recovery system of a larger piece of mining equipment — like a sluice box or dredge.

Panning all the way down to gold is really not very difficult, once you get the hang of it. It's just a matter of a little practice and being a bit more careful. Most prospectors when doing so, prefer to use the smooth surface of gold pan as opposed to using the cheater riffles. (See figure 4-15 on following page.)

When panning a set of concentrates all the way down to the gold — or nearly so, it's good to have a medium sized funnel and a large mouth gold sample bottle on hand. This way, once you have finished panning, it's just a matter of pouring the gold from your pan into the sample bottle via the funnel, as shown in figure 4-16. Pill bottles and baby food jars often make good gold sample bottles for field use because they are usually made of thick glass and have wide mouths. Plastic ones are even safer.

Fig. 4—15. Panning down through the black sands to the gold is not too difficult once you get the hang of it.

Fig 4—16. A funnel can come in handy when it's time to transfer your gold into a sample bottle.

If you do not have a funnel on hand, try wetting your finger with saliva and fingering the gold into the jar, which should be filled with water. The saliva will cause gold and concentrates to stick to your finger until it touches the water in the jar. This works, but the funnel method is faster.

PRACTICE GOLD PANNING

If you are not in a known gold producing location, but want to do some practice panning to get accustomed to it and acquire some skills before going out into the field, you can practice in your own back yard. Use a washtub to pan into and some diggings from your garden — or wherever, to simulate streambed materials. I recommend that you throw in some rocks and gravel along with the dirt so that it takes on an actual streambed consistency. Take some pieces of lead, buckshot or small lead fishing weights, cut them up into various sizes, ranging from pellet size down to pinhead size, and pound some of them flat with a hammer. This puts the pieces of lead in the same form as the majority of gold which is found in a streambed — flake form; and so they will act in much the same way as will flakes and grains of gold. Leave a few of the pieces of lead shot as they are so that gold nuggets can also be simulated.

When panning into the tub, place a few of these pieces of lead into your pan — starting off with the larger sized pieces first. Keep track of how many pieces of lead that you use each time so that you can see how well you are doing when you get down to the bottom of the pan. Practice panning in this manner can be very very revealing to a beginner, especially when he or she continues to put smaller and smaller pieces of lead into the pan as progress is made.

If a person is able to pan small pieces of lead successfully, then he or she will have no difficulty whatsoever in panning gold (higher specific gravity) out of a riverbed. And who knows? You may end up with gold in your pan — right out of your own back yard! It wouldn't be the first time.

Out in the field, one sure sign that you are panning correctly is the accumulation of heavy black sands at the bottom of your pan. If you are recovering the magnetite — specific gravity 5.2, then you will recover the gold — specific gravity 19.3.

On the large gold producing rivers of the Western United States, there are actually very few places in which you can pan for gold and not turn any up. Direct your efforts toward the lowest strata of streambed material and the bedrock irregularities. Many of these rivers or sections of them have been assayed out to carry in excess of a million dollars in gold per mile. (Minimum figures.) So there really is no lack of good gold bearing ground near water in which to perfect your gold panning techniques.

If you are just beginning and there is an experienced miner around, it's always a good idea to talk him into giving you a demonstration, as it tends to help a person to catch on faster.

The general equipment needed in order to conduct a gold panning or sampling operation is as follows: shovel — for digging, screwdriver — for breaking open bedrock irregularities and scraping them clean, whisk broom — for cleaning up dry bedrock, garden trowel — for digging out bedrock traps, small coffee can — for valuable black sand concentrates, gold pan — for processing the gold out of material, gold bottle and tweezers — for the gold (See figure 4-17).

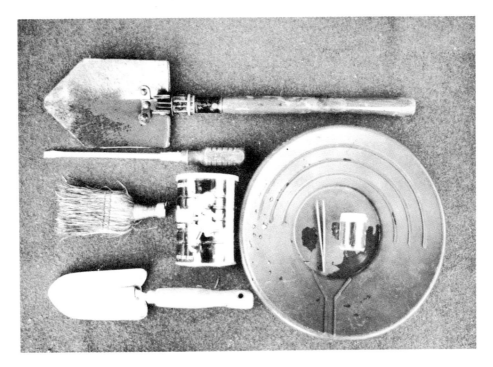

Fig. 4—17. Here are the tools that are normally used in a gold panning or sampling operation.

One other tool that sometimes comes in handy when you are cleaning up bedrock is a "gold snifter" or "suction gun" (See figure 4-18.).

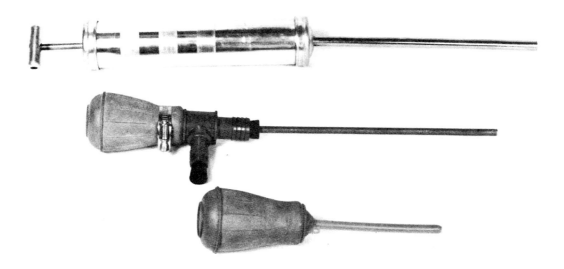

Fig. 4—18. "Suction gun" (top) and "gold snifters," used to suck material from the bottom of bedrock crevices.

Once in awhile, you will run into a bedrock crack, crevice, or some other kind of irregularity which you cannot easily get into and thoroughly clean out with the normal panning tools. In this case, you can fill the crevice with water and suck the contents out with the use of one of these suction tools — as shown in figure 4-19.

Fig. 4–19. Material can be extracted out of bedrock irregularities with the use of a suction tool.

If you are panning in a location and are not turning up an acceptable amount of gold, the thing to do is move to another likely spot in which to find it. Use your knowledge of stream placer geology and try there, and keep on trying different spots until you locate some ground which is paying in gold values to your liking. This is the basic procedure of sampling. One luxury of using a gold pan as a sampling tool, is that it's very easy to pick up and move around until you have found a place which is hot enough to work seriously.

CLEANING UP SLUICE BOX CONCENTRATES

There is really not much difference between panning off a set of concentrates taken from a sluice box, and those materials taken from a streambed. The main difference is that sluice box materials are usually much more concentrated than the normal streambed materials are, and so you will be dealing with more black sands — and hopefully, more gold, too.

Here are a few tips which can help to make the clean-up of concentrates quicker and more effective. . .

Panning concentrates goes much smoother if you remove all of the larger stones and pebbles before you start. This can be done very quickly by pouring the concentrates through a set of mesh screens. Excellent results can be obtained by passing them through a ¼ inch mesh screen first. (Hole openings ¼ inch.) See figure 4-20.

Fig. 4—20. Concentrates are much easier to pan-off if all of the larger sized rocks and pebbles are classified out first.

Before discarding the larger sized rocks and pebbles that will not pass through a mesh screen, always inspect them first to make sure that you don't throw away any large pieces of gold. These usually show themselves quite readily — but it pays to make sure.

The second screening of your concentrates should be done using window screen type mesh. A large kitchen type wire screen strainer works very well in doing this final screening. (See figure 4-21.) Separation of the different sized materials in this way is most easily done underwater. The concentrates which pass through this last screening are placed in a different container than the materials which will not pass through, and each is panned separately. Interestingly enough, it's the black sands (smaller sized concentrates) that slows down the panning of the larger sized concentrates, and the larger concentrates get in the way of your being able to pan off the black sands effectively, so separating the two and panning them apart makes the process much faster.

Fig. 4—21. A large, handled, kitchen-type wire strainer works well as a clean-up classification tool.

When panning the larger sized concentrates taken from this last screening, keep a close eye out for flakes of gold while you are sweeping; because shaking does not cause them to sink down very far in the pan when the concentrates of this size are being worked. This is especially true when you have a lot of gold in the material — which may be the case when cleaning-up a sluice or dredge.

Because of the large amount of black sands that accumulate in a sluice box which need to be panned during clean-up, it's well to develop your panning skills to the point where you can pan all the way down to the gold, or nearly so. Otherwise, you can end up spending hours on end picking with a pair of tweezers.

If you are cleaning up a set of concentrates in which the sand will fill more than one pan, rather than take each pan all the way down to gold, it's much faster to take each pan to the heavier concentrates and save them for a final pan. Then take it all down to the gold at one time.

Many experienced miners do the above process, panning each pan of their clean-up down to the point where they are afraid of losing some gold (panning quickly). Then the final concentrates are panned into a wash tub, so that the heaviest black sands can be saved (See figure 4-22). The reason for this is that it takes a lot of time to pan a set of heavy concentrates all the way down to gold without losing some in the process — even if just a small amount. Also, some of the black sands have gold inside of them. These are called "Locked in values," and are the reason why some of the black sands appear to be heavier than they ought to be.

The more fine gold that is in a set of concentrates, the more difficult it is to separate all of it from the black sands, and the longer that it takes to do so. So experienced miners will do the final panning into a wash tub — being careful to get as much of the fine gold as possible, but not bothering to take all day at it either. It doesn't matter if some of the fines are lost out of the pan and drop into the tub; because afterwards, the concentrates are poured into a coffee can or some other similar container and accumulated for later processing (See figure 4-23).

Fig. 4—22. The final concentrates can be panned into a wash tub without worry of losing any gold values.

Fig. 4—23. The final concentrates - after being panned, can be saved for further processing at a later period.

There are several things that you can do with a set of concentrates in order to profit by them. Perhaps you'll want to make a winter project out of recovering the rest of the gold out of them with the use of mercury (Covered in Chapter 7). It's possible that you know — or will be able to find - someone who owns a professional vibrating table, who will be willing to run your concentrates over the table to extract the gold values. Or, maybe you will want to sell your concentrates. There are people around who are willing to pay cash for black sand concentrates — even after you have taken out all of the values that you are able to recover. Black sands can bring in just about any amount of money — depending on how much gold and other valuable minerals that they contain. Often, black sands contain a considerable amount of gold even when it is not visible (locked in values). As much as 600 dollars a pound (dry pound) is being paid for some concentrates at this very writing. That happens to be a very rich set of concentrates that were taken from the clean-ups of a semi-large scale surface bench operation that is producing better than 60 ounces of coarse gold per day. One or two dollars per pound of concentrates is more common amongst the small time operations having a daily clean-up. Even so, that's nothing to laugh at when you are panning 10 or 20 pounds a day out of your sluice box. It pays expenses!

CHAPTER V

SLUICING FOR GOLD

A "sluice box" is a trough-like gold recovering device, which has a series of obstructions or baffles — called "riffles" along its bottom edge. (See figure 5-1.)

While a steady stream of water is made to pass through, streambed material is shoveled into the upper end of the box. The flow of water washes the streambed materials through the sluice and over the riffles — which trap the gold out of the material. (See figures 5-1 and 5-2 on following page.)

The reason that a sluice box works is because gold is extremely heavy and so will quickly work it's way down to the bottom of the materials which are being washed through the box. The gold will quickly be dropped behind the riffles and remain there, because there is not enough water force behind the riffles to sweep the gold out into the main force of water again.

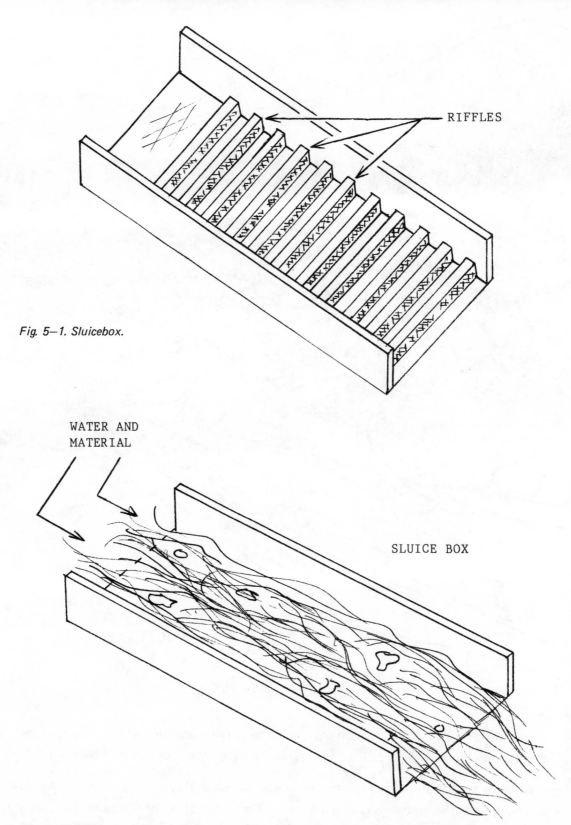

Fig. 5—1. Sluicebox.

RIFFLES

WATER AND
MATERIAL

SLUICE BOX

Fig. 5—2. Riffles catch the gold out of the material that is washed through the sluice box.

A sluicing operation, when set up properly, can process the gold out of material as fast as it can be shoveled into the box. This can be anywhere from 10 to 200 times more material than a panning operation can handle, yet with similiar efficiency in gold reçovery. How much material that can be shoveled into a sluice box greatly depends on the consistency and hardness of the material in the streambed itself, and how easily that it can be broken away.

A sluice requires a steady flow of water through the box in order to operate at its best efficiency. Most often, the box is placed in a stream or creek where water is moving rather swiftly, with the sluice being placed in such a way that a stream of water is directed through the box. In locations where water is available, but it is not moving fast enough that it can be channeled through the box for sluicing purposes, the water can be pumped or siphoned through with an excellent result (covered later). How much water that is available, and whether or not it will need to be transported to your sluice box, is something that needs to be considered when in setting up a sluicing operation.

Because so much more volume of material can be processed with a sluice over that of a gold pan, streambed materials which contain far less gold values can be mined at a profit. If the streambed material had to pay a certain amount in gold values in order to be worked with a gold pan to your satisfaction, ground containing perhaps 1/100th as much values can be worked to the same result with the use of a sluice box. This is an important factor to grasp, because it means that the modern sluice box opens up a tremendous amount of ground that can be profitable mined by the individual.

If streambed material is located which can be profitably worked with the use of a gold pan, then working the same material with a sluice greatly increases the amount of gold which will be recovered in the same amount of time.

Sluice boxes are the most broadly used recovery systems in the gold mining industry today. They come in a wide range of sizes — from the small "miniature sluice boxes," to the medium sized boxes — which are often found on the suction dredges, to the larger sized sluices employed by the large scale bench mining operations, in which the sluices are fed by heavy equipment — bulldozers, front end loaders and the like.

For a one or two man sluicing operation, a medium sized sluice box can be built (covered later), or one can be purchased from a mining equipment dealer. Figure 5-3 shows an example of a modern day medium sized sluice box.

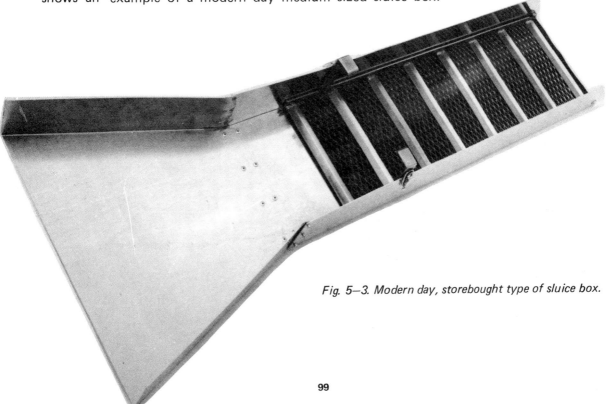

Fig. 5—3. Modern day, storebought type of sluice box.

The store bought sluice box, as shown in figure 5-3, has a few meaningful advantages over that of the homemade wooden type boxes. One example of this is that they are made out of light weight aluminum, and so are easy to carry around and will sink when you place them in the water, instead of floating off like the wooden ones tend to do. Another advantage to the store bought sluice is that it comes with a nifty set of quick release latches that hold down the riffles, so clean-up is easier and faster. Many of these models also come with a flair positioned at the head of the sluice that is designed to channel more water through the box, which means that they can be used in slower moving streams of water and still work properly. These flairs also come in handy when a miner wants to place more than one sluice box in succession to add additional recovery when very rich ground is encountered. The store bought models also usually recover gold quite well, or can be made to do so with a few minor modifications.

SLUICE BOX HISTORY

Fig. 5—4. Ground sluicing operation.

The first sluices were made by the early California miners, who dug trenches down to the bedrock or sometimes cut a trough into the bedrock itself. They would then channel water through the ditch and over the natural bed rock traps. (See figure 5-4) Then streambed material would be shoveled into the stream of water, which would allow the gold — which is heavier, to drop into the bedrock irregularities (riffles) while the lighter worthless material was washed away. This method — known as "ground sluicing," was developed in an effort on the part of the 49ers to find a faster means of recovering gold out of the streambed material, other than with the use of a gold pan. The idea of ground sluicing was originally based on the principle that if the bedrock irregularities trapped gold once, then they would do so again — and again, etc.

Over the years, many different kinds of riffle systems were experimented with, all of which trapped gold to some extent, because the yellow metal is so heavy that it doesn't take much to trap it's larger sized pieces. Figure 5-5 shows examples of some of the more primitive types of riffles systems that were commonly used by the oldtimers on the early frontier.

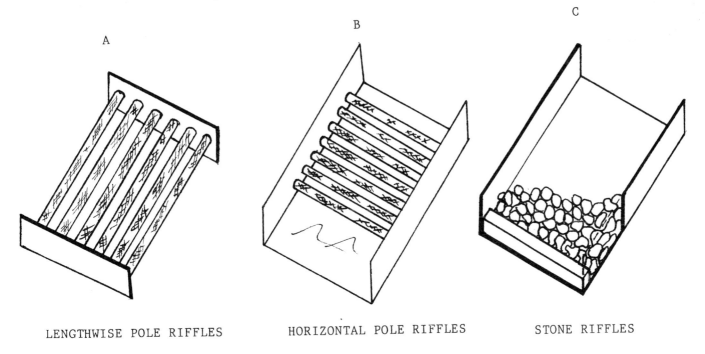

LENGTHWISE POLE RIFFLES   HORIZONTAL POLE RIFFLES   STONE RIFFLES

Fig. 5—5. Examples of early day riffles.

Parts A and B in the figure 5-5 examples, show riffles which were usually made of thin, straight, round logs — called "pole riffles." These were used to some good effect by placing them in both crosswise and lengthwise directions in the sluice box, as shown in the above examples. Part C above shows the "stone riffles," which were often used where wooden riffles would not be strong enough and no metal was available. Most sluice boxes of the old days were much longer than todays modern sluices are, and they often employed the use of more than one kind of riffle in a single box. The idea was that if one particular set of riffles did not catch the gold, another type would.

Civilization followed just behind the gold rush, and with it came more tools and supplies. And so recovery systems were improved over time, with particular attention being focused on trapping the tremendous volume of fine particles of gold — which were much more difficult to recover. Figure 5-6 shows examples of some of the more developed riffle systems used in the early days.

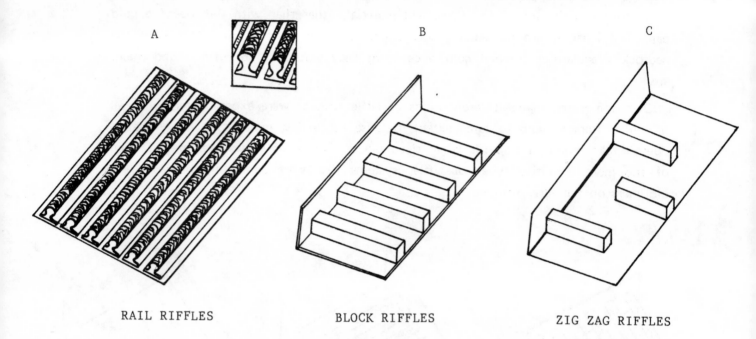

A   B   C

RAIL RIFFLES   BLOCK RIFFLES   ZIG ZAG RIFFLES

Fig. 5—6. Successful riffle systems used by the earlier miners.

"Rails riffles" (Part A), were used both in lengthwise and crosswise directions in sluice boxes. They were also used in both right-side-up and up-side down positions — all to some effect. Rail riffles are still being used today in many of the surface bench operations up in the Yukon Territory. "Block riffles" (Part B) were popular amongst many of the oldtimers as a good recovery system, and are also still used in the homemade sluice boxes seen out in the field today. Another version of the block riffle were the "zig zag riffles" (Part C). These riffles extended about 1/2 to 2/3rds of the way across the box (depending on the miner), which caused the water and material to flow around the riffles instead of over them. Many of the old timers agreed that zig zag riffles were one of the best fine gold recovery systems ever developed, and swore by it.

MODERN RIFFLES

Today, there are three main kinds of riffles that are being used — all of which work very well.

The first type, and probably the most often used of the three, is called the "Hungarian riffle" (See figure 5-7).

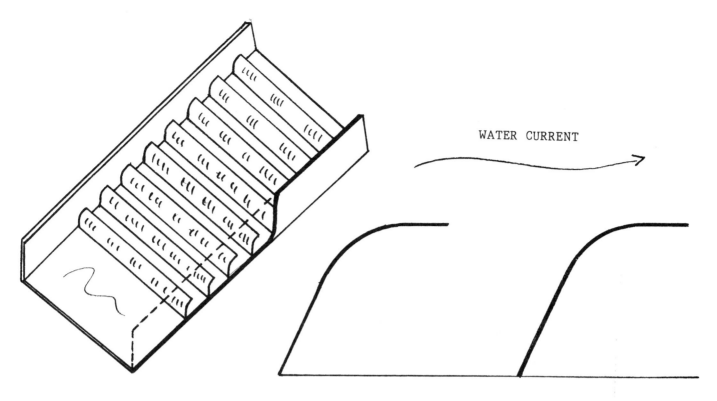

WATER CURRENT

Fig. 5-7. Hungarian type riffle.

Hungarian riffles (sometimes called "Lazy L Riffles") are usually made of a steel alloy. These are designed to recover the gold out of large volumes of material being washed over the riffles. Hungarians are found in the sluice boxes on most dredges for this reason. Hungarian riffles do more than trap gold, they concentrate the heaviest materials that are passed over them. The shape of the riffle is designed to cause a "back eddy" just beyond the upper edge of the riffle, as shown in figure 5-8. This back eddy just behind the riffle, sucks material down into it and causes a vibrating and continuous sorting action, keeping the heaviest materials and allowing the lighter materials to wash out as the new materials are sucked in. The lighter materials can

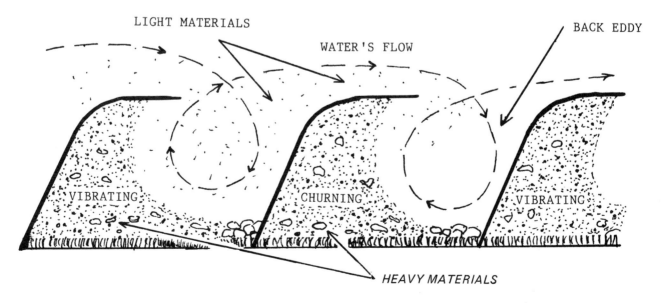

LIGHT MATERIALS

WATER'S FLOW

BACK EDDY

VIBRATING

CHURNING

VIBRATING

HEAVY MATERIALS

Fig. 5-8. Hungarian riffle action vibrates the heavy materials in and light materials out of the riffle.

then be washed down and out of the box by the main force of water. It is this same concentrating action which causes the Hungarian-type riffle to recover so well.

The second kind of riffle, which is seen on some of today's larger sized dredges and sluice boxes, is called the "Right Angle Riffle" (See figure 5-9).

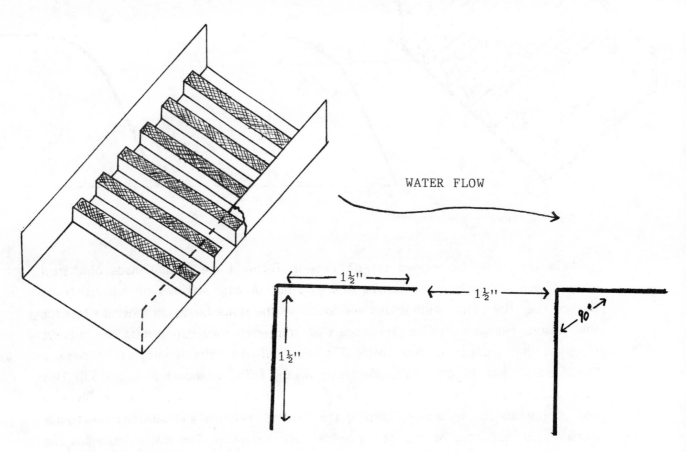

Fig. 5–9. Right angle-type riffle.

Right angle riffles, usually made out of 90 degree angle iron, are a favorite amongst larger sized operations, because of their superior strength. Angle iron comes in different sizes, but it's the 1-1/2 X 1-1/2 inch size that is most often used. Larger or smaller sizes can be utilized in the case of processing larger or smaller volumes of material.

The right angle riffle is concentrating type riffle too. Results are being obtained by placing the riffles an equal distance apart — that distance being the same as the width of the angle itself, as shown in the above diagram. These riffles concentrate best when they are tilted forward slightly — about 1/8th of an inch, in the case of a 1-1/2 X 1-1/2 inch riffle, is right (See figure 5-10). Better results are also being obtained by placing the tilted riffles about twice that distance apart — this seems to be more popular amongst today's miners.

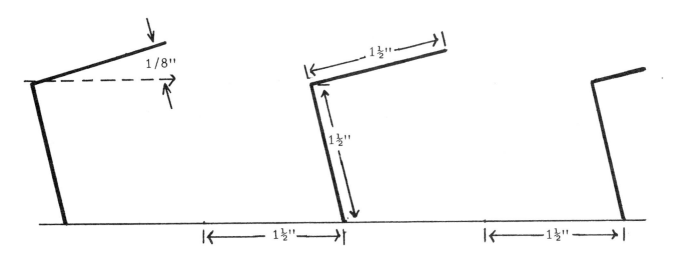

Fig. 5—10. Right angle riffles work best when tilted forward slightly.

The third type of riffle that is often seen in todays sluice boxes is expanded metal — the turned up kind, as shown if figure 5-11.

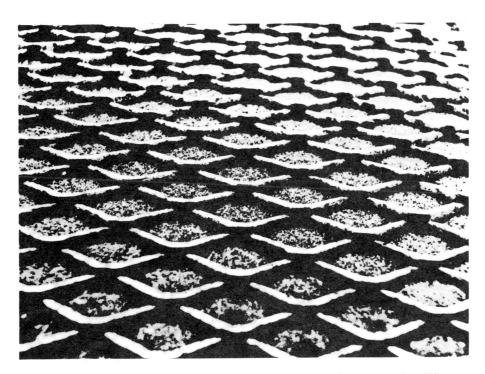

Fig. 5—11. Turned up kind of expanded metal can make an excellent recovering riffle system.

Expanded metal is used with the turned up side pointing WITH the direction of the current as shown in figure 5-12. In this way a similar type of back eddy is created just behind the turned up points, which causes the expanded metal to concentrate and recover gold very well. (See figure 5-12 on next page.)

Expanded metal, when used under the proper conditions, makes for an excellent recovery system — especially in the case of fine gold. Best results are obtained in recovery systems that have a mild flow of water passing over the box, because it only

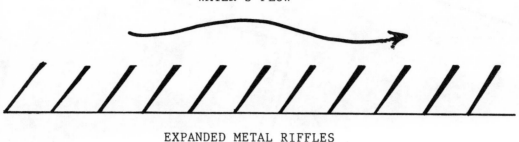

EXPANDED METAL RIFFLES

Fig. 5—12 Turned up points of expanded metal type riffles should point with the flow of current which moves through the box.

takes a mild velocity to keep expanded metal concentrating. Too much water velocity has a tendency to sweep expanded metal clean of much of it's heavier concentrated material — including gold values. The reason for this is because the expanded metal type riffle is so short in height. The best place to use expanded metal as a riffle system is in small sluice boxes or in the larger sluices where all of the larger sized material has already been screened out, so that a mild water velocity is all that is needed in the box to move material over the riffles. In these cases you will find that expanded metal recovers gold extremely well.

Most all of todays sluice boxes contain a form of rough and porous matting or carpet underneath the riffle system. It's purpose is to give the gold something along the bottom edge to work it's way down into and become permanently trapped in the sluice box. (See figure 5-13.) Various types of indoor/outdoor carpets are being used for this. The grassy types work well. Some miners prefer the use of several layers of burlap, or "miners cloth" — which is a heavier form of burlap.

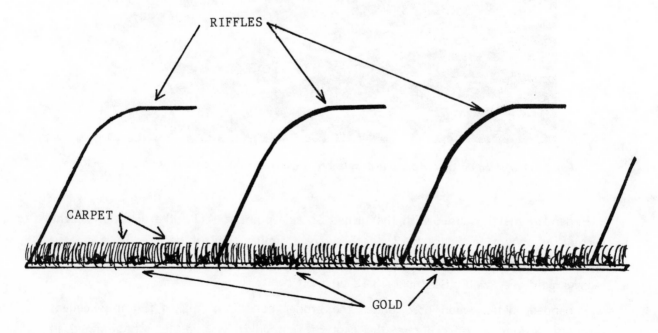

Fig. 5—13. Underlying carpet or matting will trap gold permanently in the sluicebox.

One thing to remember about any set of riffles, especially the three kinds that are outlined above, is that the entire surface of the bottom side of each riffle should be set firmly against the bottom matting of the sluice box during operation. If a space is left between the carpet and the riffles, a good deal of the back eddy effect which normally occurs behind the riffles will be lost, so some of the concentrating action will cease, and gold recovery will suffer as a result.

Sometimes expanded metal is used in conjunction with other types of riffles. In the case where expanded metal is laid down underneath a top set of riffles — like a set of hungarians, it's necessary to make sure that the underlying carpet is thick enough so that it will stick up through and around the expanded metal and fill the space between the expanded metal and the bottom edge of the overlying riffles, as shown in figure 5-14. Otherwise some of the concentrating action in the upper set of riffles will be forfeited, and a loss of fine gold recovery may result.

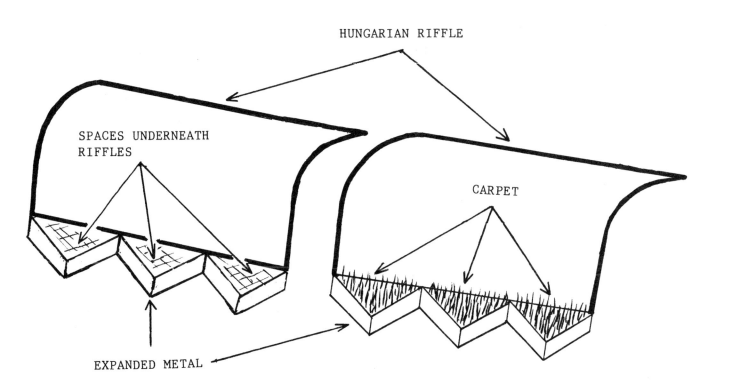

HUNGARIAN RIFFLE

SPACES UNDERNEATH RIFFLES

CARPET

EXPANDED METAL

Fig. 5–14. Recovery system on the right is likely to recover gold better, because the gaps underneath the overlying riffles are filled by carpet.

SETTING THE PROPER WATER

VELOCITY THROUGH A SLUICE BOX

There is no exact formula that can be used in setting the proper water velocity through a sluice box which will work optimumly under all conditions, for all the different types of riffles which are being utilized today. Therefore, rather than to give you a formula, I will attempt to give you an understanding of what effects the proper amount of water velocity will cause in a box and also, what the effects are of too much or too little water velocity. In this way you will be able to act from direct observation to ensure that yours, or anyone else's sluicing device will be recovering gold to the fullest extent possible.

In setting up a sluice, it is desirable to have enough water flow to move the material through the box as fast as you can shovel it in at production speed.

Most of the riffles being used today are designed so that a concentrating action takes place behind the riffles. By increasing or decreasing the amount of water velocity over a set of riffles, the amount of water action behind each riffle is also increased or decreased — which has an effect on the amount of concentrating action that takes place. Water velocity can be increased by either putting more water through the sluice box or by moving the same amount through faster. Optimumly, the water flow is just enough to keep the concentrating action going behind each riffle, yet not so much that the riffles are being swept clean of their concentrated material.

How much water velocity that is directed over the box determines how much material will stay behind the riffles. When the correct amount of water force is being put through the sluice, it's riffles will run about half full of material, and that material can be visibly seen to be dancing and vibrating behind the riffles (concentrating) when the water is flowing. (See figure 5-15.)

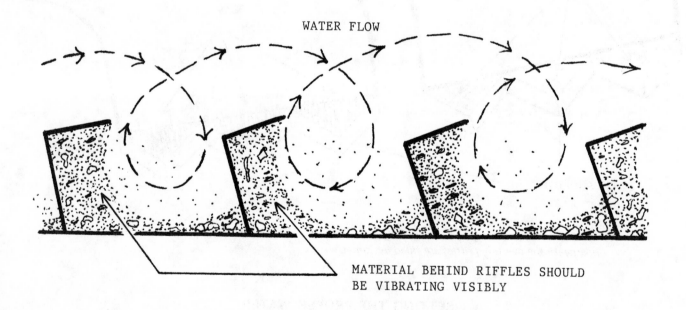

WATER FLOW

MATERIAL BEHIND RIFFLES SHOULD
BE VIBRATING VISIBLY

Fig. 5—15. The correct amount of water flow will run riffles about 1/2 full of material.

If too little flow of water is directed through a sluice box, not enough water force can get into the riffles and they will fill up with material. In this case little or no concentrating action will take place and gold recovery will be poor. (See figure 5-16.)

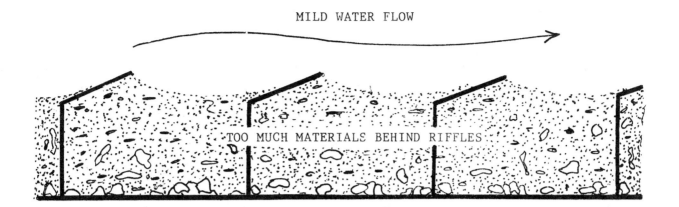

MILD WATER FLOW

TOO MUCH MATERIALS BEHIND RIFFLES

Fig. 5—16. Overloaded riffles - means not enough water velocity over box.

When this happens, no visible vibrating action behind the riffles will be seen and material will not be moving through the box fast enough to allow you to shovel at production speed without loading up the entire box, as shown in figure 5-17.

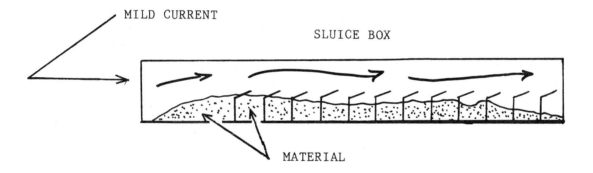

MILD CURRENT

SLUICE BOX

MATERIAL

Fig. 5—17. Too little water flow can allow the entire sluicebox to load up with material.

Too much force of water through a sluice box will put too much turbulence behind the riffles, which will cause some of the heavier concentrated material to be swept out of the box. (See figure 5-18.) When this happens, gold recovery will also suffer, because the spaces behind the riffles are not calm enough to allow a percentage of the finer pieces of gold to settle. It will be noticed in this case that the dancing action is occurring behind each riffle, but that less material will collect behind the riffles because of the increased amount of turbulence occurring there. It will also be noticed when you have too much water velocity that when the material is shoveled into the box, it passes through very quickly and has little time to make contact with the riffles.

All the above points remain true when trying to get the proper amount of water flowing over an expanded metal riffle system. However, when using such a system it's necessary to remember that the riffles are very short and so it doesn't take very much

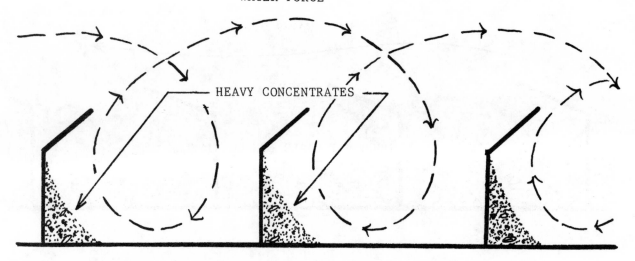

Fig. 5–18. Too much water velocity over a sluice box will sweep the riffles clean of some of the heavier concentrates, and a loss of gold may result.

water velocity to make them concentrate properly. The correct amount of flow is usually found to be just enough to move the material over the box to keep up with your shoveling.

In the final analysis, once you have your sluice box set up the way that you think it should be, run a good sized portion of gold bearing material through the box and then pan out some samples of the tailings. If you don't turn any gold up out of the tailings, you are set up properly. If you are finding gold in the tailings, some changes are in order. Another test is to mix some pieces of lead in with some material, run it through the sluice, and see where the lead stops.

On most suction dredges, the volume of water being moved through the sluice continues at the same steady flow during production speed. So, changing the water velocity is done by changing the slope of the sluice box itself — which will speed up or slow down the flow of water over the box.

It's a different matter when dealing with a single sluice box that is going to be placed in a stream or creek for its water flow. In this case the water velocity can be adjusted by either changing the slop of the box, by varying the volume of water being directed through the box, or by placing the sluice at different sites in the stream or creek where the water is moving under a more optimum condition for your sluicing needs. Getting the right flow of water to pass through a sluice box out in the field is not difficult, but it is usually necessary to do a bit of coping with the situation on the part of the miner. For example, in a location where the water is moving slow, you might be able to direct more volume of water through the sluice and gain the amount of water velocity that you need. In a stream where the flow is moving more swiftly, the water velocity through your box can be adjusted by changing the volume of water that is directed into it, and/or by varying its downward slope.

Usually, you will have no trouble at all arriving at the correct velocity through your sluice box when placing it in a fast stream of water. You can use river rocks to make a foundation in the stream so that your box can sit level from side to side; and by allowing different amounts of water volume through the box, and by changing its downward slope, you will quickly get the required combination. It's good to have a length of nylon cord along with you for the purpose of securing the sluice box to a rock or some other object upstream, to prevent it from being moved off of its foundation by the force of water. Sometimes it's necessary to pile a rock or two on top of the box to hold it in place. This is especially true when you are using a sluice made out of wood. Shovel gravel into the box while trying the different combinations, to see what effects that the changes have on the water velocity.

In a situation where you have to set your sluice into slower moving water, you will find that it is generally more difficult to get the flow that you need; because you have to first create more water force than is presently there.

If the flow of the stream itself is not enough to move material through your box, you will usually find that changing the slope of the box within the stream has little or no effect on speeding up the flow through the sluice (See figure 5–19).

SAME SLUICE WITH DIFFERENT DOWNWARD SLOPES

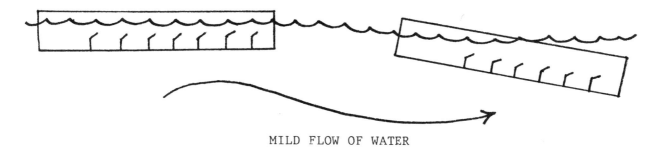

MILD FLOW OF WATER

Fig. 5–19. In a mild flow of water, just changing the slope of the sluice usually has little or no effect on increasing the amount of water velocity through the box.

In this situation, there are several things which might be done to channel enough flow through your box so that you can run material through at production speed. Sometimes the flow of water in the stream itself is enough, that by setting up a "water director" in the stream, you can move enough water through the box to give you the desired result, as shown in figure 5-20. A water deflector, or barrier like this, can usually be built by throwing river rocks out into the stream to make more water flow into and through the sluice.

If the flow in the stream is not moving fast enough that a water director can be used — but some water flow is occurring, sometimes you can get the water velocity that you need by building a small dam. By doing so, and by placing your sluice where the moving water spills over the top, you can often get more than enough water flow through the box to meet your needs, as shown in figure 5-21. It really doesn't take very much volume of water through a medium sized sluice box to get the right amount of velocity, if the water is moved through the box at speed. In the case of a small dam, as shown above, the water level usually only needs to be raised up slightly to increase the downward slope of the box enough to create the needed water velocity. How high that the dam will need to be depends mostly on how much water is flowing in the stream or creek.

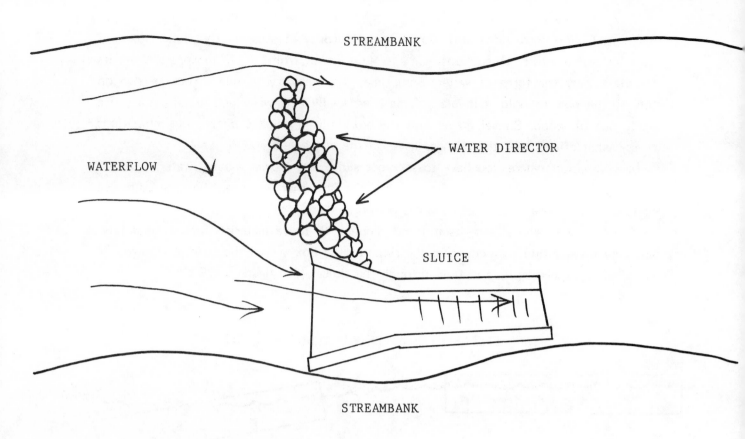

STREAMBANK

WATER DIRECTOR

WATERFLOW

SLUICE

STREAMBANK

Fig. 5–20. Sometimes more water can be directed through a sluice box in order to get the necessary amount of water velocity.

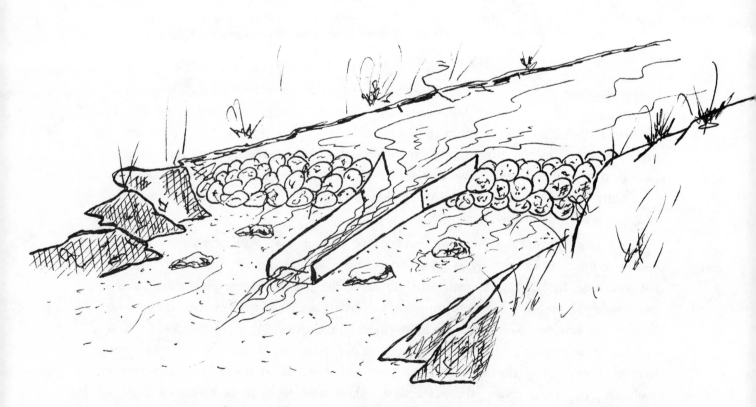

Fig. 5–21. Sometimes you can build a small dam to bring the water level up just a bit and get the needed water velocity through your box.

A sheet or two of thin plastic comes in handy when you are building a dam or water director in a stream; because the plastic will help to prevent the water from pouring through the holes in your man-made barriers.

Either a water director or dam can usually be used to a good result wherever the water in a stream or creek is moving and is not so deep that the barriers cannot be built easily.

If the water at the worksite is moving too slow, or for some reason a water director or dam won't work in that location, it will be necessary to either set up your sluice in another location — where the water is moving faster, or use a pump to put water into your box, or siphon water to your box from a higher point upstream. Siphoning can be done effectively with the use of reinforced garden hose or PVC.

PUMPING WATER TO A SLUICE

Engine-pump units are available on the market that will pump enough water to supply any sized sluice box. A medium sized sluice box can usually be fed an ample supply of water, via a large sized diameter garden hose, by one of the smaller and more economical units. Sluicing with the use of a pump is very popular amongst serious miners, because it allows the sluice to be placed in the most optimum position for production purposes. Sometimes, the paydirt that one is interested in mining is not directly near moving water; and in this case pumping or siphoning the water to the sluice is far more efficient than hauling the paydirt over to the nearest running water. Pumping water to the sluice also allows the miner to move his box into better positions as progress is made into the streambed. This allows him to continue optimum production all the time, instead of having to carry the material as progress takes him further and further away from the stream of water.

What sized engine-pump unit that an operation will need depends on the size of the sluice box being used, how far that the water will have to be pumped, and how far upward that the water will be pumped. Elevation of the worksite above sea level and outside air temperatures can also affect engine performance. Most dealers of mining equipment have the specifications on their various sized pumping units, and will be more than happy to help you find the best equipment to fill your needs.

When pumping water to a sluice box through a hose, it's usually necessary to have some kind of a "water spreader" to distribute the water effectively at the head of the box. One of these can be easily put together with the use of a short length of 2 inch diameter PVC piping, as shown in figure 5-22. In putting such a device together, an end cap should close off one end of the spreader, and the other end should be capped with a fitting which will connect to the hose that is being used to pump or siphon water to the box.

Holes should be drilled in a straight line along the length of the spreader. These should be an inch apart and about 3/8 inches in diameter — or larger, depending on how much water is needed. Generally, 3/8 inch holes are about right, but they can be enlarged if necessary. This water spreader can be clamped to the head of your box if

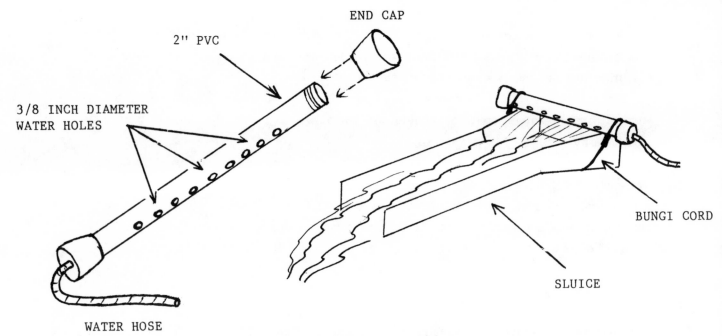

END CAP

2" PVC

3/8 INCH DIAMETER
WATER HOLES

WATER HOSE

BUNGI CORD

SLUICE

Fig. 5—22. PVC water spreader.

it is to remain there permanently, or it can be attached with the use of a heavy rubber bungi cord if it's only a temporary affair, like in the above figure. The reason why this kind of water spreader works so well is because it is relatively out of the way — being all the way to the head of the sluice, and also because the line of holes can be turned to adjust the direction in which the water hits the head of the box so that optimum performance can be obtained.

If you are out in the field and have a coffee can handy, a workable spreader can be made by punching a hole toward the upper edge of the can large enough to feed your hose through, as shown in figure 5-23. The can is used upside down with the hose

Fig. 5—23. Coffee can water spreader.

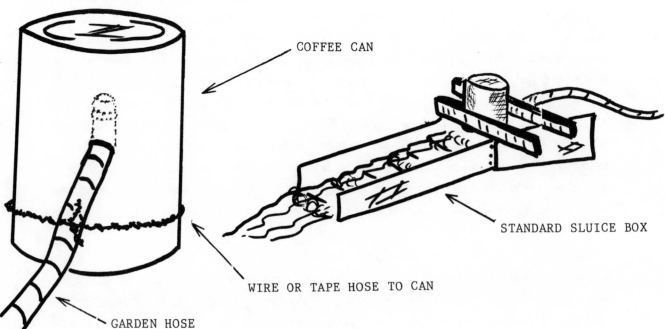

COFFEE CAN

STANDARD SLUICE BOX

WIRE OR TAPE HOSE TO CAN

GARDEN HOSE

stuck through the hole and fed up into the can. The hose can then be wired or taped to the outside of the can to ensure that it stays in place. Small sized coffee cans work best for this when being used in conjunction with medium sized sluice boxes. The can is nailed to several pieces of wood that are long enough to extend across the head of the sluice box, as shown if figure 5-23.

CLASSIFICATION OF MATERIAL

It takes more water velocity to move the larger sized material than it does to move the smaller sized material through a sluice box. To the degree that the water velocity over a sluice box is increased, there will be a loss of a certain percentage of fine gold recovery. To the degree that the water velocity over a sluice box is slowed down, there will be an increase in fine gold recovery — as long as there is still enough flow over the box to keep the riffles concentrating.

When larger sized rocks are pushed through a sluice box by water force, they can cause a great deal of turbulence behind the riffles as they pass over — which can also cause a loss on fine gold recovery.

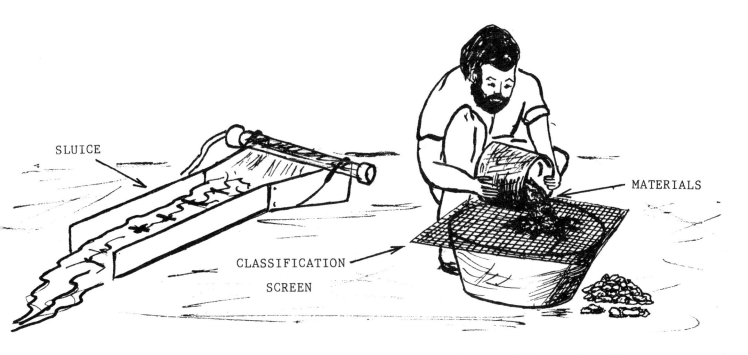

Fig. 5—24. Classifying material before running it through a sluice box will improve fine gold recovery.

In order to improve gold recovery, many miners run their material through a screen to classify out the larger sized rocks before running the material through a sluice box. In this way, less water velocity is needed through the box, which allows for a more orderly flow, and so the fine gold recovery is improved. The action of screening materials as such is called "classification." Materials which have been passed through a classification screen are called "classified materials."

Half inch mesh screen is commonly used in small and medium sized sluicing operations, because the screen is large enough that classification will take place quickly, yet no materials greater than half inch in size will get into the sluice. In this way a much milder current of water can be passed through the box, and fine gold recovery will be improved as a result.

The classification for a sluicing operation can be done in any number of ways, one of which is to place a piece of strong half inch mesh screen over a bucket, and shovel or pour through the screen into the bucket while sweeping the larger sized material off to the side, as shown in figure 5-24. Once the bucket is filled with classified material, it can be poured into the sluice box at a uniform rate. Don't just dump the whole bucket into the sluice all at once, because by doing that, you can overload the riffles and possibly lose some gold as a result.

In a situation where it is necessary to haul material for a short distance to the sluice box, probably the best method is to classify the material directly into a wheelbarrow and to cart only the classified materials over to the box.

Perhaps one of the best screening methods is to build a classification device that you can shovel into, which will stand directly over top of, and drop the classified materials into the head of your sluice box, as shown in figure 5-25.

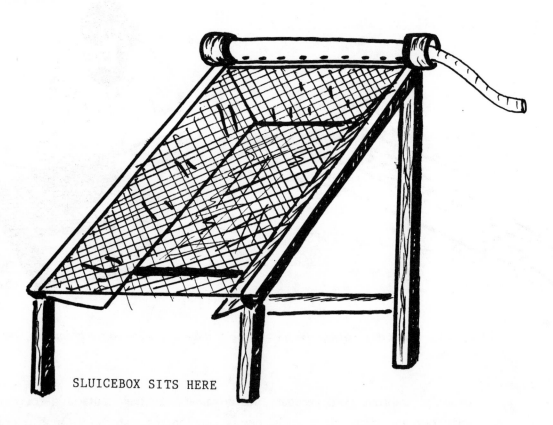

SLUICEBOX SITS HERE

Fig. 5–25. Homemade screening device used to speed up classifciation and improve gold recovery.

The device should be built with the screen set at an angle, so that the larger sized material will roll off of the screen as the pay dirt is shoveled onto it. The smaller sized materials should fall through the screen and be directed to fall into the head of your sluice box. This is actually a minature model of the big classifiers used by many of the large scale bench mining operations. A classification device such as this is rather easy and economical to build and will speed up a production sluicing operation in which screening is being done to improve gold recovery. (See figure 5-26.)

Fig. 5—26.

HYDRAULIC CONCENTRATORS

A "hydraulic concentrator" (see figure 5-27) is a highly portable sluicing device, which contains all of the best features mentioned thus far in this chapter. These units have classification screens that are designed to keep the larger sized materials out of the sluice, yet they classify fast enough to keep one or two men busy shoveling at production speed. The manufacturers of the model shown in figure 5-27 state that their unit will pump water to the concentrator as far as 200 feet above the source of water. This allows for quite a lot of operating mobility. The concentrator is designed so that the water flow over the sluice is adjustable, to get the best recovery possible.

The hydraulic concentrator is very easy to set up compared with having to set up a sluice in a streambed.

They will usually handle up to about 2 cubic yards of material per hour, which is equivalent of any medium sized sluice box when set up under the most optimum conditions.

The hydraulic concentrator is not very heavy, about 50 pounds in all — including the engine-pump unit, and so can be used successfully as a sampling tool when larger volume samples are wanted and the areas being tested are not too far off the beaten

Fig. 5–27. Hydraulic concentrator.

path. The hydraulic concentrator can also be used as a production machine with excellent results; and for this reason — and the other factors mentioned above, it is perhaps the best all around, medium sized, portable, surface sluicing equipment on the market today.

WHEN TO CLEAN-UP

Some miners like to clean-up their sluice boxes after every hour of operation. Some prefer to clean-up at the end of the day. Others will go for days at a time before cleaning-up. This is all a matter of preference and probably has little or nothing to do with the actual needs of the sluice box. Some of the large scale operations which ran during the early 1900's used to allow the lower 2/3d's of their boxes to run for months at a stretch without cleaning them up — and without worry of losing gold. However, it is true that sluice boxes were longer in those days.

There is a way of determining when a sluice box needs to be cleaned up in order to keep it operating at it's utmost efficiency.

If the majority of gold is catching in the upper third section of the sluice box, then the recovery system is working well.

After a set of riffles has been run for an extended period of time without being cleaned, they will have concentrated a large amount of heavy materials behind them. Sometimes a lot of heavy concentrated material in a sluice box will affect the efficiency of the riffles to recover gold. This is not always the case, it depends on the type of riffles being used and how they are set up in the box. The true test of when a set of riffles are losing their efficiency because of being loaded down with heavy concentrates, is when the gold starts being trapped further down the length of the box than where it normally catches. When this occurs, it is definitely time to clean-up your box. Otherwise, clean them when you like.

Expanded metal riffles — being short, will tend to load up with heavy black sands faster than the larger types of riffles. However, a visible, large amount of black sand being present is not necessarily a sign that you are losing gold. Gold is 4 times heavier than black sand; and in some cases, the black sand will have little or no effect on gold recovery. Again, it depends on how the system is set up. The best way to tell about your recovery system is by direct observation of where the gold is being trapped.

TRIPLE-SLUICES

One of the most important recent developments in gold mining equipment is the "triple-sluice box." These are mostly being used on suction dredges at this time. They could also be used in straight sluicing operations to a good result — especially in the case of small hydraulic operations, where a large volume of material is being processed.

The idea behind the triple-sluice is to have a classification screen at the head of the box, which allows the smaller material to be separated out and run through side sluice boxes, where the water flow is controlled to move much slower. Most gold, platinum and gem stones are of a size which will drop through the screen at the head of the box and end up in the slower currents of the side boxes (see figure 5-28), and so the gold recovery is excellent in these triple-sluice recovery systems.

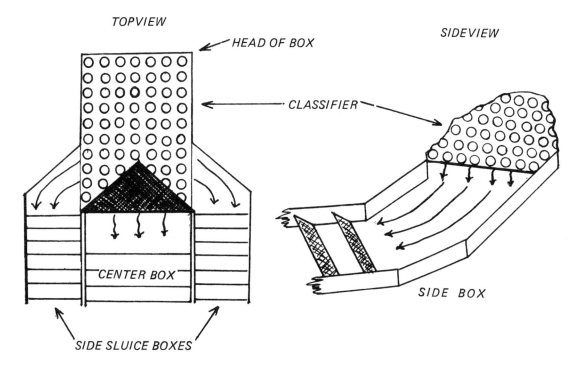

Fig. 5—28. On a triple-sluice type of recovery system, most of the finer sized values will drop down through the classifier and be swept into the side boxes, where the flow of water is moving much slower.

The center box in a triple sluice has a current passing through that is fast enough to move the larger materials. Yet, the current is not strong enough to wash the larger pieces of gold out of the box.

These boxes are well used in the case of suction dredges, where large amounts of streambed materials are being processed and classification is necessary in order to recover a large percentage of the fine gold. (See figure 5-29.)

Fig. 5—29. Triple sluice dredge in action.

TOOLS

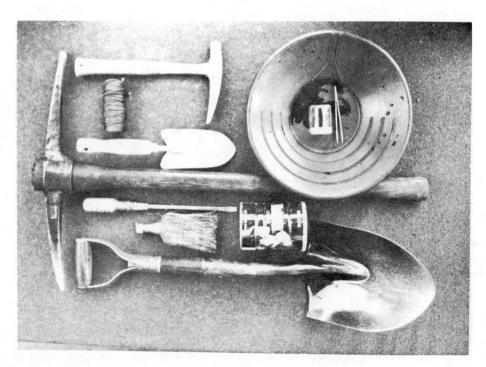

Fig. 5—30. Additional sluicing equipment.

The following tools are usually of use to a sluicing operation: shovel, pick — comes in very useful for breaking material out of the streambed, rock hammer — to help break up bedrock and clean out crevices, screw driver, garden trowel — for fine work in digging out bedrock irregularities, whisk broom — for cleaning bedrock, plastic sheets — for building water barriers, nylon cord — for anchoring sluice in running water, coffee can — for concentrates, gold pan — for clean-up, tweezers and gold bottle — for the gold.

BUILDING A SIMPLE SLUICE BOX

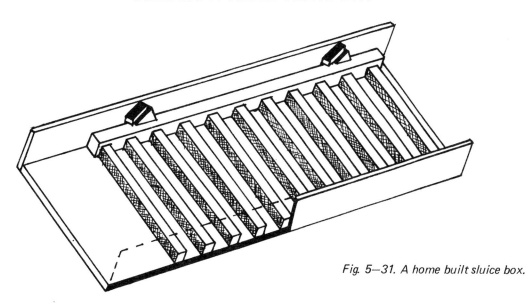

Fig. 5—31. A home built sluice box.

A very simple, but effective, sluice box can be built out of wood, that can be used in a small one or two-man operation with good results.

The sluice is put together as follows: Using marine or a good grade of outdoor plywood, cut the rectangular pieces for the basic floor and walls of the box to the dimensions as laid out in figure 5-32.

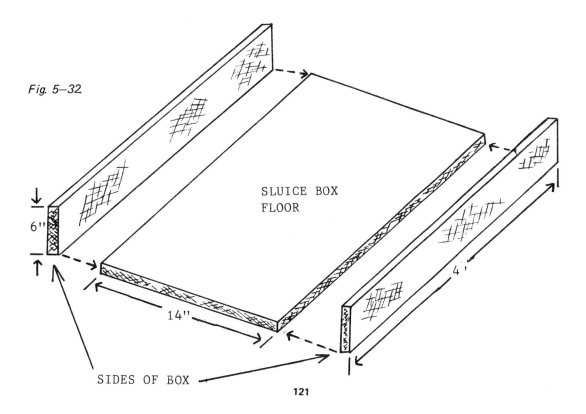

Fig. 5—32

SLUICE BOX FLOOR

6"

14"

4'

SIDES OF BOX

The sideboards should now be nailed or screwed tightly to the bottom board — making sure that the sideboards are attached to the side edges of the bottom board, as shown in figure 5-33. Once the sideboards are securely fastened to the bottom side, caulk the seams with silicone rubber. This is to insure that no gold is lost through these cracks. Use just enough silicone to fill the cracks — no more.

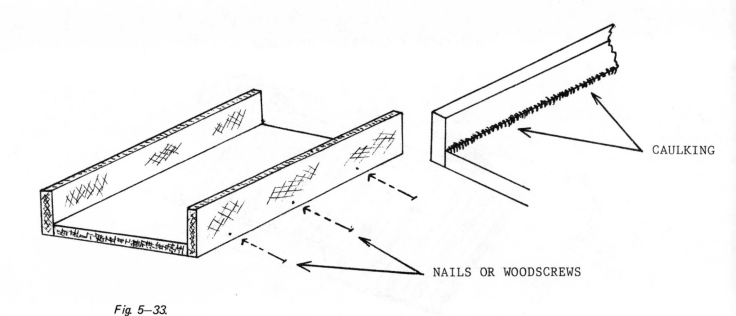

CAULKING

NAILS OR WOODSCREWS

Fig. 5—33.

Now, we'll build the riffle system. It will be made of 1 inch by 1 inch pieces of oak. The riffles themselves should be cut 12 inches long, and the side rails should be 3 feet long, as shown in figure 5-34.

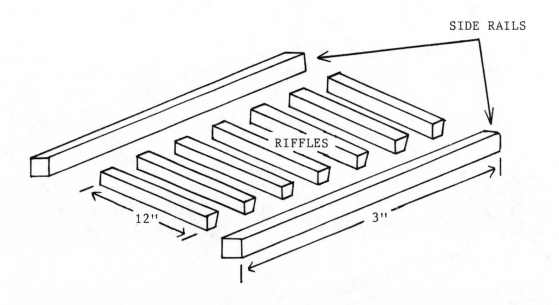

SIDE RAILS

RIFFLES

12"

3"

Fig. 5—34. All pieces made of 1 x 1 inch oak.

These riffles will be placed one inch apart down the length of the side rails. There will be 18 of them in all. Best results will be obtained from these riffles by cutting a small angle off the lower rear part of each riffle, as shown in figure 5-35. The riffles will work without this cut, but better results are obtained with it; because it creates a better back eddy behind the riffles, causing more concentrating activity.

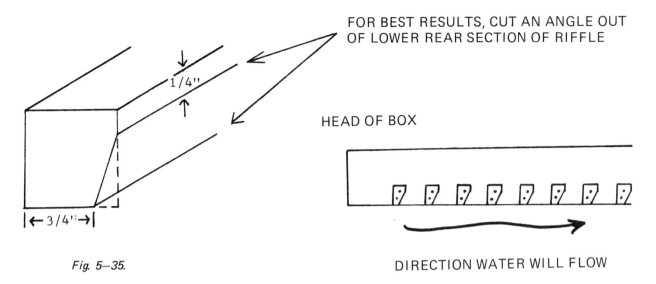

FOR BEST RESULTS, CUT AN ANGLE OUT OF LOWER REAR SECTION OF RIFFLE

HEAD OF BOX

Fig. 5-35.

DIRECTION WATER WILL FLOW

Nail or screw each riffle to the side rails with the riffle angles all facing to the rear, along the bottom edge. The riffles should start at the forward edge of the side rails and be placed 1 inch apart, with care to make sure that the bottom edges of all the riffles are even. Two nails on each side of each riffle should be used, as shown in figure 5-35. Smaller holes should be drilled first if you have trouble with nails splitting the wood.

Now cut a piece of indoor/outdoor carpet or several pieces of burlap the size of 3 feet by 14 inches. This will be placed in the lower section of the box, with the riffles laid on top.

The riffle locks now need to be made, and figure 5-36 lays out the dimensions for these. Four of each should be made.

LOCK BLOCK

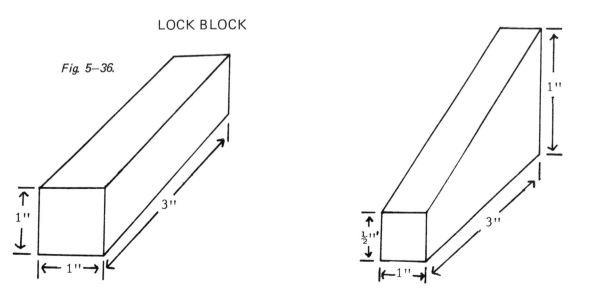

Fig. 5-36.

Now lay the matting in place within the box with the riffles on top facing the right direction. Put the wedges on top of the side rails, pointing forward about 6 inches from each corner of the riffle system, as shown in figure 5-37. The lock blocks should be placed over the wedges and bolted to the sides of the sluice box. Be sure to attach the lock blocks up and away from the side rails as far as possible, but not so far that you cannot tap the wedges into place to hold the riffles securely down. The reason why you want the lock blocks up away from the side rails is so there will be plenty of room to slide the riffles out when you want to remove them during clean-up.

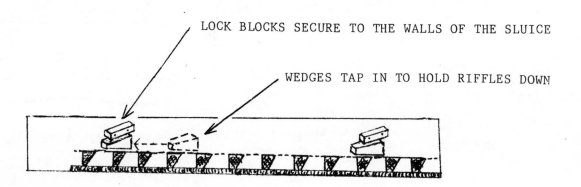

LOCK BLOCKS SECURE TO THE WALLS OF THE SLUICE

WEDGES TAP IN TO HOLD RIFFLES DOWN

Fig. 5—37. Installing lock blocks.

Now the box is complete and the riffle system can be locked in tightly by tapping the wedges into place and removed by tapping the wedges out. Notice that the head of the box has no riffles. This is where the material is tossed during sluicing.

CHAPTER VI

DREDGING FOR GOLD

Suction dredging for gold is a relatively new subject in the field of gold mining, with a large amount of development in equipment and procedure having occurred within the last few years.

Because a prospector can process so much more volume of material with the use of a gold dredge than he can with hand operated sluicing gear, and because of the relatively inexpensive dredging equipment which is available on today's market, gold dredging is probably the best thing that has ever happened in the field of mining for the small time operator. (One or two man operation.)

With the use of a gold dredge, under the proper conditions, a single person can process up to 20 cubic yards — or more - of gold bearing streambed material per hour, which is approximately 10 to 20 times more material than he or she could move using pick and shovel methods under excellent conditions at the surface.

He or she? Yes, women are operating gold dredges too, and some of them are recovering gold in large quantities!

Gold dredging today has put the small time operator in the position of being able to process very large portions of streambed, and thus putting him in a position of being able to find and recover large paying quantities of gold. The only type of gold mining activity that can out produce a suction dredging operation is a professional high-bench type of operation which employs the use of heavy earth moving equipment. Such operations usually cost hundreds of thousands of dollars to get started.

A one or two-man dredging operation costs very little to get started in comparison to how much gold that can be recovered in a short period of time — once the operators have gained an understanding of how to locate gold deposits.

Being that a great deal of gold has continued to be washed into the present streams rivers and creeks — which are and have been rather inaccessible to the surface type operations, the individual with a suction dredge is in a good position to locate and recover plenty of substantial sized placer deposits.

It takes far less effort to move a much greater volume of streambed materials than it does when using a pick and shovel. The reason for this is because the dredge operator does not need to pound away at and lift material out of the streambed. The suction dredge is an underwater vacuum cleaner, and processing the streambed materials is just a matter of sucking them up into the hose. The dredge does all the rest. Those larger sized rocks and boulders that are too big to be sucked up are much easier to move under the surface of the water than they are at the surface. The dredge operator does not even have the weight of his own body to move around, because it is in a state of suspension in the water — only being weighted down enough to remain on the bottom.

During recent years, as the market value of gold has increased, so has the interest in gold mining, and many people have turned to suction dredging. As a result, a large competitive market in dredging equipment has sprung up, which has been the cause of many, many improvements in the field, and has brought the costs of equipment way down.

Because most dredging is done during the hot summer months, and is done under the cool clear water of mountain streams, and because so much more streambed material can be explored with the use of a suction dredge — to uncover more and larger quantities of gold than was ever possible by earlier methods; gold dredging is more like treasure hunting than anything else. As a result, the gold rush of the 80's is largely due to suction dredges.

I'm not kidding you; once you get good at it, it's like hunting treasure — which you know you are going to find. It's exciting and fun — even during the cold winter months for me.

Don't misunderstand me in thinking that gold dredging is not hard work. There's plenty of hard work involved. Generally speaking, any gold mining operation will produce only as well as the operator is willing to put his energy into it. It's just that so much more can be done with a suction dredge. The same amount of energy produces a lot more in a dredging operation, and so the guy — or gal — who is really willing to put out in an effort to succeed well at gold dredging, usually does! And that's one of the points that makes suction dredging so popular.

WHAT A GOLD DREDGE IS

Suction gold dredges come in a wide range of sizes and variety, but any and all of them basically break down into five major components. These are the floatation system, engine/pump assembly, jet/hose system, recovery system, and the air breathing system.

FLOATATION

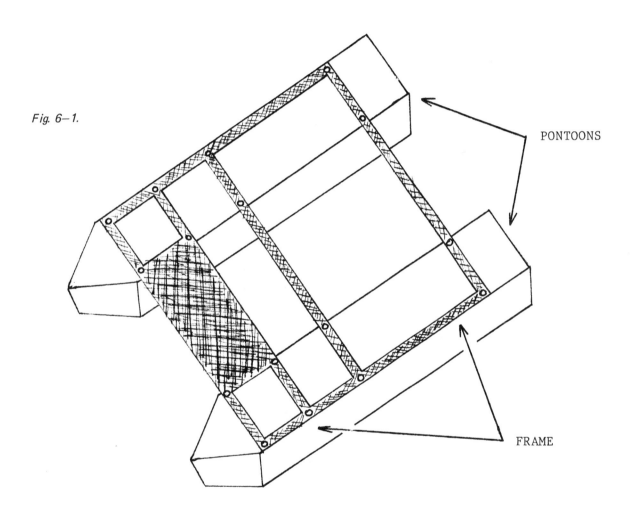

Fig. 6—1.

PONTOONS

FRAME

Todays dredges — meaning the entire units, are usually floated either on a set of innertubes, or on a set of pontoons. The larger the size of the dredge, the more floatation that is needed. Innertubes are used on many of the smaller and intermediate size dredges, and have the advantage of deflating. So they can be packed away and hauled around easier than the larger pontoons can.

Pontoons today are usually made out of lightweight styrofoam, aluminum, durable plastics, or some combination of these. Some homemade rigs employ the use of empty steel drums.

When shopping around to buy a dredge, look over the floatation system to ensure that the floats can be securely fastened to the dredge's frame, and that they are wide enough to give the dredge good stability on the water.

PUMP/ENGINE

Portable gasoline type engines are being used to power most suction dredges found on the market today. These are the same kind of engines that are found on lawn mowers and industrial equipment. The advantage to these is that they are light and easy to pack around, and it takes very little maintenance to keep them operating.

Some of the larger-sized professional dredges employ the use of car engines in order to get the needed power to run them. These are popular on large professional production dredges.

Some dredge manufacturers utilize more than one small engine to get the amount of power needed for their larger sized dredges. This makes the larger sized dredge and its various components easier to haul into and out of a production location.

Most often, for a water supply, the centrifugal type of pump is used, which bolts directly onto the engine (See figure 6-2).

ENGINE

AIR COMPRESSOR

PUMP

Fig. 6—2. Engine/pump assembly

The different sized dredges have different sized engine/pump assemblies, because larger amounts of water and pressure are needed in order to power a larger sized dredge.

Centrifugal pumps are usually mounted on the engine in an above water location, and a tube or water hose is usually used to get water to the pump, as shown in figure 6-3.

PUMP IS PRIMED
HERE

PRIMER AND PUMP INTAKE

Fig. 6—3. Pumps which are mounted above the water's surface suck water up to themselves through an intake tube or hose.

Pumps which have been mounted above water almost always need to be primed before they are operated, because the centrifugal pump is made to pump water and so it must be emersed in water, or connected with water in order to start pumping. Once primed and started, the pump will suck water to itself and no further service will be needed to keep it running properly.

On most of todays gold dredges, priming is being done in three different ways. Some of the larger professional rigs have automatic primers and all that's necessary is to start the engine and the pump will be primed automatically. Many of the large and intermediate sized dredges have a combination intake tube and primer, which has a screw cap at the top, and water is poured into it from the surface in order to prime the pump before starting. (See figure 6-3.) On these, it's necessary to remember to put the cap on tightly before the engine is started. Otherwise the prime will be lost. Most of the smaller sized gold dredges employ the use of the intake hose as a primer. Such hoses are equipped with a screening device at the lower end — to prevent pebbles and rocks from being sucked up into the pump, and they also have a one way flow valve — so that water will be allowed to enter the intake hose but will be prevented from leaking back out again. To prime such a hose, it is necessary to take it in your hand and quickly push it up and down under the water. This action forces water up into the intake hose. The one way valve prevents the water from flowing back out again, and after a bit of pumping in this way you are able to get enough water up through the hose to prime the pump. This procedure is usually done while the pump is running at low speed. (See figure 6-4.)

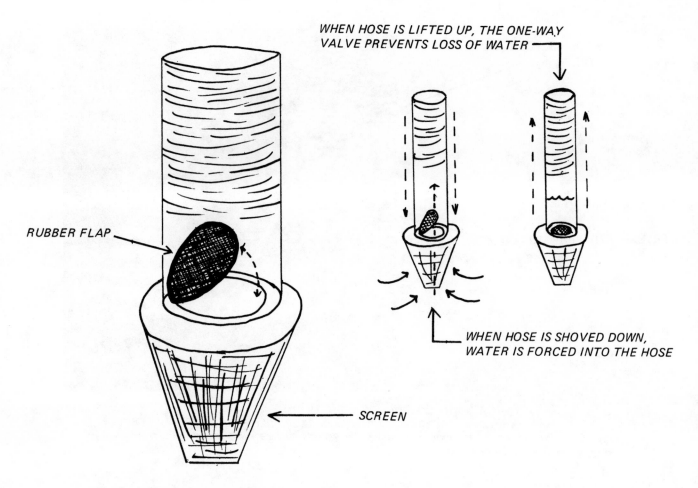

WHEN HOSE IS LIFTED UP, THE ONE-WAY VALVE PREVENTS LOSS OF WATER

RUBBER FLAP

SCREEN

WHEN HOSE IS SHOVED DOWN, WATER IS FORCED INTO THE HOSE

Fig. 6—4. One-way valve on a primer hose.

Just about all primers and pump intakes — no matter what kind, are equipped with a screening device at the lower end to keep rocks from being sucked up into the pump, and a one way flow valve so that the pump's prime is not lost when the engine is shut down temporarily — to refuel or whatever.

Some of the smaller dredges on the market use vertical shaft engines, and the pumps are mounted on the underside of the dredge beneath the water. No priming is necessary in their case.

Some home built dredges use jet boat type pumps, which mount underwater too and need no priming.

Centrifugal pumps require little to no maintenance. The one thing to remember is that they should not be operated for an extended period of time without water being run through them. The reason for this is that these pumps use a rubber type seal which fits snugly on the shaft to keep water from leaking out around where the shaft enters the pump. This seal depends on the water passing through the pump to keep it lubricated and cool. If the pump is operated for awhile without water passing through, the seal can become too hot and thereafter lose it's efficiency in preventing water from leaking around the shaft. The way to avoid this is to never run the pump for more than a few seconds at a time without water. You can tell if water is being pumped by looking to see if it is running into the dredge's sluice box.

If it does happen that the pump's seal on your dredge becomes defective, it is not a difficult job to replace it. An extra seal is good to have on hand in case it should occur out in the field. It is done by unbolting and removing the outer pump housing and then the impeller. Very few impellers on today's centrifugal pumps are pressed on. Most of them are screwed onto the shaft. Usually it's necessary to get a firm grip on the engine's flywheel and hold it steady, so that the impeller can be unscrewed off the shaft. Once the impeller is removed, the pump's inner housing can be unbolted and removed from the engine. The seal can then be replaced on the inner housing. The pump goes back together in the opposite way that it came apart.

The engines that are used on most of today's dredges require very little maintenance. Usually they do not come with oil in the crankcase; so they will need to be filled to the proper level first — before being started. The oil level should be checked periodically, and a log of operating hours should be kept so that the oil, spark plug, and breaker points can be changed according to the manufacturer's instructions. The air and gas filters should also be checked and cleaned every once in awhile.

When the pump is primed and the engine is started, water will be pumped through a pressure hose to the jet.

JET SYSTEM

The earliest suction dredges pumped water, mud, sand, clay, rocks and gravel — all through the pump itself. Needless to say, that must have been extremely hard on pumps!

Most of today's suction dredges employ the use of a "venturi system," in which a volume of water under pressure is pumped into a steel tube at an angle. As shown in figure 6-5, this causes a vacuum effect (venturi effect) just behind where the water enters the main tube (jet), which pushes/pulls the water, sand and gravel up through the suction hose and main jet. In this way, no streambed material needs to be run through the pump.

The jet system is probably the most important component part on a suction dredge. The idea is to get the highest pressure and greatest volume that is attainable out of the pump, in order to get the most suction power at the nozzle. This is done by reducing the size of the power jet just before it enters the main tube of the jet. The highest volume — highest pressure mixture is difficult to get right without a lot of trial and error on the part of the dredge builder, and is the main reason why most dredgers buy their equipment instead of building their own. Different pumps have different pressure and volume capacities - which require different sized power jet reductions. These changes also affect how wide the sluice will need to be in order to accommodate the amount of water that is being pumped through the box — which calls for additional trial and error on the part of the dredge builder. It is possible to build your own dredge, and it's really not too difficult to do if you are naturally inclined in that area. However, I assure you that it would be difficult to build a better dredge than some of the improved models that are being offered on today's market, and almost impossible to

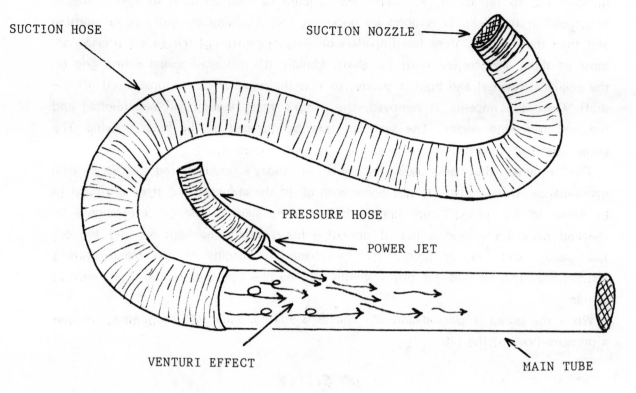

SUCTION HOSE

SUCTION NOZZLE

PRESSURE HOSE

POWER JET

VENTURI EFFECT

MAIN TUBE

Fig. 6—5. Venturi effect creates a suction through the jet and suction hose.

do it at less cost than it would take to buy one. Many miners have built their own dredges, and some of them are excellent machines, mine included. Also many of them are complete failures. If you are naturally inclined towards building your own dredge and choose to do so from scratch, speaking from experience, I recommend that you put aside some extra money and prepare to spend at least an entire season to work out all the bugs to get the entire dredge operating to YOUR satisfaction.

There are several different kinds of jets that are being used on the dredges found out in the field today that you should be familiar with.

Nozzle Jet: The nozzel jet was the first type of jet to be used on suction gold dredges. (See figure 6-6 on following page.)

In this case, water is pumped through a pressure hose down to the suction nozzle itself where it is directed into the suction hose to push the water and material through. The nozzle jet was a great improvement over that of pumping material directly through the pump. This kind of jet system is most often seen on smaller sized suction dredging equipment, which is designed to operate in shallow water, because one of the main advantages to this kind of system is that the suction nozzle can be raised out of the water and put back under again without worry of filling the entire suction hose up with air.

Power Jet: The power jet, as shown earlier, utilizes a volume of water being directed into a main jet tube under high pressure to cause a suction up through the suction hose. (See figure 6-7.)

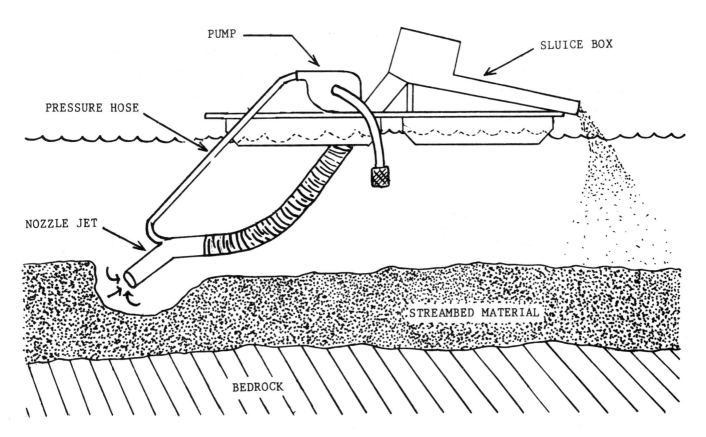

Fig. 6–6. Nozzle jet type gold dredge.

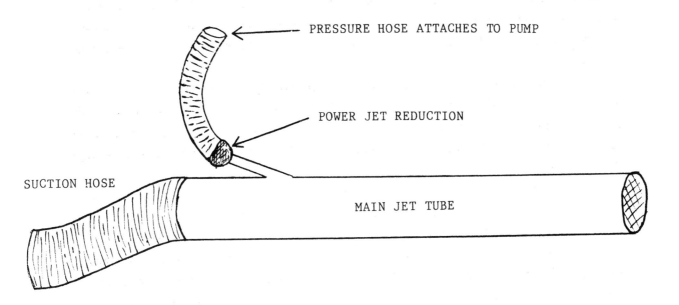

Fig. 6–7. Power jet.

This kind of jet system is most often used on the intermediate and large sized production dredges. One advantage to this kind of system is that the operator only has one hose to manipulate around while working underwater — as opposed to the two hoses that are involved with a nozzle type jet system.

There are power jets which use more than one jet intake, some using as many as 4 or 5 of them to cause a more orderly and effective mixture in the main tube. This is especially true of the larger sized dredges that employ more than one engine/pump assembly (See figure 6-8).

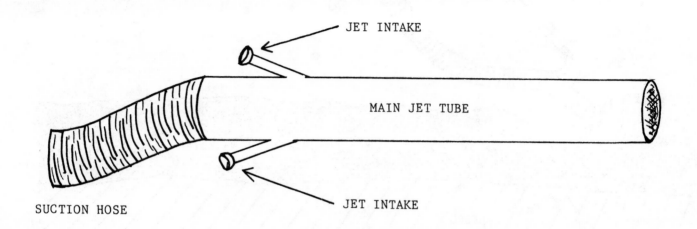

JET INTAKE

MAIN JET TUBE

SUCTION HOSE

JET INTAKE

Fig. 6—8. Some power jet systems utilize more than one jet intake.

For example, one of the larger dredge manufacturers puts out an 8-inch production dredge that uses a double power jet, powers it with two twin cylinder 18 horsepower industrial engines, and gets excellent results (Shown in figure 6-20). Yet the dredge still maintains its portability.

Couple Jet: In theory, the best type of jet would be one that was positioned directly in the center of the main jet tube. In this way, optimum mixing would result with the minimum amount of friction loss. However, this type of jet cannot be used on a dredge system, because it would obstruct the flow of rocks and material through the main jet.

There is another type of jet which is being used by some dredge manufacturers today — called the "couple jet," in which a volume of water is forced into the main jet tube from the outside surface of the tube (See figure 6-9 on next page).

This kind of jet is usually made to allow the jet tube to slide further in or out of the outer housing, so that it can be adjusted to the most optimum pressure/volume setting for the pump and engine assembly that is being used — which is handy.

Sometimes, after a couple-type jet has been used for awhile, a few rocks or pebbles can become jammed into the space between the jet tube and the outer housing. These, when accumulated, can cause a power loss to the suction nozzle. To remove them, all that is necessary usually is to loosen up the jet tube and slide it back just a bit, and run water through the jet. Then the tube can be slid back to its normal position and the pebbles should be gone.

SIDEVIEW   FRONTVIEW

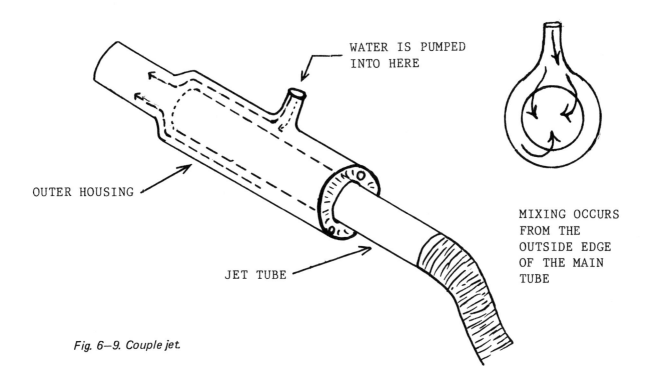

WATER IS PUMPED
INTO HERE

OUTER HOUSING

JET TUBE

MIXING OCCURS
FROM THE
OUTSIDE EDGE
OF THE MAIN
TUBE

Fig. 6–9. Couple jet.

Most jets are designed so that the suction hose slides onto the jet and clamps on tightly. A nozzle clamps onto the other end of the suction hose. It is the nozzle which the operator moves around to suck material up into the suction hose. Suction hose comes in different sizes. For example, "6-inch suction hose" will be found to have an inside diameter of 6 inches. "Four-inch suction hose" will have an inside diameter of 4 inches, and so on. Suction nozzles usually have an inside diameter that is reduced in size slightly. This prevents rocks of the same size as the inside diameter of the suction hose from being sucked up and jamming inside the hose. The idea is to slightly reduce the size of the material that passes in, so as to allow a little leeway inside the suction hose. In this way, there are far less plug-ups and more production can occur.

So the engine powers the pump which forces a volume of water under pressure into the jet, which creates a venturi effect — causing the water and material to be sucked up through the suction hose and jet, to be poured into a sluice box.

RECOVERY SYSTEMS

The majority of dredges today use a sluice box to recover gold out of the material. Most of the basics concerning sluice boxes were covered in the last chapter — which all apply to the sluice boxes found on dredges. Still, there are a few additional points that should be mentioned.

First, many dredges have a "baffle box" at the head of the sluice, which is designed to break up the material further as it enters the box, and also to slow the water and material down and spread it out so that it can flow evenly down the length of the sluice box (See figure 6-10).

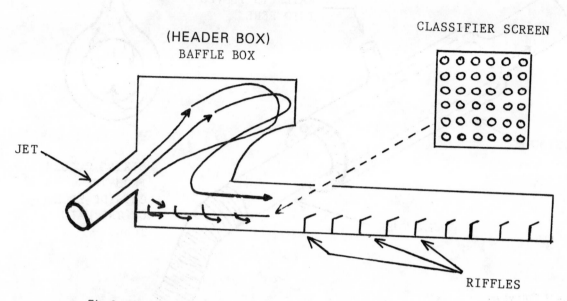

Fig. 6—10. Many dredges have a baffle box to slow down material and spread it evenly over the box.

The sluice boxes on many gold dredges also have a classifier screen located at the head of the baffle box, as shown in figure 6-10. This screen is usually made out of steel punch plate, and is designed to allow the smaller pieces of gold to drop down through the holes and become trapped under the classifier, or be pushed along by the slower current that flows underneath the punch plate. This makes it easier for the gold to become trapped behind the first few riffles, as shown in figure 6-11.

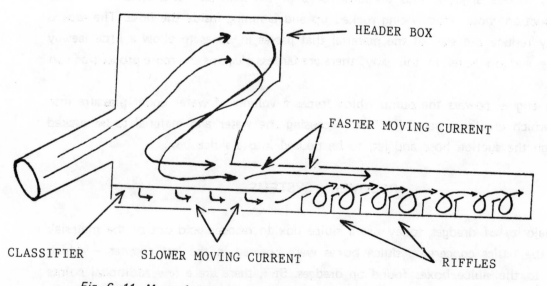

Fig. 6—11. Most of the gold should drop down through the classifier into the slower moving current, to become trapped behind the first few riffles.

136

At operating speed, a gold dredge has a steady flow of water moving through its sluice box. So, water velocity adjustment is normally done by changing the slope of the sluice box. This determines how fast the water will travel over the box, and so determines how much concentrating action will be created behind the riffles.

Hungarian-type riffles are almost always used in the store bought gold dredges. With a suction dredge which is using either hungarian or right angle-type riffles, the proper slope of the box is obtained when a small amount of carpet is showing just in front of each riffle in the box (See figure 6-12). To test this, run a good amount of material through the dredge at operating speed. Then allow the dredge to run at the same speed for about 20 seconds or so without pumping any material; then shut down. If no carpet is showing in front of each riffle in the sluice box, it will be necessary to increase its slope slightly. If more than just a little bit of carpet is showing in front of each riffle, then you should lessen the slope of the box slightly. Always set the proper slope of your sluice box to catch properly when the dredge is running at production speed. The water velocity must be enough to keep material from loading up in the sluice box.

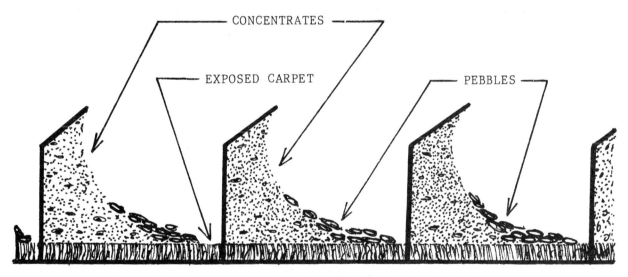

Fig. 6—12. The correct velocity over a dredge's sluice box is obtained when a small amount of carpet is exposed in front of each riffle after running.

When a sluice box on a gold dredge is recovering properly, the majority of gold will be found behind the first 3 or 4 riffles in the box; and in the final analysis, this is the way to tell if the correct adjustments have been made. And, of course, it's always a good idea to test your tailings with a gold pan to make sure. You can also use pieces of lead to test your recovery.

Once the sluice box is properly set, it does everything for you automatically. It's just a matter of going down to the bottom and sucking material up into the nozzle — and it doesn't really matter from how deep, except that when you are underwater you will need air breathing apparatus.

AIR SYSTEMS

The earliest gold dredgers used scuba equipment to stay down underwater for extended periods of time. In fact, it was the evolution of scuba equipment that brought on the development of suction dredges.

Today, scuba equipment is not used very often in dredging activities. The "hooka air system" on a dredge consists of a low pressure air compressor, which is powered by the same engine that powers the dredge. While the engine is operating, low pressure air is pumped through an extended air line to a regulator — which the diver breathes from while dredging.

There are various sized compressors available for the different sized dredges that are offered on the market. The larger compressors are able to pump more air when it is needed, in case more than one diver is operating the dredge, or when work is being done at greater depths. Some of the larger compressors will pump enough air to supply up to 4 divers at once at a depth of 30 feet.

Most of these compressors are constructed with sealed type bearings, so that no oil is needed for lubrication. In this way, the larger scrubbing air filters used on the high pressure scuba compressors are not required to filter out oil vapors.

These hooka air systems also usually contain a small air storage tank, which is designed to store a small amount of reserve air for the diver. So if the dredge should run out of gas and quit, or stop running for some other reason while the diver is underwater, he will have a small supply of air to breathe enroute to the surface (See figure 6-13).

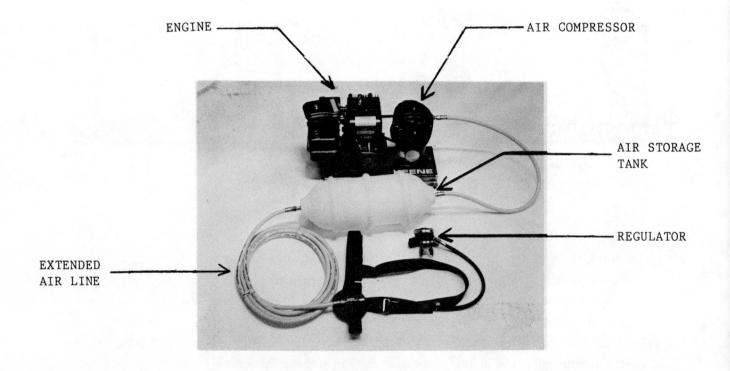

ENGINE ———————————————————— AIR COMPRESSOR

AIR STORAGE TANK

REGULATOR

EXTENDED AIR LINE

Fig. 6—13. Air breathing hooka system for a suction dredge.

As a safety feature, on most hooka air systems, a one-way flow "check valve" will be attached to the airline just before it connects to the regulator. The check valve basically consists of a spring — which forces a ball bearing against a seating inside of the valve, as shown in figure 6-14. The check valve is positioned on the airline so that it will not allow air to be sucked back up the line from the diver. In this way, if the airline happens to part at the surface, the pressure differential between the depth at which the diver is dredging, and the surface, is not permitted to suck air back up through the hose from the diver. It is a good safety feature, and will be found on most any dredge on the market.

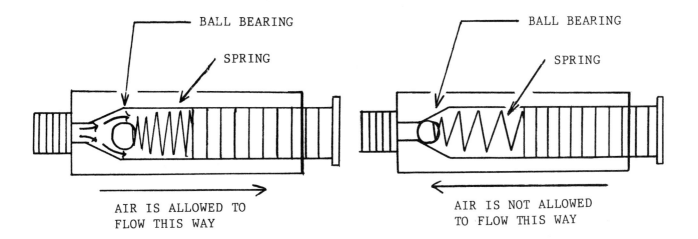

BALL BEARING

SPRING

AIR IS ALLOWED TO
FLOW THIS WAY

BALL BEARING

SPRING

AIR IS NOT ALLOWED
TO FLOW THIS WAY

Fig. 6—14. One way flow "check valve."

The regulators used on these hooka systems are the same components which are used as the final stages in scuba apparatus. However, they are modified to breathe easily on low pressure air, and a regulator that is normally used for scuba purposes will not work very well on a hooka air system until it has been modified also. The regulator fits into your mouth, and you breathe in air just as you would at the surface. Then you exhale into the regulator, which has its own one-way exhaust ports to get rid of the air that you breathe into it.

The regulator can be taken out of your mouth while underwater and then replaced, but will be found to have a small amount of water inside of it — which can be blown out through the exhaust ports by exhaling into the mouthpiece, or by pushing the "purge button" that is located on the front face of the regulator, as shown in figure 6-15. When the purge button on the regulator is pushed, it will cause an automatic flow of air into the regulator, which will force any water there out of the exhaust ports.

The hooka system on a gold dredge requires very little maintenance. The small air filters should be replaced or cleaned in soap and water every once in awhile — depending on what kind they are. Care should be taken to not spill gasoline onto the compressor's air filter when the dredge is being refueled. Sometimes the air filter is located just below the gas tank, and it's necessary to place a bucket or something over

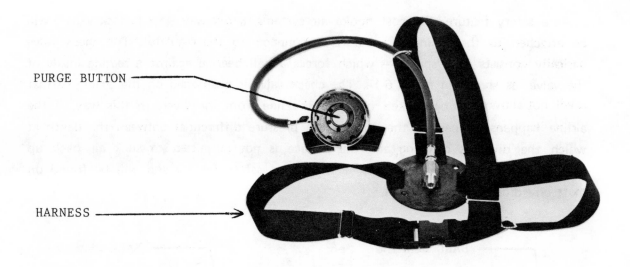

PURGE BUTTON

HARNESS

Fig. 6—15. Purge button (in this case is white) is located on the center of the regulator's front face plate.

top of the filter to prevent spillage from getting onto it. Needless to say, the resulting gasoline fumes — being pumped down to the diver through a hooka air system, can make for a very uncomfortable dive. If gasoline is spilled on an air filter by mistake, it should be removed and thoroughly cleaned before the dive is begun.

SETTING UP A GOLD DREDGE

Carry your dredge to the location where you will enter the water, near the place that you intend to dredge or sample, and assemble it. Be sure that all of the clamps are securely fastened, that the engine has the proper amount of oil, and that the gas tank is filled. Float the dredge to the location where you want to work and tie it off according to the water currents in play at that location. If there is more than just a mild current flowing down river, it will probably be necessary to tie the dredge off from a position upstream to keep it from floating down river with the current. If there is little or no water flowing in that location, you will probably need to tie the dredge off from the rear to keep it from motor boating forward on you.

Once the dredge is tied off, ensure that the suction hose is full of water and that the suction nozzle is under the water.

Prime the pump and start the engine. Allow the engine to run at low speed and warm up while you put your diving gear on — weights, hood, mask, etc.

Once you are ready for the dive, accelerate the engine to operating speed and start vacuuming up the riverbed materials, gold and all.

DREDGE SIZES

The size of a suction dredge is labled according to the inside diameter size of it's suction hose. Dredges come in a wide range of sizes.

A larger sized suction hose requires more power to make it suck well than does a smaller sized suction hose. This means that a larger pump/engine assembly is needed, and that more water will be pumped. So a larger dredge will also require a larger sluice box to handle the additional flow of water and material, and an additional amount of floatation will also be needed to float the entire works and keep it stable above water.

A larger dredge will pump more volume of streambed material and also will move larger sized rocks — which means that less rocks will need to be moved by hand, and so much more production can occur. However, the larger a suction hose diameter is, the thicker and heavier it is, and so it becomes more stiff and unwieldly, and takes more energy to move around.

Additionally, the larger a dredge is, the more energy it takes to pack it from place to place. For this reason the larger sized gold dredges are mainly used for production dredging, the intermediate sized dredges are mostly used for sampling — because they can move a healthy volume of material but are not too difficult to pack around, and the small sized dredges are usually best suited for the smaller sized streams, and the remote locations — where accessibility is a problem.

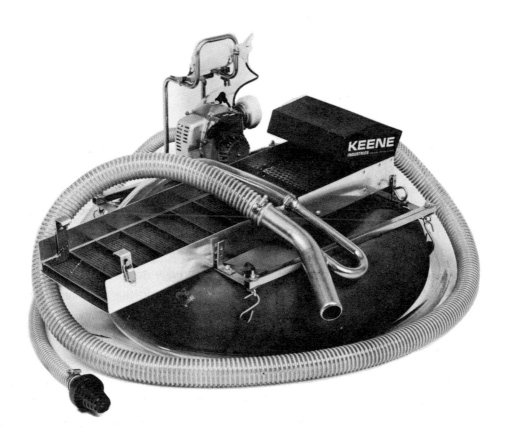

Fig. 6—16. 2 inch back pack mini dredge.

One of the smallest dredges found on today's market is the "2 inch mini dredge." (See figure 6-16.) This model is powered by a new two stroke 1-1/4 horsepower engine and pump, with the entire dredge weighing about 38 pounds. It is very economical on gasoline and can be rigged easily into a back packing unit — which makes this dredge an excellent machine for sampling the small streams and creeks in the high country, and the other remote locations. The 2 inch mini dredge can process up to two cubic yards of gravel per hour under the most ideal conditions — which is about the equivalent of what a hand sluicing operation can do under similarly good conditions.

Fig. 6–17. 4-inch intermediate sized gold dredge.

Intermediate-sized suction dredges are available in a wide variety. Figure 6-17 shows a good 4-inch sized dredge, an intermediate, weighing a total of just under 200 pounds. This dredge breaks down into individual pieces — each which can be carried by a single person. It can also process up to 12 cubic yards of streambed material per hour under the most ideal conditions. This makes it a very effective sampling machine for the professional who is attempting to find the larger sized underwater placer deposits, so that he can bring on a larger sized dredge to mine them once they are located. This dredge is also excellent recreational gear for the hobbiest, who wants a piece of equipment that will create a significant effect on a streambed, so that paying quantities of gold can be found. I have know professionals, myself included, who have used this same intermediate as a production machine and made a living at it.

The 5-inch sized triple-sluice dredge is perhaps the best all around dredge that can be found on the market today (See figure 6-18). This dredge is just slightly heavier than the 4-inch sized intermediate that was covered above, yet it can process a third more volume of streambed material because of its larger size. The extra one inch sized diameter of its nozzle intake also allows larger rocks to be sucked up — which means just that many less rocks that need to be tossed by hand. So the 5-incher ends up being able to move double the volume — or more, over that of what the 4-incher can produce in experienced hands, making it a much more efficient machine for its size and weight. Also, the triple-sluice design is one of the best recovery systems available on the market today, it being able to recover gold down to the ultra fine stages because

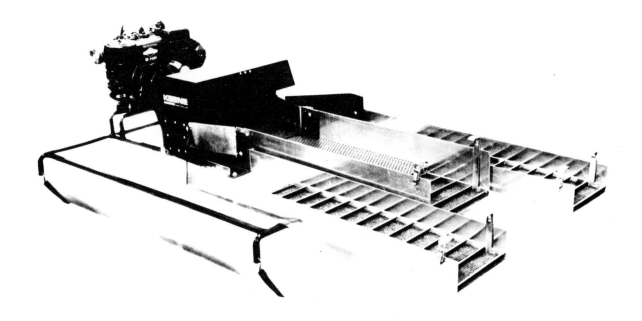

Fig. 6—18. 5-inch triple sluice intermediate sized production gold dredge.

of the controlled slower currents which flow in the side trays. Because of all these features, the 5-inch triple-sluice is not only the best recreational dredge found on the market; but also, it's probably the best all around one-man professional rig too. It is light enough that a single person can carry all of its individual parts around by himself if he has to. Plus with excellent recovery, it is able to process enough material to make it a worthwhile piece of production equipment.

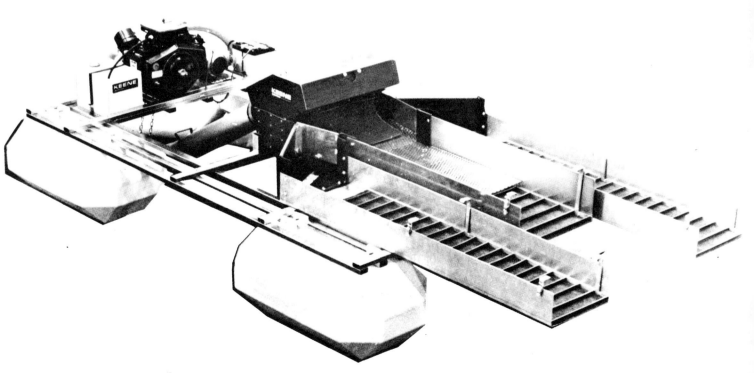

Fig. 6—19. Triple sluice 6-inch production gold dredge.

The 6-inch triple-sluice dredge is a machine, which has been designed to give excellent gold recovery, and can move up to about 25 cubic yards of streambed material per hour under ideal conditions (See figure 6-19). This 6-inch dredge can be operated by one strong person, but many prefer to team up when using a dredge of this size. The "6-incher" can be packed around easily by two people — when broken down into seperate component parts, so it can also be used for sampling purposes. Yet, they are utilized best as production machines, because of the large amounts of streambed material that they can process, and with excellent fine gold recovery.

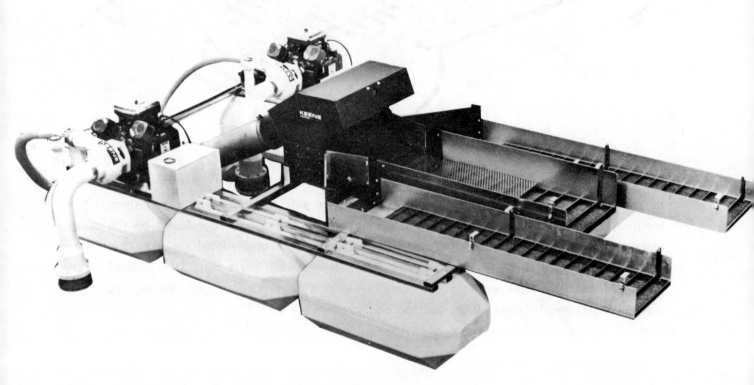

Fig. 6—20. 8-inch triple-sluice, twin powered, production dredge.

The 8-inch triple-sluice dredge is definitely considered to be a professional production machine (See figure 6—20). This dredge is powered by two lightweight, twin cylinder, 18 horsepower engines, and is capable of processing up to about 40 cubic yards of streambed material per hour under ideal conditions — with good fine gold recovery because of the triple-sluice design. Because of the twin engine power system, the entire dredge — when broken down into individual components, can be packed around by a two-man team. Again, a single strong man can operate one of these on his own; but it really takes two if it is to be operated for extended periods of time day after day, like a professional dredge should be. This is the kind of dredge that you bring on once you have found a sizable deposit. And it makes little difference whether the gold is of course or fine size; because when set up properly, this dredge will recover well.

The dredges which have been shown above are just a few of the many different kinds and sizes that are available on the market. Those above have been chosen in an effort to show some of the various models which are available, and to illustrate the wide range of dredge sizes — from the mini dredge, to the intermediate, and up to the large production machines, to give the reader some idea of what they are and how they are best utilized according to their sizes.

UNDERWATER DREDGES

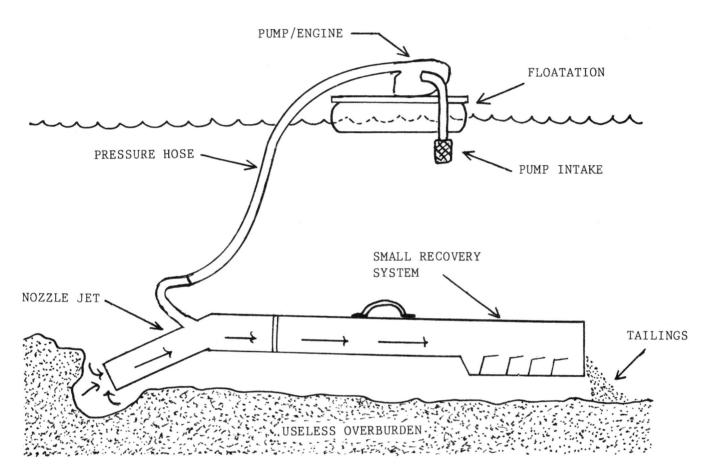

Fig. 6—21. Underwater-type gold dredge.

Underwater-type suction dredges have the advantage of being able to pump a greater volume of material with less power, than the surface-type gold dredges. The reason for this is that the surface-type dredge — as covered earlier, pumps its water and material from the bottom of the streambed up to the sluice box above the surface of the water. It takes a lot of power to lift up a volume of streambed material any distance — especially when it is being lifted 8 or 10 inches above the water. The underwater-type dredge pumps streambed material to a sluice box that is located just behind it underwater, as shown in figure 6-21.

The underwater-type dredge is an instance where the nozzle jet is being put to a very efficient use; as with this kind of system, a pump/engine unit at the water's surface is able to pump water down through a pressure hose and power an underwater dredge that is capable of moving about double the volume of streambed material as the same pumping unit could process when powering a surface-type dredge. For example, the power plant on the 4-inch dredge covered earlier, is able to power a 6-

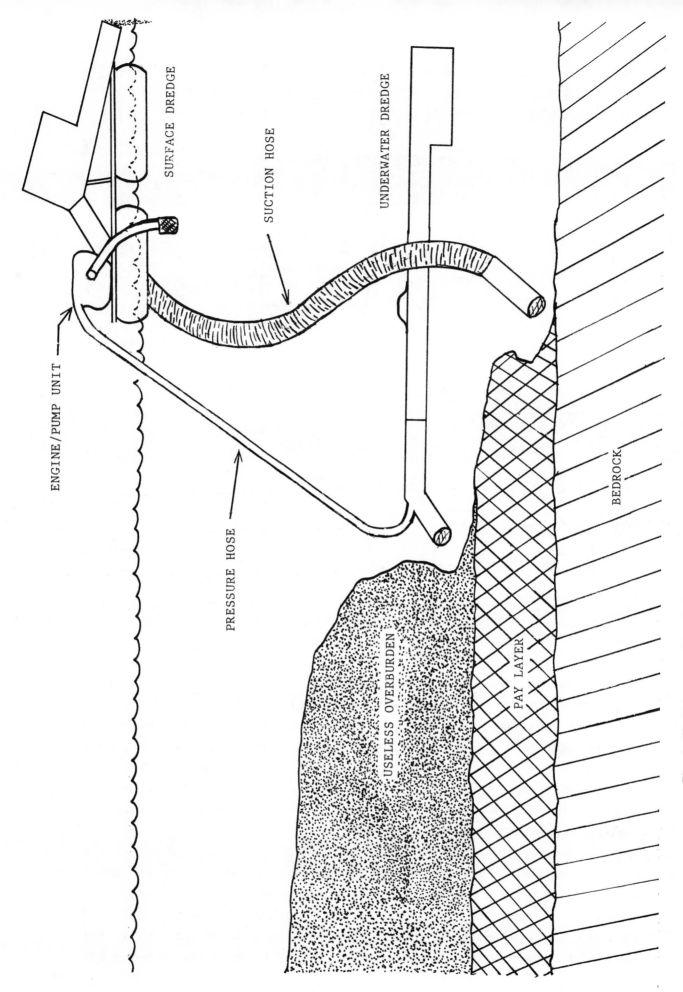

SURFACE DREDGE

SUCTION HOSE

UNDERWATER DREDGE

ENGINE/PUMP UNIT

PRESSURE HOSE

USELESS OVERBURDEN

PAY LAYER

BEDROCK

Fig. 6—22 Using a surface dredge and an underwater dredge in combination, to get the best results.

inch sized underwater dredge, the power plant on the 6 inch dredge is able to power an 8 inch sized underwater dredge, and the power plants on the 8 inch dredge that was covered earlier are able to power a 12 inch sized underwater dredge to a good result.

The drawback to the underwater type dredges is that their recovery systems are very limited as to size, and so they are not able to recover gold nearly as well as the surface-type dredges are able to — especially those having the triple-sluice design.

The underwater type dredge is most effectively used in conjunction with a good recovering surface-type dredge. It is not uncommon to locate a nice paystreak that is lying underneath 5 feet or more of flood layer ("overburden"), which sampling tests have shown, does not have any significant amount of gold in it at all. In this case the idea is to move the overburden off the paystreak as quickly as possible so that the gold can be recovered. An underwater dredge comes in handy here as the engine/pump unit on a surface dredge will be able to power an underwater dredge of greater size, which will be able to move the useless material out of the way approximately twice as fast — or more, than a surface dredge can do it. The underwater dredge is equipped with a small recovery system that will catch the medium and course gold — should some be present in the waste material and be overlooked by the dredger. Most often, if sampling has shown that a top layer of overburden does not have paying quantities of gold, then very little gold will be found in that top layer when it's being moved. So there is little need to worry about loss of gold when moving such a layer of overburden with an underwater dredge. Usually, it's a case of having found a nice paystreak underneath a large amount of useless overburden — too much for your surface dredge to move and still make it worthwhile to dredge the paystreak which lies underneath. (Not an uncommon occurrence.) In this case, often an underwater dredge can be attached to the power unit of a surface dredge and can be used to move the waste material out of the way, resulting in the paystreak being able to be recovered effectively and at a profit. (See figure 6-22.)

SUBSURFACE DREDGES

Subsurface-type gold dredges are similiar to underwater type dredges in that the water and material is pumped to a sluice box that is located below the water's surface. The recovery system on this type of unit is suspended just below the floatation system which supports the engine/pump unit. (See figure 6-23.) Subsurface type recovery systems are larger than those found on the underwater type dredges of the same hose diameter — about twice as large, and so the subsurface type dredge offers better gold recovery than the underwater dredge does, but still not as good as the surface type dredge. Yet, because the material and water is not pumped above the water's surface, a subsurface dredge can pump about twice as much volume as a surface dredge that is being powered by the same engine/pump unit. So the subsurface dredge is the "go between" of the surface dredge and the underwater dredge, it being able to pump more material than a surface rig and recover better than the underwater dredge can.

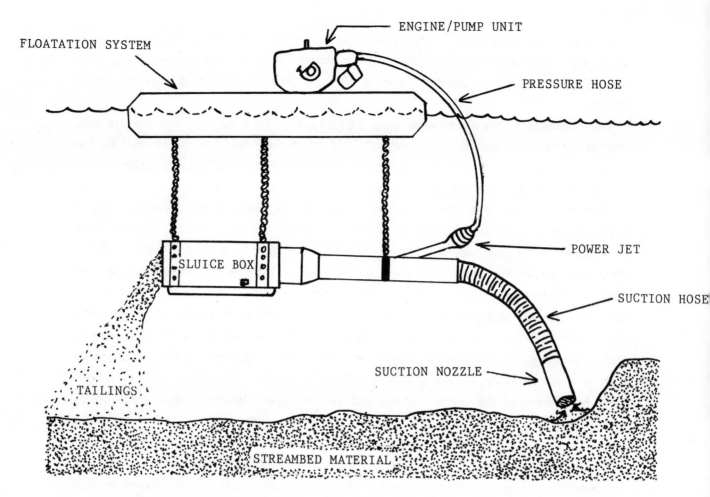

FLOATATION SYSTEM

ENGINE/PUMP UNIT

PRESSURE HOSE

POWER JET

SUCTION HOSE

SUCTION NOZZLE

SLUICE BOX

TAILINGS

STREAMBED MATERIAL

Fig. 6—23. Sub-surface type gold dredge.

Subsurface type dredges are best used when a great deal of overburden needs to be moved off an underlying paystreak, yet the overburden has proven to pay to some degree, and also where the water current is flowing mildly — or not at all, so that it doesn't cause a great pulling effect on the sluice box, which hangs just below the water's surface.

DREDGE CAPACITIES

The production ability of any dredge varies with differing conditions. Hotter weather can cause a power loss to a dredge, as can dredging at higher altitudes above sea level. Also, the deeper that you dredge, the more power that it takes, because the material will need to be lifted a greater distance against the effects of gravity.

The manufacturer's specifications as to what a dredge is capable of producing is not likely going to be the same amount that you are going to be able to make it produce out in the field, because the manufacturer's specifications are given for the dredge when operating under the most ideal conditions. Plus, classified material is used during these tests. Very seldom does one run into a large deposit of gold out in the field where loose classified material is all that needs to be pumped. Usually the streambeds where one finds gold are composed of a wide range of different sized rocks and material that is packed tightly together. Streambeds like this need to be systematically picked apart, with the larger sized rocks tossed aside, the boulders rolled out of the way, and the smaller material sucked up into the dredge as it is exposed. All this takes time and energy. So you are never able to move as great a volume of material out in the field as the manufacturers can under totally controlled conditions. I wanted you to be aware of this so that you won't get the false impression that you can go out into the field and move 12 cubic yards of material per hour just because the manufacturer says that his dredge is capable of moving that amount. How much material you will be able to move out in the field depends greatly on the consistency of the streambed material that you will be pumping and in your skill at operating the suction nozzle. The main idea is to get a dredge which has good enough suction power to be able to move material through the suction hose as fast as you are capable of feeding it into the nozzle. Most dredges available on today's market are able to supply you with enough power to do this.

If you are planning to dredge gold under more severe conditions — like at higher altitudes or in deep water, you should get a dredge which has a larger power/pump unit so that you will have the additional power that is needed to operate under those conditions. Dredging equipment dealers are usually quite knowledgeable as to what is needed by way of equipment to handle abnormal conditions, and can help you to choose the proper equipment for your needs if you are uncertain as to what is required.

Small sized gold dredges usually come with 10 foot lengths of suction hose. Intermediates and large sized dredges usually come with 15 feet of suction hose, which is enough length to do the job well under the majority of circumstances. Most dredging is done in less than 10 feet of water. Extended pieces of suction hose are available. Short lengths of suction hose with couplings are also available if you should want to extend the length of your hose.

The suction hoses on larger sized dredges — 6 inchers and 8 inchers in particular, are commonly more stiff and much easier to manipulate around if you have 20 feet of suction hose, instead of 15 feet. This is something to keep in mind when buying a gold dredge of this size, as they can be bought with longer lengths of suction hose if you want them that way. It costs a little more, but you'll get more production done too.

PROTECTIVE SUITS

If you are planning to do a lot of dredging in cold water, it will probably be necessary for you to wear some kind of a protective suit to keep your body comfortably warm.

There are two different kinds of protective body suits that are being used amongst gold dredgers — "wet suits" and "dry suits."

Wet suits are the more economical to buy, and generally work well during the summer months when the water has warmed up. These are designed to allow water to get inside the suit. (Wet-suit) Your body heat then warms that water up and it works as an insulator against the colder water which remains outside of the wet suit. Wet suits are available in a wide variety of sizes and design, of which the respective dealers will have information.

A dry suit (artic diving suit) is similar to a wet suit in that it is made of neopreme rubber, only it is made with waterproof zippers and watertight seals at each extremity to prevent any water at all from entering the suit. This type of suit will keep a person warm when diving in extremely cold water for extended periods of time, and it is almost a necessity for a dredger to own one if he plans to work during the colder months, when the river water gets ice cold. Thermal underwear can be worn inside a dry suit to give extra warmth when it's needed. Dry suits also come in a wide variety of sized and design, which you should look into before spending the money. I highly recommend that you buy one with a relief zipper as part of the suit, so that you don't need to take the whole thing off every time you have to urinate. Dry suits generally cost 2 to 3 times as much as a wet suit of similiar quality, but they are definitely worth the extra money if you are planning to spend extended periods of time in cold water.

When wearing a protective rubber suit, you will also need to wear extra weight to compensate for the additional buoyancy caused by the suit. Lead weights on nylon belts are most commonly used for this purpose, and can usually be found wherever the diving suits are sold. If you want to save money, a mold is generally available; and you can buy the lead from a scrap metal yard and make your own. The dealers who sell these protective rubber suits usually have a rough idea of how much weight you will need. This varies with the different kinds of suits. Between 30 and 40 pounds of lead would be a fair estimate. You will want to have enough to sink you to the bottom and make you heavy enough that you can move around on your feet. The more water current you are working in, up to a point, the more lead weight that you will need to wear in order to hold your position on the bottom. So it's a good idea to have some extra weights on hand for the sake of changing dredging conditions.

The proper nylon belts for the job always contain some kind of quick release buckles — which are very important to have in case the dredger needs to get to the surface in a hurry. It's good to know how to release this buckle, and to know where to find it on your body when dredging — just in case.

Some dredgers also prefer to use some ankle weights to help keep their feet on the river's bottom. This is not necessary, just a preference amongst some dredgers.

OTHER DREDGING EQUIPMENT

Some of the other equipment that is commonly needed in a dredging operation, as shown in figure 6-24, are as follows: face mask, snorkle — if you are using a smaller sized dredge that has no hooka system, hood — to keep your head warm if one is not already attached to your protective suit, booties — to keep your feet warm if they are not already attached to your protective suit, boots — to fit over and protect your booties, knee pads — to protect your suit and your knees, rubber gloves — to protect your hands, crowbar or prybar tool — to help pick apart the streambed materials and

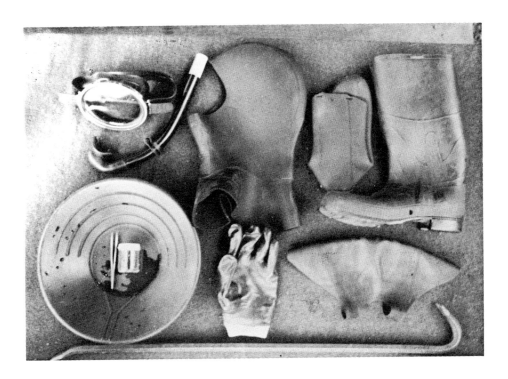

Fig. 6—24. Additional dredging equipment.

break up bedrock, rope — to tie off the dredge, spare gas can — for extra gas, classification screens and wash tub — to help with clean-up (optional), gold pan — for clean-up, tweezers and sample bottle — for the gold.

DREDGING SAFETY*

Because one is working in the water when dredging, most of the rules of swimming safety apply. And because one is usually underwater, many safety rules for scuba diving also apply.

Probably the first rule of safety is to not do it alone. Have someone else around to keep an eye on you in case you should get into some kind of trouble and need assistance.

The activity of gold dredging often puts you in the position of needing to move large boulders. There is the possibility of one of these rolling on you in some way and pinning you to the bottom. Or a rock could fall out of the streambed material, bounce off your head, and stun you. These things simply won't happen if you pay attention to what you are doing and avoid putting yourself in that position; but the possibility is always there — in which case it's good to have someone else around.

DIVING SAFETY

As you go further beneath the water's surface, there is an increase in the amount of water on top of you, and so there is more pressure against your body. For dredging purposes, this increased pressure has little or no effect on the liquid and solid parts of a body, because they are not compressible. An air space with an increase of pressure upon it will tend to become compressed into a smaller size. That is, unless an

*See Safety in Gold Dredging (Page 1).

additional amount of air is pumped into that air space to keep it the same size.

As an air space is taken further down below the water's surface, the outside pressure will be increased and so the airspace will be further compressed. (See figure 6-25.)

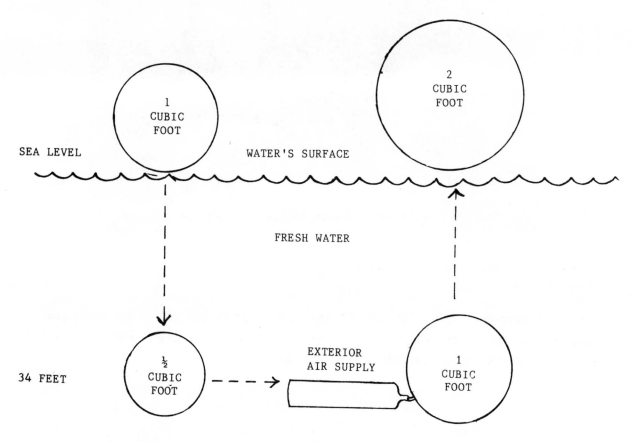

AIR IN THESE SPACES ARE COMPRESSED TO TWICE ITS NORMAL DENSITY

Fig. 6—25. The pressure increase at 34 feet in depth will compress an air space to half it's normal size.

At a depth of 34 feet in fresh water, there will be twice as much outside pressure on an air space as there would be at the water's surface (at sea level). So at this depth, an air space would be compressed to half it's normal size. If there is an exterior air supply available (like a hooka system), and additional air can be pumped into that air space to keep it the same size as it descends in depth, it would need to have twice as much air at a depth of 34 feet. Then if that same air space is brought up to the surface without allowing the additional air to escape as it expands, the space will expand (or burst) to twice the size that is was at 34 feet in depth. (See figure 6-25.)

The main air spaces in your body which will normally be affected by increased pressure during dredging are the ears, sinuses and lungs.

Ears: In taking up the ears first, see figure 6-26 and take note that the middle ear and external ear are separated by the ear drum. The middle ear has an air space which is connected to the breathing passage by the "eustachian tube," as shown in the above mentioned figure. At the water's surface, the middle ear space contains air at surface

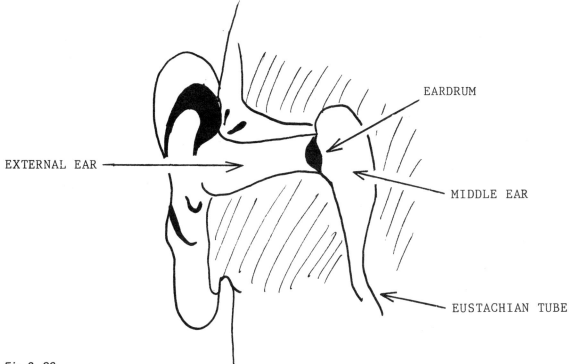

EARDRUM

EXTERNAL EAR

MIDDLE EAR

EUSTACHIAN TUBE

Fig. 6–26.

pressure. As descent is made further underwater, the outside water pressure increases, and the middle ear space will be compressed, unless more air is allowed into that space through the eustchian tube. Compression on the middle ear space puts pressure on the ear drum, making it uncomfortable — or even painful if one continues to go deeper without equalizing the ear pressure. Many people have experienced this when swimming to the bottom of a swimming pool.

The eustachian tube does not always allow air to pass freely into the middle ear, and few people have easy control over this passage. Sometimes, it's necessary to do some jaw moving, swallowing, or some yawning to open up this air canal and equalize the middle ear pressure when going deeper under the water. Sometimes, it's necessary to hold your nose and blow air up into the middle ear in order to equalize the pressure. This almost always works, unless a person has a great deal of sinus congestion. The idea is to blow more air up into the middle ears as the increased pressure of water depth makes them uncomfortable. The ears will be comfortable, like normal, when the inside and outside pressures are properly equalized.

If you are descending and the pressure increases on your ears, and you are not able to equalize one or both of them, the thing to do is go back upwards a few feet and equalize them there and then continue downward, continuing to equalize as you go. Sometimes, it's necessary to go to the surface and get rid of some mucus congestion in order to free up the passages to the ears.

When the middle ear pressure is not equalized, the ear will be uncomfortable. To descend further without equalizing can cause pain. To descend further than that without equalizing the middle ear pressure, is to invite the ear drum to become ruptured. This in itself may not be a serious injury — but it will have you out of the water for a matter of weeks while it heals.

If too much pressure is forced on your eardrums and one or both of them are allowed to rupture, water may enter the middle ear. If the water is cold, it can offset a person's equilibrium and also possibly cause nausea, until the water is warmed up inside the middle ear. Sometimes, the equilibrium can be affected so severely that the diver cannot tell which direction is up. Again, should this occur, the condition should only last for a few moments — until the water in the middle ear is allowed to warm up. Regulators are especially built with large exhaust parts to accommodate nausea, should it occur to a diver while underwater. However, it's probably not a very pleasant experience!

Really, there is no reason for a diver to ever burst an eardrum; because as outlined above, the warning pain happens long before the point where it will occur, and equalization should be done long before the pain starts.

As one ascends towards the surface, the additional air within the middle ear will expand and automatically release itself through the eustachian tube. So, it takes no effort or attention on the part of the diver to re-equalize ear pressures on the way to the surface.

Tight fitting hoods: Sometimes a diver will acquire a tight fitting hood, which fits so tightly over the ears that it does not allow water to enter the external ear space. Instead, it causes a trapped air space in the external ear as shown in figure 6-27.

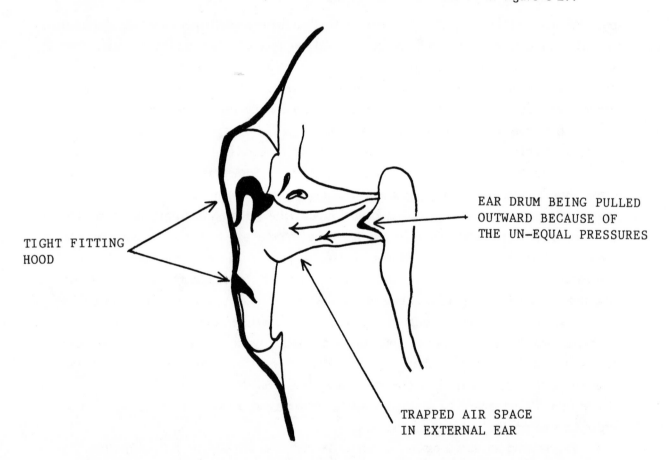

Fig. 6—27. A tight fitting hood can set up a trapped air space inside the outer ear — which cannot be equalized.

In this case, the air space within the external ear will compress as the diver goes deeper underwater, and there will be no way to equalize that pressure. This will cause the ear drum to be drawn outwards, as shown in the above figure. When this occurs, the unequalized pressure on the eardrum will cause an uncomfortable sensation just like before — and pain, and a possible puncture if descent is continued. An "external ear squeeze" can be prevented by avoiding very tight fitting hoods. Or, if you should happen to already have one, the thing to do is to make a few small holes in the hood where the ears are located, so that water will be allowed into the external ears while diving. One other thing that can be done, is lift that part of the hood off your face when you enter the water — just enough and long enough to ensure that water is allowed to pass into and around both ears.

Earplugs: Never place earplugs in your ears when you plan to dive. An earplug will set up a trapped air space inside the external ear which cannot be equalized — in the same way that a tight fitting hood can. Earplugs will prevent you from going more than just a few feet down without causing an external ear squeeze, and possible damage to the eardrums.

Sinuses: The sinus cavities are also affected by the increased pressure of depths underwater, but these automatically equalize themselves because they are connected directly to the nasal passages. The only time a diver will have trouble with his sinus cavities is when he is having trouble with a lot of mucus congestion. When a diver descends underwater and his sinus cavities are too congested to equalize the pressure, he will feel the increased compression just inside the forehead, above the nose. When your sinuses won't clear (equalize) by themselves, sometimes you can go to the surface and get rid of some mucus and then go down successfully. If this is not the case, it may be necessary to postpone the dive until your sinuses have cleared up.

Lung Cavities: The other main air spaces that are affected by pressure changes when a person dredges at a depth below the water's surface, are the lungs. These automatically equalize pressure themselves, as long as the dredger continues to breathe normally as he goes down to and returns from a depth underwater. The only real danger with the lungs is in holding your breath when coming to the surface. The reason for this, is that when a person goes deeper underwater, the pressure on his lungs increases, causing them to compress. As he breathes normally from the hooka-air system, additional air passes into his lungs to compensate for the increased pressure — which prevents his lungs from being compressed smaller in size. This is all automatic and the dredger will never feel any difference in pressures as long as he is breathing normally. At a depth of 34 feet in fresh water, when breathing off of a hooka system, a diver will have twice as much air in his lungs as he would have at the water's surface. His lungs will be normal in size, but the air inside is compressed to double its normal surface density. Now if that diver starts moving up, the outside pressure on his body will decrease, which will allow the air in his lungs to expand. If the diver breathes normally as he moves towards the surface, the excess air will be expelled and never noticed. If the diver holds his breath while ascending from 34 feet, there will be enough excess air in his lungs, when he gets to the surface, to expand them to about twice their normal size. Unfortunately, lungs are not equipped to withstand this kind of treatment and they will not expand to a larger size, but instead will burst to release the excess pressure. This is called an "embolism," and can be a very serious injury. Diving physicists say that it only takes an average of about two pounds of excess pressure on a lung to cause an embolism, and that this amount of excess pressure will occur from rising about 4 feet in depth while holding one's breath. However, for this to happen, the diver — or dredger, would already need to have his lungs filled to capacity.

Embolisms seldom occur in gold dredging. In fact, I have yet to hear of a single case of it. Regardless, the possibility is there when working at depths of water greater than 5 or 6 feet while breathing from a hooka system. So you should be aware of these principles and make sure to breathe normally when surfacing. Most embolism cases occur in scuba diving accidents when a diver panics and heads for the surface at full speed and forgets to expel the excess air on the way up. It's probably a natural tendency when in trouble while underwater for a person to not want to expel that life air out of his lungs. Nevertheless, when breathing from a hooka air system and returning to the surface, it is necessary to expel the excess air from your lungs -- regardless of the natural tendencies!

Bends: Bends — or "decompression sickness," occurs when a diver breathes compressed air for extended periods of time at depths greater than 35 feet (at sea level), and then rises to the surface too quickly to allow time for the expanding air to be flushed out of the body tissues. There is little chance of a gold dredger having any difficulty with decompression sickness, because very little dredging is ever done in depths greater than 25 feet of water. If it happens that you decide to dredge for extended periods of time at depths greater than 25 - 30 feet, I highly recommend that you get hold of the U.S. Navy decompression tables (available in any diving equipment shop), and calculate your dives accordingly. Also take into consideration that those decompression tables are figured for dives which are made in salt water at sea level. So they will need to be adjusted to fit the altitude for which you are diving. Perhaps someday, someone will publish a set of decompression tables that apply to altitude fresh water diving. Again, if you are planning to dredge at depths less than 25 feet — and most standard store bought equipment is not very effective beyond that depth, then none of this really applies to you. However, the necessity of having to start figuring for decompression dives needs to be mentioned for those few who will venture to greater depths.

Summary of diving safety: Gold dredging is not a dangerous activity as long as you are aware of — and pay attention to the above mentioned points on diving safety. Yes, to some the consequences — as mentioned above-of not paying attention to the safety rules may be a bit too gruesome to confront, but I would like to mention that the consequences of not driving a car properly can be even more gruesome; and there are many, many, many more safety rules to pay attention to when driving a car then there are when dredging for gold. Anybody can do it safely really. It's just a matter of getting into the habit of breathing normally while underwater, and in not forcing any more pressure on your ears past the uncomfortable stage before equalizing the pressure. A person can practice equalizing ear pressure at the surface by holding his or her nose and gently blowing air up into the middle ear space. It's easy once you get the hang of it. Usually, swallowing will cause the excess air in the middle ear to release itself.

OTHER TIPS ON DREDGING SAFETY

Probably one of the most important safety factors in gold dredging is to ensure that the exhaust fumes given off by the engine are swept down wind from the air intake of the hooka air compressor. Carbon monoxide has a cummulative effect, making one groggy and causing a certain amount of loss of judgment — which really cannot be afforded when working underwater. The necessity to avoid breathing in such gasses are increased as a dredger works at greater depth; because increased pressure will cause a greater density of air to be inhaled into the diver's system — which can make the adverse effects just that much stronger.

So when setting up your dredge in a stream, it's well to pay attention to the wind direction. Sometimes the wind will change while you are dredging and cause some of the engine's exhaust fumes to be pumped down through the air breathing system to you. When this happens, you can usually taste the difference. Carbon monoxide by itself is odorless — but when emitted from an engine's exhaust system, it is usually in association with other byproducts which do have an odor. Exhaust fumes are rather foul tasting. If you are dredging along and suddenly taste exhaust fumes in your air supply, sometimes it's just a freak change in the wind only for a moment. If the fumes continue in your air supply, you should go to the surface and change the position of your dredge slightly, so that the compressor air intake is in more of an upwind direction. Sometimes you can run into a similar problem when positioning two dredges side by side. The thing to do is to continue to try new positions until you finally have one in which all the divers are breathing fresh air.

Clearing water from mask while underwater: There are two things which any gold dredger should be able to do well and should be prepared to do at any time. These are: (1) to be able to take a face mask off, put it back on, and clear all of the water out of it — all while underwater, and (2) to be able to do the same with a regulator. There are just too many ways for your mask to get knocked off your face, or your regulator to become bumped out of your mouth, or both of these things to happen at once while dredging for gold. You need to know how to handle it without it upsetting you.

In the case of the regulator — as mentioned earlier, it's just a matter of putting it back into your mouth and exhaling into it — or by pushing the purge botton to clear any water out of it.

A face mast can be cleared of water by putting it back onto your face properly (right side up and in place), then tilting your head backward slightly — as in looking up at the water's surface, pressing the top part of the mask firmly against your forehead, and gently blowing through your nose into the face mask, as shown in figure 6-28. By blowing into your mask in this way, the water inside the mask will be forced out of the bottom edge. With a little bit of practice at this, you will be able to remove every bit of water from the inside of your mask — all while underwater.

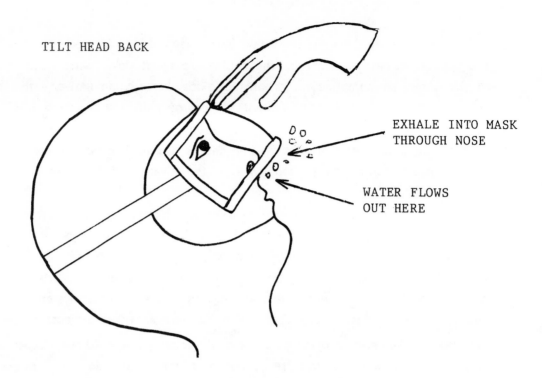

PRESS TOP OF MASK
AGAINST FOREHEAD

TILT HEAD BACK

EXHALE INTO MASK
THROUGH NOSE

WATER FLOWS
OUT HERE

Fig. 6—28. Clearing water out of mask — tilt head backwards slightly, press top of mask firmly against forehead, and blow into mask through your nose.

Some masks come with an exhaust valve on the face of the mask itself, which is designed so that water can be flushed out of the mask simply by exhaling into the mask through your nose. Some divers like this kind of mask and some don't, it's a matter of preference.

If you are new to underwater diving, the first thing that you should do before you start dredging is to practice removing your mask and putting it back on — all while underwater, and keep on practicing it until you feel very confident about doing it and are certain that you can keep your cool should your mask become swept off your face during an unexpected moment. You should also practice with the regulator in the same way. It should be mentioned that if something happens to cause both your mask and your regulator to become filled with water or swept off your face at the same time, the first thing to set right is your regulator, because that's your air supply. Remember, you'll have lead weights attached to your body keeping you on the bottom. So you'll want to get this down well, your life could depend on it. Practice makes perfect!

The buddy system: One safe system of dredging is in having two divers team up on the same dredge. One person controls the nozzle ("nozzle man"), and the other person helps him by moving the larger sized rocks out of the way ("rock man"). The rock man in an operation such as this is usually put in charge of safety — it being his duty to keep an eye out for any possible rocks or boulders that could be hazardous, and to see that they are removed before they can cause any trouble. When a team such as this is working a larger-sized dredge, in which it takes a lot more effort to move the suction hose and nozzle around, the two men can switch jobs back and forth so that neither person gets overworked.

Another good way to team up, is to have two individuals with separate dredges working in the same hole together. This way each can keep an eye on the other — for safety reasons; and also, each can help the other to move the larger sized boulders.

WINCHING BOULDERS

COME–ALONG

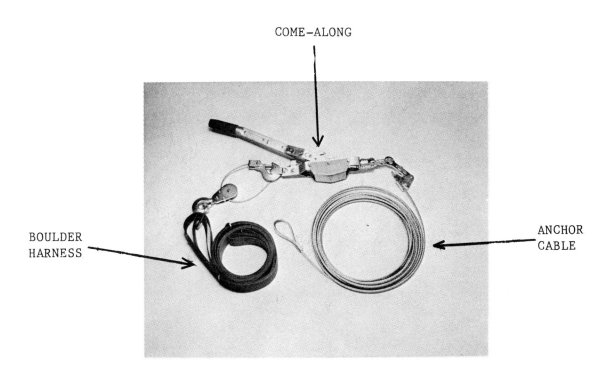

BOULDER
HARNESS

ANCHOR
CABLE

Fig. 6–29. The "come-along" is a common tool for a gold dredger to move larger sized boulders.

One tool that is commonly used amongst gold dredgers is the "come-along" (See figure 6-29.). The "come-along" is basically a hand operated winch. These come in various sizes, with the larger and better ones being able to move greater sized loads.

When a gold dredger runs across a boulder that is too large to be moved by hand — or with the use of a steel pry bar, and he feels that it is worth the effort to move the boulder so that he can dredge under it, he can sometimes do the job by himself or with the help of another by using a come-along.

The boulder itself can be attached to with a harness, which is available on the market — as shown in the above figure; or a tow chain can be used, as shown in figure 6-30 (Next page).

Many dredgers prefer a heavy tow chain for the use of slinging boulders when winching because they are quickly adjustable. They also hold up well, despite the pounding that they are subjected to when being used to pull large boulders around.

The come-along is best positioned next to the boulder, rather than next to the anchoring object. In this way, the dredger can observe what is occuring with

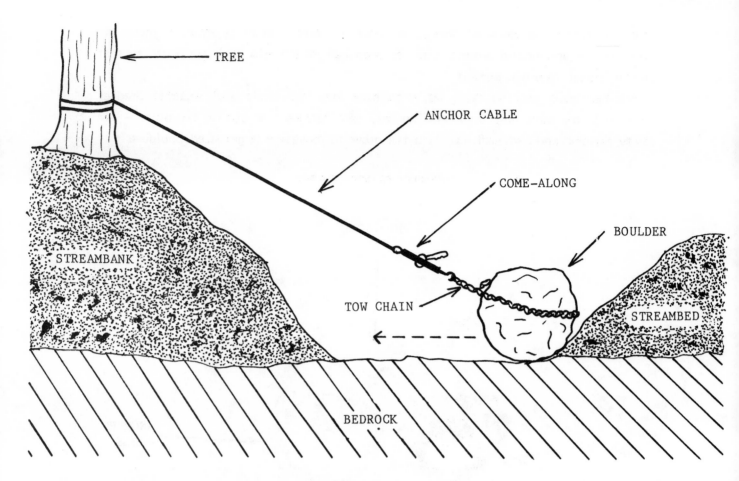

Fig. 6—30. Winching a boulder with a "come-along."

the boulder while he winches it along.

Steel cable is best used for attaching the come-along to the anchoring object, the reason being that it is very strong and won't stretch like rope will when being used for the same purpose.

It's necessary to be extra careful when winching boulders around while underwater — especially if you are doing it alone.

The idea is to move the boulders to the rear of your hole where bedrock has already been cleaned-up by dredging.

CAUTION: If the come-along that you are using (or the cable or boulder sling) to move boulders with is damaged in any way, have it repaired or replaced before you use it further. If a person is using a faulty come-along to move boulders and he puts a lot of strain on it, and it comes apart in his hands, it can injure him seriously. So keep a close eye on the winching equipment to make sure that it's fit for use.

EXTRA TOOLS AND PARTS

It's always a good idea to have a small tool box on hand as part of your standard field dredging gear. Place the basic tools inside that you will need to assemble the dredge and make minor field repairs, along with an extra sparkplug, extra hose clamps, engine manual, pump seal, etc., and if your dredge floats on innertubes, throw in a small tire patch kit and bring along a small tire pump — just in case.

HOW FAST TO RUN YOUR DREDGE

Many of the mini dredges are powered by 2 stroke type engines, which give their power in the high RPM range, and so these types of dredges usually need to be run at full throttle.

Some of the dredges that are being powered by 4 stroke engines have a little extra power in the high RPM's and might not need to be run at full speed all the time — depending on the altitude above sea level and the depths at which you are running.

The proper speed to run your dredge is at that speed which gives you enough suction power so that you can move material as fast as you are able to feed it into the nozzle. Your recovery system should be adjusted to recover well at this same rate of operation.

When you are dredging along in a pay streak and suddenly uncover a lot of gold, it's good practice to let clean water run through the dredge for a few seconds to allow the riffles to clean out the lighter material, and then suck up the gold. Most experienced dredgers, when into a heavy pay streak, will suck up the gold a little bit slower than they normally suck up other material. This is probably not necessary if the dredge which you are using recovers gold properly, but it is safer to slow down just a bit when sucking large quantities of gold into the nozzle, to ensure that the riffles are not loaded up — so that all of the gold is recovered.

DREDGING PROCEDURE

Dredging basically consists of sucking up the streambed material off of the underlying bedrock and tossing or rolling the larger sized rocks out of the way.

It's always a good idea to dredge in an up-stream direction, when possible, and place the dredge behind you so that the tailings are dumped down stream from where you are dredging, so that they will not be washed into your hole by the water's current. In this way you can place the larger sized rocks and boulders behind you as you move forward and they will only have to be moved by hand one time. As you move your hole forward, the tailings off the back end of your dredge will drop into the hole behind you and fill it in.

If you are dredging in a pay-streak which is paying a penny weight in gold or more, per hour (20th/ounce), you will be seeing plenty of gold while you dredge. Gold usually shows up as very bright and shiny when uncovered underwater and so is easy to see.

When moving your hole forward, be careful to clean out all the cracks, crevices, and other bedrock irregularities, because this is often where much of the gold is trapped — especially if you are into a bedrock pay streak, instead of a flood gold pay streak.

If you are dredging in shallow water, be sure to keep an eye on your dredge's pump intake to make sure that it is not allowed to rest on bottom where it can suck sand and small rocks into the pump. Otherwise this can cause a great deal of unnecessary wear on your equipment. If the water in which you are dredging is so shallow that this cannot be avoided, dredge a small hole for the pump intake to rest inside of and place a small bucket around the intake, as shown in figure 6-31.

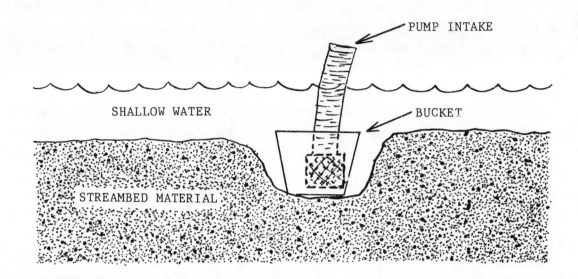

Fig. 6—31. In shallow water, place a bucket around the pump intake to prevent sand and gravel from being sucked into the pump.

LOSS OF POWER: TROUBLE SHOOTING

If your gold dredge has a noted loss of suction power at the intake nozzle, the following points should be checked and handled accordingly;

Plugged-up pump intake: Sometimes leaves or grass or even pebbles can accumulate on the outside screen of the pump intake. This will prevent a full force of water from being pumped into the jet, and so cause a power loss at the suction nozzle. When this happens, shut down the engine and clean the intake screen thoroughly.

Clogged pump impeller: It is possible for some pebbles to be sucked up and become lodged in the pump's impeller. This usually only happens after the pump intake has been close to, or has been lying on the river bottom while operating, or when another dredge has been dumping it's tailings in the water just upstream of your dredge's pump intake.

A clogged impeller can be detected by pulling the pump intake off the pump and by looking at the impeller. Any rocks or other foreign material that are lodged in the impeller should be removed. Sometimes a screwdriver is needed for this.

Air leak in the primer: Occasionally, an air leak will develop in the upper section of a primer on the pump intake of a dredge. When this happens, the amount of air that is sucked into and through the pump, subtracts from the amount of water and pressure to the jet, and a loss of suction power to the nozzle will result. An air leak can be recognized by the air bubbles being passed through the pressure hose. There is no place underwater for air to come from. So when air is seen to be pumped through the pressure hose, you know that there is some kind of an air leak on the upper section of your primer, and every effort should be made to find the source and plug it. Sometimes silicone rubber glue comes in helpful in repairing such leaks.

Water leak in the pressure hose: Once in awhile a pressure hose will spring a leak — which will subtract from the amount of water and pressure to the jet and cause a suction loss at the nozzle. This usually only occurs after the pressure hose has had lots of wear. These holes can usually be patched with the use of silicone rubber glue and duct tape. A pressure hose that has many such leaks should be replaced at the earliest convenience.

Holes in the suction hose: Holes in the suction hose itself can subtract from the amount of suction at the nozzle. Also, gold can be lost out of such holes. These too can and should be patched with the use of duct tape.

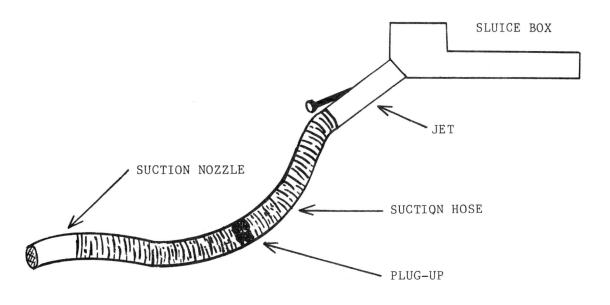

SLUICE BOX

JET

SUCTION NOZZLE

SUCTION HOSE

PLUG-UP

Fig. 6—32. A plug-up in the hose is a major cause of sudden loss of suction power at the nozzle.

Plug-ups: The most common cause of a sudden loss of suction while dredging is when a rock, or a combination of rocks, lodge themselves in the suction hose or the jet. (See figure 6-32.)

When a plug-up occurs in the suction hose, usually it can be quickly freed by gently tapping around the obstruction with a heavy rubber type hammer or with the smooth surface of a hand sized rock. If the obstruction is located inside the jet, it can usually be freed up easily with the use of a plugger pole from the surface, as shown in figure 6-33. Most store bought dredges come with a plugger pole that has been designed for the purpose of tapping free jet obstructions from the surface.

Some times a plug-up in the upper section of a jet can cause the water to reverse the direction of water flow in the suction hose. If you are dredging along and the water suddenly starts to pour out of the suction hose instead of into it like it is suppose to, it's almost a sure thing that you'll find an obstruction in the jet. The only

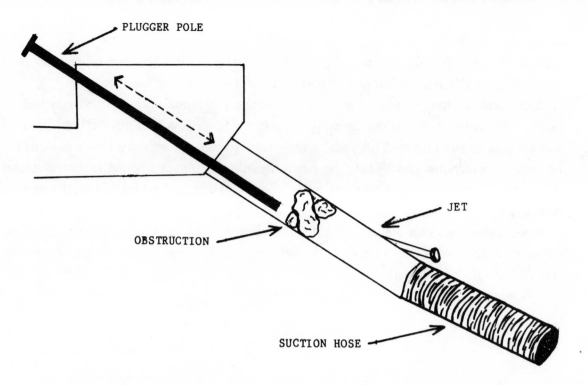

PLUGGER POLE

JET

OBSTRUCTION

SUCTION HOSE

Fig. 6—33. Obstructions in the jet can be knocked out from the surface with the plugger pole.

other time that water will reverse flow like this is when the dredge quits running — out of gas or whatever, or when running at low idle.

When your dredge undergoes a power loss, always check thoroughly for a plug-up before looking into the other possible causes. If you do not have a plug-up and none of the other earlier mentioned causes seem to be the reason for your loss of suction power, you should pull the spark plug and clean it, or replace it if needed.

There's a lot more to learn about gold dredging: Gold dredging is a very large subject, to which there is much technology — it being today's fastest progressing field in gold mining. In this chapter, I have attempted to cover all the data that you will need to know about what suction dredging is, what dredges are, and how they are used, how to dredge safely, and basics of how to run a successful dredging operation. In no way have I covered everything that there is to know about dredging.

There is another book available which I have written on the subject, giving a professional viewpoint at how to succeed in gold dredging. The book covers many of the "do's and don'ts" and "tricks of the trade" that a gold dredger normally picks up after lots of actual field activity and experience in dredging. I picked up most of the data by hanging around and working with some of the most successful professional gold dredgers in the field. I highly recommend it as good reading to anyone who wants to do better at gold dredging — no matter on what scale of operation. The book is called **Advanced Dredging Techniques - Professional Gold Dredgers Handbook** by Dave McCracken, and it should be available wherever mining equipment is being sold. If for some reason you cannot get hold of the book, write me and send me 8 bucks (plus 48c sales tax if you are located in California). I'll be happy to send you an autographed copy myself. (All orders shipped within 24 hours.)*

*See other available books on dredging on .page 1.

CHAPTER VII

FINAL CLEAN-UP PROCEDURES

After you have finished panning off the set of concentrates from a production period, usually there are a small amount of impurities remaining that need to be separated from your gold. These impurities most often consist of a few pieces of lead, some small iron rocks, and a little bit of black sand.

There are probably many different ways to go about separating the impurities from your gold in the final clean-up steps. Here follows a workable procedure which has proven fast and effective.

These final clean-up steps can be done at camp, preferably in a dry environment, where the wind is not blowing heavily and where there is a table top or some other such flat surface that is available.

STEP 1: The first thing to do is to dry out your final concentrates. This can easily be done by pouring them into a metal pan and slowly heating them over an open fire or a stove — whichever is at hand, as shown in figure 7-1.

Fig. 7—1. Final Clean-up step 1: Dry out concentrates.

You don't want to heat the concentrates too much at this stage, because usually there is still some lead in the concentrates. Excessive heat at this point has a tendency to melt the lead onto some of the gold within the concentrates. So pay attention to heat just enough to thoroughly dry out your concentrates.

STEP 2: Once the concentrates have cooled enough so that they can be handled, they should be screened through a piece of window screen. A small piece of window screen, about 6'' square, is handy to have and use for this purpose, as shown in figure 7-2.

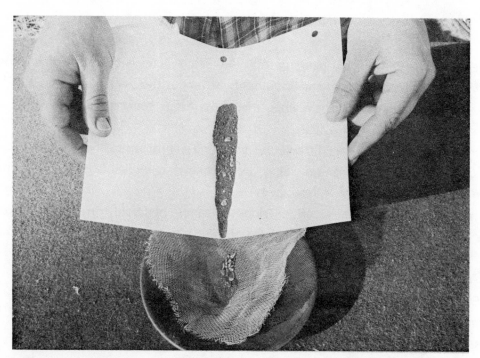

Fig. 7—2. Final clean-up step 2: Classify concentrates through window screen.

STEP 3: Take the larger sized concentrates — the stuff which would not pass through the window screen, and pour them onto a clean piece of paper. If there is a lot of this sized concentrate, then this step will have to be done in stages, handling a little bit at a time. Once the concentrates are poured onto the paper, it's easy to separate the pieces of gold from the impurities. The impurities should be swept off the paper and the gold should be poured into a gold sample bottle. This is another place where a funnel comes in handy for making pouring easier (See figure 7-3).

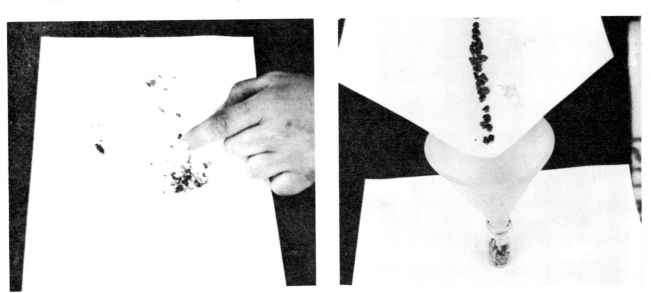

Fig. 7—3. Final clean-up step 3: Separate gold from the largest classification of waste material and pour into gold sample bottle.

STEP 4: Once the larger sized concentrates have been handled as shown above, the remaining concentrates can be classified through a finer mesh screen. A stainless steel, fine tea strainer works well for this, and one can be found in most any grocery store (See figure 7-4).

Fig. 7—4. Final clean-up step 4: Classify remaining concentrates through finer mesh screen.

STEP 5: Take the larger classification of concentrates from this screening, pour them onto a clean sheet of paper, and separate the gold from the impurities in the same way that it was done with the larger material in step 3 above. Some prefer to use a fine painters brush to do this step, although it can also be done by using your fingers. This step goes faster if you only do small amounts of concentrate at a time. Pour the gold recovered in this step into the gold sample bottle.

STEP 6: Take the fine concentrates that passed through the final screening and spread them out over a clean sheet of paper. Use a magnet to separate the magnetic black sands from these final concentrates. The magnetic black sands should be dropped onto another sheet of clean paper, spread out, and gone through with the magnet at least one more time, because some gold always seems to be carried off with the magnetic black sands. Once the magnetic black sands have been thoroughly separated from the gold to your satisfaction, pour them into your black sands collection. There are probably still some values left with them that can be recovered by other methods. (Covered later)

STEP 7: Now all that should be left is your fine gold, possibly some platinum, and a little bit of non-magnetic black sand. These final black sands can easily be removed by blowing lightly over them and vibrating the sheet of paper while doing so. The sand is about 4 times lighter than the gold and so will be blown off the paper, leaving the gold behind. Once all the black sands are gone, you can pick out the pieces of platinum, if present, and separate them from the gold. Pour the gold into the same gold sample jar used in the earlier steps.

This process as shown above (steps 1-7) goes very quickly if an effort was made during the final panning stages to get as much black sand and other waste material as possible separated from the gold. In other words, the less impurities that you have to deal with in the final clean-up steps, the faster they go and the easier they are to complete.

CLEANING GOLD

Sometimes placer gold, just out of a streambed, is very clean and shiny. If this is the case with your gold, after the final clean-up procedure is completed, your gold is ready to be weighed and sold or displayed or stored away in a safe place.

Once in awhile gold will come out of a streambed with a coating of mercury or some other impurity stuck to it, and it will be necessary to go a few steps further in order to make the gold's natural beauty stand out.

If your gold is not clean and shiny and you want to get it that way, place it in a water tight jar about half full of water and pour in some dishwashing liquid. Fasten the top on the jar and shake the contents vigorously until the gold takes on an unnatural glittery color. Sometimes this happens quickly and sometimes it takes a little longer. It depends on how much gold is in the jar. The more the better, because it is the friction of gold against gold which does the cleaning. Once the gold is glittery, rinse the soapy water out of the jar, pour the gold into a metal pan, and heat it up until the gold takes on a deep, natural, shiny luster.

Sometimes the gold will be deeply coated with a layer of mercury and will need to be heated to vaporize off the mercury or emerged in a solution of nitric acid first, before washed in soap and water. (Covered later in this chapter.)

Gold has a tendency to turn a dull color after having been stored in an airtight container for an extended period of time. For this reason, many gold miners and dealers store their gold in water filled jars, and dry it out just before displaying it or making a sale. In this way the gold keeps it's beauty all the time.

If you should happen to store your gold in an airtight container and notice that it's color does not seem to be as bright as it once was, just wash it with soap and water and re-heat it, as shown in the above steps. In this way you will be able to make your gold look it's best whenever you want to.

The best time to weigh your gold in order to get the most accurate measurement is after you have completed all of the final clean-up steps.

AMALGAMATION

Mercury ("quick silver") is a silvery white, liquid metal, which has a tremendous affinity for many other metals. When clean, mercury tends to attract to itself and ball up into a single mass. A ball of mercury also has a tendency to attract pieces of gold to itself and swallow them up into it's mass. A droplet of mercury will continue to attract more pieces of gold into it's body until it becomes so packed full, that it cannot hold together as a single mass any longer. (See figure 7-5.)

Fig. 7–5. Right-hand picture shows gold and mercury separately. Left-hand picture shows them mixed together.

Mercury is often used in mining to separate the fine pieces of gold and silver from other heavily concentrated materials. The process of mixing mercury with another metal, like gold, is called "amalgamation." The resulting mass of gold and mercury — mixed together, is called "amalgam." Amalgamation is one of the oldest gold refining techniques in existence, and is still widely used in the field of mining today.

Mercury is very heavy — having a specific gravity of about 13.5. Many of the old-timers used to place mercury in their sluice boxes in order to catch more of the extremely fine particles of gold, which otherwise would have been swept out of their boxes because of their minute size.

Gold must be clean in order for mercury to be able to attach itself. Sometimes placer gold will be covered with a thin layer of oil, which will prevent the gold from being amalgamated unless the oil is cleaned off first. If you are going to use mercury to amalgamate the gold and silver values out of a set of concentrates, it's always a good idea to bathe the concentrates first in a 10 to 1 solution of nitric acid — meaning 10 parts water to 1 part acid. This process should not be done in a metal pan, because the acid solution will attack the metal of the pan itself. Plastic gold pans and glass jars both work well for cleaning concentrates with a nitric acid solution.

CAUTION: Working with nitric acid can be very dangerous! Be extra careful to avoid spilling it onto yourself, splashing it into your eyes, or breathing in its fumes. If contact is made, fresh water will help to dilute the acid. Always pour the nitric acid into water when mixing up a solution. This prevents the full strength acid from making contact with impurities which can cause the full strength acid to spatter out of the container and onto you or your equipment.

When a solution of nitric acid is poured onto a dirty set of concentrates, the effect will be a bubbly reaction. A set of concentrates, when being cleaned with an acid solution, should be allowed to bathe until all such visible reaction has stopped. Then the concentrates should be rinsed with fresh water so that the acid is diluted and washed away. Once this is done, the concentrates are properly set up for amalgamation.

A small amount of concentrates can be amalgamated in a gold pan — either metal or plastic. Approximately the same quantity of mercury should be used as the estimated amount of gold in the concentrates. Too much mercury should be avoided, because it becomes unwieldy to work with in the pan. If anything, attempt to pour in a little less than the estimated amount that you will need. Then more can be added if it is needed. A little bit of water should also be used in the pan during amalgamation.

Take the pan in your hands, and jiggle and vibrate it around until all of the visible gold is attached to the ball of mercury (See figure 7-6).

Mercury will not grab onto black sands. So in essence, what you are doing is getting the mercury to grab all of the free gold out of the black sands. Then you will pan off the black sands and be left with a mercury ball filled with gold.

Once all of the visible gold is gone, pan off the black sands into a tub of water. The reason why it's a good idea to pan into a tub during this step, is because it is not too difficult to goof and toss your amalgam ball, or part of it, out of the pan — especially if you are using too much mercury. If you use a tub to pan into, and some

Fig. 7—6. Amalgamating in a gold pan.

of the amalgam is lost from your pan, you can retrieve it from the tub and try again at no loss. During this final panning, it sometimes comes in handy to have two gold pans so that the amalgam can be poured from one to the other, while the remaining black sands can be washed from that pan which doesn't contain the amalgam. In this way all the black sands can quickly be separated from the amalgam with no loss.

Mercury in general use will not grab onto platinum either. So care must be taken to watch for it during this final panoff if you wish to save the platinum. Platinum is heavier than the black sands and so will be located at the bottom of the gold pan and can be picked out of the pan after most of the black sands have been washed out.

During amalgamation, if you do not have enough mercury in your pan to accomodate all of the gold which is present, you will notice the amalgam starting to break apart into separate pieces. In this case, add a little more mercury so that the entire ball of amalgam can hold together and still collect all the gold out of the pan.

A thoroughly packed ball of amalgam will be found to be about 50% gold and 50% mercury.

After mercury has been used a number of times in an amalgamation process, it can become dirty itself. When mercury becomes dirty it tends to break down into smaller separate bubbles, instead of it all coming together into a single mass. The way to clean dirty mercury is to bathe it in a nitric acid solution of 30 parts water to 1 part acid. This will clean the impurities out and allow it to amalgamate properly again. Mercury can be used over and over to amalgamate, and cleaned when necessary in this way.

If you have a larger sized set of concentrates, a rock tumbler can be used to amalgamate the gold out by placing the concentrates and a correct estimation of mercury into the tumbler and allowing them to turn for a few hours. Some larger scale operations employ the use of portable cement mixers in order to amalgamate their concentrates.

Mixing lye (Draino) with your tumbling mixture will help keep the mercury alive — that is, keep the mercury grabbing the gold well.

Once all the gold has been amalgamated and the amalgam has been separated from the black sands, it's necessary to squeeze off the excess mercury from the amalgam ball. This is usually done by tightly squeezing the amalgam ball within a wet chamois until all of the excess mercury is forced through the pores. A thick cloth, piece of canvas, or a nylon stocking can also be used for this, but a thin leather chamois is preferred amongst most experienced miners. The squeezing should be done over a gold pan, or some other open container, to catch the excess mercury as it is squeezed through. If the catching container is filled with water, the mercury will be prevented from splashing or bouncing out as it drops into the receptacle.

It is always a good idea to use rubber gloves when doing the squeezing step. This will prevent any amounts of mercury from becoming absorbed into the cuts or bruises that may be on your hands.

Fig. 7–7. Squeezing the excess mercury out of amalgam with a chamois.

Mercury that has been used to amalgamate fine gold and then squeezed through a chamois or some other finely woven material as shown above, will be found to hold onto some of the extra fine gold. These remaining gold residues seem to cause the mercury to have even more affinity for gold when used in later amalgamation processes.

Once all of the excess mercury is squeezed out of the amalgam ball, the next step is to separate the mercury from the gold. This is usually done in two different ways. The first way is by heating the amalgam until all of the mercury has been vaporized off the gold. The other way (covered later) is to burn off the mercury with nitric acid.

VAPORIZING SMALL AMOUNTS OF MERCURY

If you are only dealing with a small amount of amalgam and the mercury is not worth saving, it can be vaporized off by heating the amalgam in a steel pan over a stove or an open flame. Mercury vaporizes at 675 degrees fahrenheit, which can be obtained over any open fire and over most propane stoves.

CAUTION: Mercury vapors are extremely poisonous and can cause death if enough of them are injested. NEVER VAPORIZE MERCURY INSIDE AN ENCLOSED STRUCTURE! Mercury can give off dangerous vapors at room tempreture. So anytime mercury is being heated at all, it should be done outside and from a position where the wind will blow the vapors away from you and anyone else in the vicinity. Mercury can attach itself to gold in small amounts and it's not uncommon to have some present, even if it is not showing in any great amount. It is for this reason that I suggest, when you heat up your gold during the final clean-up steps, that you do it outside and downwind. Mercury should be stored inside water filled containers.

Aluminum pans do not work well when working with mercury; because the aluminum reacts to the mercury in an amalgamation process of its own — which tends to make the clean-up procedure much more difficult. The small steel gold pans — about 6 inches in diameter — work very well as all-around clean-up pans for heating and amalgamation purposes.

When heating up an amalgam ball in a steel pan, a good effort should be made beforehand to remove as much excess mercury as possible from the amalgam. Also, it should be heated slowly at first, to prevent the mercury from boiling and spattering values out of the pan. Once enough mercury has vaporized off so that there is no longer any danger of this, the heat can be increased to make the job go faster. Best results with this method can be obtained by placing a carved out half of a uncooked potato over the amalgam, to prevent the spattering and loss of values (Instructions later in chapter). If your gold just has a small amount of mercury attached to it, you won't have to worry about spattering, and just heating your gold will suffice. Don't forget: Those vapors are dangerous, do it outside and downwind!

RETORTING

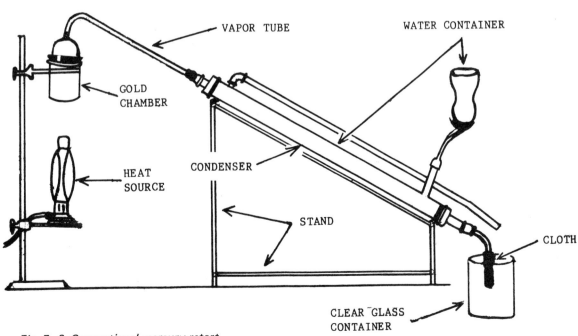

Fig. 7—8. Conventional mercury retort.

A "retort" is an apparatus that is used to vaporize the mercury off of gold. It then distills the vapors back into native mercury, and drops it into a separate container so that none is lost. A standard retort (figure 7-8 above) consists of a gold chamber, a vapor tube, and a condenser, as shown in the above diagram. The retort is usually held in place with the use of a stand. Sometimes a propane torch is used as the source of heat. The condenser is basically a water jacket, that surrounds the vapor tube with cool water, which acts to cool the mercury vapors as they emerge from the heated gold chamber. As the vapors are cooled, they condense back into liquid form again and run down the tub to fall into a container at the bottom (See figure 7-9).

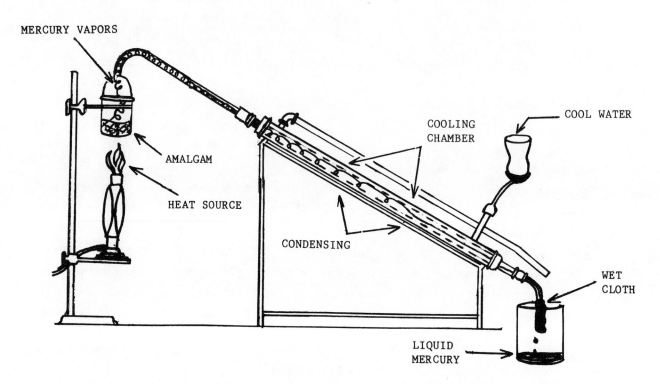

MERCURY VAPORS

AMALGAM

HEAT SOURCE

COOLING CHAMBER

COOL WATER

CONDENSING

WET CLOTH

LIQUID MERCURY

Fig. 7—9. Retort condenses the mercury vapors back into liquid form again.

The procedure commonly used in setting up a mercury retort is as follows:

STEP 1: First, look over the vapor tube to ensure that there are no obstructions inside it. Sometimes it's necessary to blow through it to make sure. Don't get any remaining mercury residues in your mouth!

STEP 2: Coat the inside of the gold chamber with chalk or graphite and allow to dry. This will prevent gold and silver spatterings from adhering to the cast iron interior of the gold chamber. A double thickness of newspaper lining on the inside of the chamber will also prevent spatterings from sticking to the inside walls of the chamber, but if used repeatedly, will cause an undesirable residue to collect inside the vapor tube.

STEP 3: Place the amalgam inside the gold chamber. The amalgam should be broken apart and placed loosely at the bottom of the chamber for best results. When using amalgam, the chamber should not be filled more than 2/3rd's of the way to the top. When retorting liquid mercury, the chamber should not be filled more than 1/3 to 1/2 way to the top. This is to prevent spatterings from getting into and possibly blocking the vapor tube passage.

STEP 4: The cap should be sealed (luted) with the use of a clay or sealing compound. A water/flour mixture works well for this. Once the compound is placed on the upper outer edge of the gold chamber, the cap should be tightly screwed shut.

STEP 5: Check the seal on the gold chamber by blowing into the vapor tube. No air should escape from the seal around the upper edge of the chamber. If any does, re-seat the chamber and check again until you are certain of a good seal.

STEP 6: Securely fasten the retort to it's stand so that there is no danger of it falling or being disturbed while retorting is being done.

STEP 7: Place a small clear water filled jar just under the vapor tube opening so that the mercury will fall into the jar as it drops out of the vapor tube. Ensure that the end of the tube is close to the water, but not submerged. Also make sure that the jar is filled with water to the brim, so that water will overflow from the jar as the mercury drops in. This is to prevent the water from rising up in the jar, as it is displaced by the mercury, and submerging the end of the vapor tube.

STEP 8: Tie a piece of cloth securely around the lower end of the vapor tube so that it surrounds the end of the tube and enters the water in the collecting jar. (See figure 7-8 for example.)

STEP 9: Fill the cooling chamber with cool water.

STEP 10: Start with a low heat on the gold chamber for the first 10 or 15 minutes. This prevents excessive boiling at first, that could in theory cause pieces of gold to become lodged in the vapor tube and possibly block the exit of further vapors — which could cause an explosion.

STEP 11: Slowly increase the heat on the gold chamber until mercury starts to flow from the vapor tube into the collecting jar. Continue with just enough heat to keep a steady flow of mercury into the jar.

STEP 12: When mercury stops flowing from the vapor tube, continue the heat on the gold chamber for a few minutes.

STEP 13: Turn off the heat and allow the retort to cool. Ensure that the end of the vapor tube is not submerged under water in the collecting jar during cooling.

STEP 14: Return the mercury from the collecting jar to its proper container.

STEP 15: Unseal the chamber and remove the gold. **CAUTION:** Some mercury vapors always remain in the gold chamber just after retorting. Be careful to not breathe them in when you unseal and take off the lid.

If retorting is completed, you will be left with yellow sponge gold as the final product.

PRECAUTIONS: There are several things to keep in mind when setting up a retort, so as to prevent the possibility of an explosion from occurring. One is to never fill the gold chamber with amalgam or liquid mercury. Retorts come in a wide range of sizes, from the smaller ones that are designed to retort about 2 ounces of amalgam, to the largest ones that are able to handle up to two hundred pounds of amalgam at once. The idea is to acquire one that is a bit larger than is necessary to service your needs. In this way, there is less chance of your needing to over fill it.

Another precaution is to make sure you start with a slow heat on the gold chamber to ensure that excessive boiling does not occur.

Always check the vapor tube, before using the retort, to make certain that it is not blocked, and will pass vapors freely.

And finally, the lower end of the vapor tube should not be allowed to be submerged under the water in the collecting jar. The reason for this is because the heating of the gold chamber causes the gases there to expand and be forced out of the vapor tube. When the chamber is allowed to cool, a vacuum is created within that will pull air back up the vapor tube and into the chamber. If the end of the vapor tube is submerged when cooling is started, water can be sucked up into the extremely hot chamber, where it will suddenly expand into super heated steam and have nowhere to go — and possibly cause an explosion. This has occurred in the past, and so is the reason for the cloth at the end of the vapor tube. A damp cloth is enough to ensure that no vapors are allowed to escape during retorting, yet will also allow air to pass back into the vapor tube during cooling.

Retorting should be done outside and downwind of nearby occupancy. Even though the retort is supposed to recover all of the mercury, you can never be too safe. Plus, there are a certain amount of vapors released when the gold chamber is opened after retorting has been done. *So be safe and do it outside, eh?*

POTATO RETORTING

A form of retorting can be done with the use of a large uncooked potato. If you are out in the field and are working with enough mercury that you want to save most of it, but don't have the conventional retort on hand, the procedure is as follows:

STEP 1: Cut the potato in half and carve a cavity in the center of one of the halves, as shown in figure 7-10. The cavity should be made a bit larger than the size of your amalgam ball.

Fig. 7—10. Potato retorting step 1; cut an uncooked potato in half and carve out a cavity larger than the size of your amalgam ball.

STEP 2: Place the amalgam in the cavity, put the other half of the potato on top, wire the potato tightly together, and wrap the entire potato in aluminum foil.

STEP 3: Place the potato as wrapped in the hot coals of a campfire for about an hour, or a little longer. Some vapors will escape in using this method of retorting, so make sure that you stay upwind. Also, once in awhile a potato will explode, so keep your distance.

STEP 4: Remove the potato from the fire and allow it to cool.

STEP 5: Open up the potato and remove the gold, If retorting is complete it should be yellow and spongy.

STEP 6: Thoroughly crush the potato in your gold pan and pan it off. This should leave you with most of the mercury that you started out with.

This is a rather easy and effective way of retorting mercury when out in the field. The main precautions to keep in mind when retorting in this way are to stay upwind and DON'T EAT THE POTATO! Don't laugh, it's happened.

HALF POTATO METHOD

Here's another method of vaporizing off the mercury from gold which is often used when a miner wants to save as much of his mercury as possible, yet he doesn't have a conventional retort, and it's inconvenient to start up a camp fire.

STEP 1: Cut a large sized uncooked potato in half in the crosswise direction. (See figure 7-11 for example).

STEP 2: Cut a cavity for your amalgam ball into one of the potato halves.

STEP 3: Put the amalgam in the center of your small steel clean-up pan, and place the carved-out half of the potato over top of the amalgam, so that it is covered by the potato as shown in figure 7-11.

Fig. 7—11. Half potato retorting step 1: Cut an uncooked potatoe in half in a crosswise direction and carve out a cavity larger than the size of your amalgam ball.

STEP 4: Place the pan over a source of heat for about 30 minutes for each ounce of amalgam being retorted, and stay upwind.

STEP 5: Allow to cool, remove potato, and extract the gold.

STEP 6: Crush the potato thoroughly in your gold pan and pan off the waste material, so that the mercury can be recovered.

BURNING OFF MERCURY WITH NITRIC ACID

Nitric acid will attack mercury, whereas it has no effect on gold. A solution of 6 parts water to 1 part acid (or stronger solution) will eat up the mercury that has attached itself to your gold. If you are dealing with only a small amount of amalgam, or some gold that has a small amount of mercury attached to it, nitric acid can be used to dispose of the mercury.

The process can be done in a plastic gold pan, although it is done most efficiently in a small glass jar.

STEP 1: If working with amalgam, make sure that all excess mercury is squeezed free.

STEP 2: Place the gold or amalgam in a small glass jar and set it in a safe place, downwind of any presently populated area within the vicinity.

STEP 3: Pour in a solution of 6 to 1 nitric acid (or stronger) and allow it to boil until there is no visible reaction occurring. BE CAREFUL TO NOT BREATH THE FUMES GIVEN OFF BY THE CHEMICAL REACTION!

STEP 4: Carefully flush the jar with fresh water to dilute and wash out the nitric acid.

STEP 5: If all of the mercury is not yet dissolved out of the jar, with the gold back into it's natural flake and powder form, use a screwdriver to poke it around and break it up. Pour the water out of the jar, and pour in another dose of nitric acid solution. Sometimes it's necessary to poke at the gold just a bit to help break it up while it's being worked on by the acid. An old screwdriver works well for this.

STEP 6: When the reaction stops, flush again with fresh water. If the gold is still not back into it's natural form, increase the strength of the acid solution and do the above steps again.

When dealing with small amounts of mercury, usually the gold will be thoroughly cleaned of it after the first bath in the acid solution. Sometimes when working with larger amounts of mercury, it is necessary to do the steps a few times, as shown above.

When the mercury is dissolved out of an amalgam mixture with the use of nitric acid, often the gold is left with an unnatural dark film covering it afterwards. This film can be removed easily by putting the gold in a jar with some vinegar and salt, placing the top securely on the jar, and vigorously shaking until the gold is clean of the dark film. The vinegar solution can then be flushed out of the jar with fresh water and for best results, the gold should be washed with soap and water and then heated, as outlined earlier in this chapter.

CHEMICAL RETORTING

If you are burning off larger amounts of mercury with the use of nitric acid and it's worth your while to save most of the mercury in the process, it can be done simply by pouring the acid solution into a separate glass jar after all visible reaction has stopped — instead of rinsing it out of the jar as in the earlier method. That acid solution has dissolved the mercury off the gold and into the solution. Once the solution is in a separate jar, some aluminum foil should be dropped into the acid solution. When this happens, a chemical reaction takes place and the acid solution will drop the mercury to attack the aluminum. This causes the mercury to revert back to it's natural liquid metal form at the bottom of the jar. The acid solution can then be rinsed out and you will be left with most of your original mercury.

INTERESTING INFORMATION

A solution of sodium cyanide will dissolve gold into the liquid state of the solution. Some refiners use such a solution as a method of removing all of the gold out of a set of concentrates. The solution is then removed and placed in a container from which there are various methods of extracting the gold. One way is by adding powdered zinc to the solution, which will form a compound. The compound is then heated in a furnace until the entire content is melted, which allows the zinc to float to the surface where it can be skimmed off, leaving pure gold behind.

Another advanced refining method that is generally used in hardrock recovery of gold particles which are extremely fine and difficult to recover by other methods is called the "floatation process." Chemicals are used which cause the particles of gold to attach themselves to the air bubbles that are blown into the chemical solution. The fine particles of gold then float to the surface where they form a froth, which can be skimmed off or allowed to float off, leaving the useless waste material behind.

SELLING GOLD

There are numerous markets on which you can sell your gold. Refineries will pay you for the fineness of the gold itself and subtract a certain amount for refining charges. In this case you will receive a little bit less than the actual value of the gold itself. Generally, the refineries will not pay you for the silver and platinum contained in your placer gold unless you are delivering it in large quantities. The refineries prefer that you bring in your gold to them in large amounts and so will often charge less for refining and sometimes pay just a bit more for the gold when it is brought to them in larger quantities.

Flakes of gold and nuggets have jewelry value, and if marketed properly can bring in twice as much as a refinery will pay — or sometimes even more.

If you are located in gold country and ask around, you can always find someone who is buying placer gold from the local miners. These individuals usually pay cash. Unless the fineness of the gold within the area is extremely low, there is no reason to settle for less than 70% of the market value of the gold for that day. This means that the gold is weighed and he pays you for the weight of what you deliver. Impurities are never calculated into this type of deal. There is always someone in gold country who will pay you at least 70% for your gold — as is. Usually if you look around, you can find someone who is willing to pay 75%, and sometimes you can find an 80% straight out buyer — which is good.

There are also plenty of guys out there who are ready to gyp you out of your gold if they can get away with it. It's always well to bring your own pocket calculator along when going to deal with a new buyer. If you go to a dealer who starts figuring a certain percentage of the fineness etc., and his final figures end up lower than a straight out 70% of the bulk weight of your gold as it is, go find some more dealers. This is not to say that 70% is the going rate. You can do better if you look around a bit. You should never have to accept less than 70% for your gold. If a dealer starts to tell you all sorts of reasons why your gold is not worth what you want for it, go find someone else. There are plenty of gold buyers around who will at least validate your gold, so there's no reason at all to hang around and listen to someone who's trying to steal it from you.

Always clean your gold well before you take it somewhere to be sold — it helps a lot.

Sometimes dentists will give you a good price for your gold, and a phone call or two can pay off. Also, some lawyers and businessmen like to invest in gold. Sometimes you can get up to 100% of spot for your fines when dealing with them.

Some jewelers will pay well for your flakes when they have a demand for them, and it's not uncommon to get as much as 90% or better when you make such contacts.

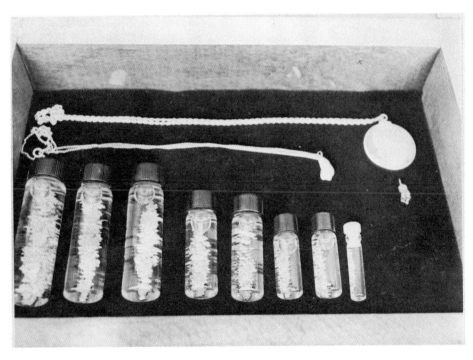

Fig. 7-12. Top dollar can be had for your gold by selling it out of jewelry boxes placed in tourist areas.

Probably one of the best ways to market your placer gold, is to build some small jewelry boxes and place your gold in different sized gold bottles and lockets and display them in the well frequented stores and restaurants in your area. (See figure 7-12.) The price can be marked up to about double the spot market value of gold, plus the store commission can be tacked on. There is enough gold in the gold bottles and lockets to make them nice keepsakes, gifts or souvenirs, and they do sell well to the tourists. You can fill up the gold bottles with clean water, which tends to magnify the gold to a degree, making it sell even better. A jeweler can place bails on your larger pieces of gold. Then those can be put on a chain and sometimes can bring in as much as three times the current market value — or more, depending on the individual characteristics of the various pieces. Smaller sized pieces can be made into earrings to the same result. Even your fine gold can be placed in gold bottles with water and sold for double spot. This is a good way to sell your gold when you don't need the money immediately. Nine or ten boxes as such, placed in well populated areas, can bring one in a good income, as long as they are kept up and moved when the sales drop off.

The best way to get top dollar for your gold is to do a lot of inquiring, always with the intention to find more and better markets. Then when you need some cash, you sell to the buyer who pays the most. One way to make a lot of gold buyer contacts, is to connect up with "Miners Referral" — who will give a list of the gold buyers in your area (See page 257).

CHAPTER VIII

DRY WASHING FOR GOLD

The deserts consist of huge deposits of sedimentry material, which have been affected by ancient ocean tides, ancient rivers, glaciers, floods, gully washers, huge wind storms, and are literally a gold mine of placer deposits.

There is also an enormous amount of gold bearing mountainous dry placer ground which has remained relatively untouched by large scale gold mining activity because of the scarcity of water in the area, that is needed for wet recovery methods.

Generally speaking, dry methods of gold recovery are not as effective or as fast as wet recovery methods. Yet, dry methods do work well enough to make some ground pay in sufficient amount to be worked in this manner at a good profit. Plus, recent developments in dry washing equipment — namely the "electrostatic dry concentrator" (shown later in figure 8-10), have made it possible for a one or two man operation to work larger volumes of dry placer ground without the need of water, and get really good results in gold recovery too.

Dry processing methods employ the use of air currents to do the same job that water does in wet recovery methods, namely washing off or blowing off the lighter worthless materials. Under controlled conditions, air currents can be made to do this very well.

183

For best results in dry processing methods, the larger sized classification of materials should always be screened out. The reason for this is that the amount of air current force that it takes to blow off larger sized pebbles, is also enough to blow off the fine and smaller sized flakes of gold. Best results in dry processing also require that the material be totally dry. Moisture and dampness tends to hold streambed materials together in clumps and adds weight to them. This prevents the air currents from affecting the different kinds of materials the way they should be, and so lessens gold recovering effeciency. It's not uncommon to run into damp material a foot or two beneath the surface in many dry placer locations. When this is the case, the material can be effectively worked by drying it out first on top of large pieces of dark plastic laid out on the ground near the work sight. The pay dirt can be shoveled first onto one plastic sheet, and then more can be placed on top of a second sheet — and additional sheets can be used if necessary. Once the material on the first sheet has dried in the sun, that material can be run through the drywashing plant — whatever is being used. Then more material can be shoveled onto that sheet to be dried. By that time, the material on the next sheet should be dried out, and it can be run through the dry washing plant. Then, further material can be spread out over that sheet of plastic to dry. Paydirt can be dried out and worked very effectively in this manner of alternating from sheet to sheet. This procedure works best when the larger sized material has been classified out by screening before drying is done. The heaviest plastic sheeting that can be found should be used for this purpose, because it takes a lot of heavy wear and tear during the process.

"WINNOWING" — OLDEST FORM OF DRYWASHING

"Winnowing" is one of the oldest methods of working dry placer materials. This procedure was probably first developed by the early Spanish miners — who used it a great deal. That they used this method on a very broad scale and for a long time is evidence that the procedure works well enough to pay, and is also further evidence of the extensiveness of well paying placer deposits that are situated out in the desert regions. It is done with the use of a heavy duty, large, wool blanket, two men, and a mild amount of wind.

The procedure basically consists of placing a conservative amount of paydirt in the center of the wool blanket. Each man then grabs hold of two corners of the blanket, and they toss the material up into the air, where a breeze can blow off the lighter waste materials (See picture next page). During this process, the two men should be positioned in such a way that the waste materials do not blow on top of them or back onto the work site. Best results are obtained when the material being worked has already been screened through 1/8 inch mesh screen (or smaller). Otherwise, it takes a great deal more wind to blow off the larger sized materials — and when you have that much wind, you will start losing a much higher percentage of the fine sized values. How far down in size that the material needs to be classified to get the most efficiency out of winnowing depends a great deal upon how much wind is blowing. A very mild current requires that the materials be classified to a smaller size for

Fig. 8—1. Winnowing.

winnowing to work effectively. So it's good to have a few different classification of mesh screens on hand for changing wind conditions. With a little bit of trial and error, the operators will quickly get the idea of what classification is necessary to get the most out of the amount of breeze which is blowing at the time.

The wool of the blanket will tend to latch onto and trap some of the smaller sized pieces of gold during the winnowing process.

The most optimum gold recovery in winnowing can be obtained by working materials down to the heaviest concentrates, picking out the larger pieces of gold, and then pouring the concentrates into a container to be worked later by wet processing methods. In this way, a large amount of material can be worked into a much smaller amount of concentrated gold bearing materials, which can then be more easily packed to a water site. To get the concentrates from the wool blanket into a bucket without losing any of the values in the process, a strong sheet of plastic can be used. The concentrates can be poured from the blanket onto the plastic, and then from the plastic to the bucket. When this method is used, care should be taken to winnow the materials down to the heaviest of materials before pouring into the bucket. This way, less material needs to be packed and worked again at a later time. Winnowing, when being done properly, is effective — more so than dry panning, and perhaps even more so than some of the dry washing plants available on the market. You'd be surprised after trying it for awhile! The secret is in screening the material properly and in not trying to winnow too much material at once. It doesn't take long to get the hang of it. The main disadvantage is that you are depending on a steady mild breeze to continue.

Winnowing is probably not best used as a production activity — because of the limited amount of material that can be effectively processed, and because of the dry production plants that are now available, at rather low cost, which can produce so much more. (Covered later.)

Probably the best use for winnowing is in a two man sampling activity, in an effort to locate some good production ground. A winnowing operation has great accessibility, the only tools needed being; wool blanket, bucket, shovel, classification screens, a few sheets of plastic, and a gold sample bottle, which really is nothing at all for a two man team to carry around. Also, winnowing is pretty fast and it takes very little time in setting up. Actually, it's just a matter of laying the blanket down and screening the sample material onto it. A dedicated, two man winnowing team can get a lot of area sampled in a days time — and the samples would be pretty accurate too, if they were packed back and worked later by wet processing methods. And in this way good paying ground could be located which could be then mined with larger equipment.

DRY PANNING

Panning dry placer deposits without the use of water can be done with some success after just a little bit of practice. The method is really not any more difficult to do than wet panning is. However, no matter how well that dry panning is done, it won't be as effective as wet panning can be — when done by someone with experience. This is especially true when it comes to fine gold recovery. Also, wet panning methods are able to process much more material than dry panning. To put it plainly; wet processing methods are much more thorough and much faster than the dry processing methods are. But when no water is available, and you are in a potentially high producing gold location, you have to use whatever methods that are available to you which work, and the gold pan can be used to process dry material to some result.

Dry panning is not best used as a production activity, although records show that it has been used to this purpose in the past with success. Today there are simply too many economical machines that can do a better job in a dry production operation. Dry panning can be used rather effectively in a sampling activity, especially when used in conjunction with wet methods to process the heavier concentrates that are recovered in dry panning.

The procedure is as follows:

STEP 1: Fill your gold pan about half way to the top, or perhaps just a little less, with sample material. Ensure that all of the material that you put into the pan is broken up thoroughly into separate individual parts, instead of clumps of conglomerated material. (See figure 8-2.)

Fig. 8—2. Dry panning step 1; fill pan a little less than half full of thoroughly broken up dry material.

STEP 2: Classification of material through 1/8th inch screen before it is panned is best, but if such a screen is not available, use your fingers as a rake to sweep the larger sized stones and pebbles out of the gold pan. Do this until most or all of them are out. (See figure 8-3.) Be extra careful to look for the larger sized pieces of gold while doing this step so that you don't throw any away along with the larger sized pieces of waste material. Keep in mind that pieces of gold in dry material do not show themselves nearly as well as when uncovered in water.

Fig. 8—3. Dry panning step 2; rake the larger stones and pebbles out of the gold pan.

STEP 3: Toss 3 pieces of lead shot or BB's into the pan of material. These will help you to see what is happening to the heavier materials within your pan while you are working it. Lead is best for this because it is closer to the specific gravity of gold than BB's are, and so will act more like the gold will in your pan. (See figure 8-4.) Once you have learned how to dry pan and have some experience in knowing what to look for, you can skip using the lead shot. Many prospectors prefer to use them though, because they show a lot of what is happening with the heavy material within the gold pan.

Fig. 8—4. Dry panning step 3; drop 3 pieces of lead shot into the material within the pan.

STEP 4: Vigorously shake the pan back and forth to start the heavier materials working down towards the bottom of the gold pan. (See figure 8-5.) This is the time to crumble up any conglomerated material which has not yet been broken up, as it shows itself. Be careful to not overdo the shaking so much that any material is spilled from the pan.

Fig. 8—5. Dry panning step 4; vigorously shake contents.

STEP 5: Now, take the pan in one hand, holding it in a level position, and start tapping the side of the pan with your other hand. The tapping should cause quick jerks to the pan — which should make the material inside jump slightly. (See fig. 8-6.)

Fig. 8—6. Dry panning step 5; start tapping pan to the side to cause the material to start jumping slightly.

STEP 6: While continuing to tap the pan on the side, slowly tilt it forward just enough to regulate a small amount of lighter materials to flow over the forward edge of the gold pan as the tapping action vibrates them forward. (See figure 8-7.) Watch closely for the location of the pieces of lead in your pan while doing this. If the pieces of lead start moving towards the forward edge of your pan, tilt the pan back to the level, start a new tapping action and then tilt forward again to vibrate the lighter materials out of the pan.

Fig. 8—7. Dry panning step 6; tapping the lighter materials out of the forward edge of your pan.

STEP 7: Every once in awhile — or whenever the pieces of lead show themselves to be moving towards the forward edge of the gold pan, tilt the pan back to the level position and reshake the materials. Then continue to tap the lighter materials off the forward edge of the pan. This is to prevent any heavier material (gold) from being worked up the forward surface towards the edge because of the friction caused by the tapping action.

The tapping of the pan is the main key to successful dry panning. It's this action which vibrates the material in the pan and shakes it into somewhat of a suspended state, which will allow the heavier materials (gold) to work their way downward in the pan. So how the pan is tapped can make a big difference as to the results of this activity. A person can see the results of this tapping action by watching what happens to the lead shot in the pan, while trying different kinds of tapping actions. When the tapping action makes the lead shot stray down towards the lower end of the pan — while the lighter materials are vibrated out, you have got it right. You'll catch on with a little practice at this.

Dry panning can be continued until there is nothing left in your pan except the lead shot and gold — if present. Yet I recommend that instead of panning all the way down to gold, that you only dry pan down to the heavier concentrates, and then take them — once enough are accumulated — to a water site and finish them off by wet panning. The reason for this is that dry panning is not real efficient — and becomes less efficient after you have worked your way down to the heaviest concentrates within the pan, and are attempting to vibrate the lightest of these out. Fine gold and small flakes can be lost in the process anyway. This becomes increasingly the case once you are down into the heavier materials within the pan. If you are sampling around in an attempt to locate a paystreak, often these fine flakes of gold are the only sign that rich paydirt is present. So you don't want to lose any more of them than you can possibly prevent — especially in a sampling activity. Otherwise, you can waste all your time and effort and pass right over paystreaks and even test them and never know of their existence.

So one of the best plans when sampling out dry areas with the use of a gold pan, is to bring along a container. After the sample material is worked down to the heaviest concentrated material, pick out the lead shot and larger pieces of gold and pour the concentrates into the container for more efficient processing methods to be done later. In this way, you can get a somewhat accurate index of how rich certain areas are by dry panning. A large coffee can works good as a container for dry samples. Sometimes a larger sized container is needed, depending on the amount of sampling that is to be done on a single trip.

One thing worth mentioning is that if you pan down to the concentrates, and find pick-out sized pieces of gold in your pan, consider that you have found a likely hot spot and start figuring out how to best work it production-wise. Smaller pieces of gold don't usually show themselves readily when using dry methods. So if you are seeing it, it's definitely a good sign.

One of the first things to do when you've found a hot spot in the desert areas is to take note of it's location. It's very easy to lose a spot in the desert, once you have

Fig. 8—8.

left it. On top of that, a single wind or rain storm can change everything around to look different. The best way to mark a spot in the desert is by checking its position with regards to the large fixed objects in the near vicinity — or those further away if none are close. Here's where your magnetic compass comes in handy, because with it, you can note the exact bearing to 3 or 4 permanent objects in different directions, and write them down. Then you will always be able to get back to that exact position, no matter what happens to the face of the desert. And believe me, if you find a rich deposit out in the desert, you can never be too careful about not losing track of it.

DRY PAN SAMPLING PROCEDURE

Here's an effective dry panning procedure which can be utilized successfully to locate paying placer ground in dry areas:

STEP 0: Tools needed: gold pan, bucket, 1/8 inch mesh screen — to fit over the mouth of the bucket, shovel, concentrates container (coffee can), and some black plastic sheets.

STEP 1: Uncover the material that you want to take a sample of.

STEP 2: Screen the prime sample material into the bucket until it is filled to the top.

STEP 3: If the sample material is not perfectly dry, spread it out thinly over your plastic sheet in the direct sun until it drys. This usually does not take too long. If for some reason this step takes awhile — it's well to have extra plastic sheets on hand and to move on and lay out your next few sample locations in the same way, and then come back later to complete each sample.

STEP 4: Dry pan the screened sample material down to the heavier concentrates and pour these in the sample container.

STEP 5: Once the entire bucket sized sample is dry panned down to heavy concentrates, bring them back to your car or truck and wet pan them into a washtub to get an idea of how much gold that is present in each sample.

If you have a large car or a truck, you can haul lots of extra gallons of water and several washtubs out into the field with you to assist in your sampling activities.

Sometimes you can drive your vehicle directly to the sights where you want to sample, and in this case you can skip dry panning, and wet pan your samples directly into your wash tub. A second washtub can be used to pour the water into from the first tub, once it starts getting too much material accumulated inside of it from the panning. When panning raw material like this directly into a washtub, the water becomes muddy very fast and it is a little more difficult to see what you are doing — but you get used to it, and it's still much more effective and a lot faster than dry panning.

If you can't get your vehicle out to the sampling sight, then you will have to settle for hauling the dry concentrates back to the vehicle to be wet panned. If you do not have room in your vehicle for wet panning supplies (filled water jugs, and washtubs , then you really don't have the proper vehicle for the job — but it can still be done, you'll just have to bring more sample containers along with you and take them somewhere else to be wet panned later.

If you plan to take more than one sample on a single trip out into the field, it's always good practice to bring along a magic marker and ensure that you mark each sample separately, so that you can keep track of which sample came out of which hole, etc. You can also bring along some paper and make a map if necessary.

Never mix the samples from different locations together in the same container before you have finished testing them. If you do so, then you no longer have an accurate index of the material value from each separate location that you have sampled. For example, if you sample 6 different locations and one is very rich and the others carry little or no amount of gold, and if you mix all of the samples together, the result will probably show a poor average of values, and you might never realize that one of the samples was very rich. And if you do realize that one of them might have been rich, you'll have to go back and resample each one separately to find out which — but that's what you are supposed to do in the first place. Get the idea? So always keep your samples separated from each other and keep track of where each one has come from, at least until you have finished testing them. This holds true of any kind of sampling activity in mining — no matter what it is that you are doing.

If you are able to haul water in your vehicle, yet you cannot quite get your vehicle out to your sampling sight, you might consider the idea of also bringing along a wheelbarrow, if there's room. A wheelbarrow can be a large help in either hauling sample material to water, or in hauling water filled jugs to your sample sight. Sometimes you can get your vehicle to a good generalized location where you'll want to do lots of sampling. Then the wheelbarrow can be used to haul different samples to the water so that they can be wet panned. This can be lots faster and more effective than the combination wet panning/dry panning method. It depends on how far the samples will have to be hauled and what the terrain is like, etc. It's something that you'll have to decide. If a wheelbarrow is to be used for hauling sample material, you should consider the idea of building a screening device that will rest over top of the wheelbarrow — to speed up the procedure. The Chinese were well known for hauling material to water sights in this manner.

Needless to say at this point, sampling for gold deposits in the dry regions is a lot of work. This is true of sampling in any area, but a little bit more so in the dry areas, because often it entails hauling material a distance, or setting it out to dry, etc. However, do keep in mind that the dry regions — deserts especially, are almost entirely virgin of earlier mining activity, and the gold deposits that were once there millions of years ago, just about all still remain there today. The deserts of today remain as virgin as the mother lode area in California was when the 49er's first found gold there. Some extremely rich deposits have been found in the deserts during the past. Most of them still remain in place. To find them means sampling activity. Sampling activity means hard work and persistence to make it pay off. The sampling activities as layed out above work.

One other thing to keep in mind about the dry regions, is that you don't usually have to get off the main beaten trail in order to locate virgin ground. It is often necessary to get off the beaten trail in order to find entirely virgin ground when you are prospecting for gold in the gold bearing mountainous areas where water is available. But in the dry regions — especially in the deserts, this is almost never the case, because these areas are pretty well entirely unworked by large scale mining activity — not because of the lack of gold, but because of the lack of water being immediately available for large scale processing methods. So you don't need to get way out in the middle of no-where in the deserts to find the most likely areas to carry bonanza sized deposits. You are just as likely to find them in the washes located just off of the highway. It's just within the last 60 years or so that the deserts have been accessible to the interested miners, because of the availability of transportation that will get you, your equipment, and water, to the promising locations. It's just within the past few years that interest has picked back up in mining gold. In taking all of this into account, very little effective gold mining activity has been done in the dry regions. Yet, with the equipment that is available today, these areas probably show more potential for the small scale miner than any other single area, possibly with the exception of gold dredging. Which area shows more promise? That is a question which will be answered truthfully within the next few years. I'm hoping that the desert areas prove themselves out — simply because of the vast size of the totally virgin ground that is presently available.

WORKING DRY GOUND ON A PRODUCTION SCALE

Once you have located ground in a dry area which is paying well enough to be worked on a production scale, in order to recover paying amounts of gold, you will need to figure out the best way to work the ground.

Often a road can be bulldozed to your spot. Sometimes you can drive right in with a 4 wheel drive truck. In these cases, you might consider the idea of screening the paydirt into the back of a truck and hauling it to a wash plant to be processed elsewhere. Actually, this is just slightly more difficult than in shoveling directly into a wash plant. The hardest part is usually a matter of breaking the material away from the streambed and classifying it. It takes a little more time to haul the material to the wash plant — but that depends on the distance and the condition of the road. It's also a little more difficult to shovel up into a truck. Some small operations use a conveyor belt to lift the material into their truck. Feeding the material from a truck into a wash plant is not difficult — because it's usually downhill. A one or two-man team could probably move the equivalent of a pickup sized load of screened paydirt, plus run it through the wash plant at another location, in the period of a full day's work. And if the material was paying well, they could do right well at it too. This is just one possibility of working dry paydirt on a small production scale that should be considered.

DRY WASHING PLANTS

If conditions do not allow you to truck the paydirt to a nearby water sight to be processed by wet methods, you will have to consider processing the rich material by dry production methods.

While dry panning and winnowing do work, and have been used as a means of production in the past, they are not nearly as effective as some of the modern dry washing plants which are available on today's market.

Dry washing machines usually employ the use of an air blowing fan or bellows — type device to blow a controlled amount of air current up through the dry material which is being processed. The air current will blow off the lighter materials and allow the heaviest particles — gold included — to collect.

Dry washing plants are available which can either be operated by hand, or by light weight engine/air fan assemblies.

The hand operated dry washing plant — as shown in figure 8-9, has its own classification screen as part of the unit, so the raw material can be shoveled directly onto it. The bellows air blower is worked by pulling on a cord, which is conveniently located so that one man can both shovel work the bellows at the

Fig. 8—9. Lightweight, hand operated, drywashing plant — used for sampling or production purposes.

same time . Two men working together can process up to a ton of gravel per hour — or more, by taking turns at one man shoveling — while the other works the bellows. The particular machine as shown in figure 8-9 only weighs a total of 19 pounds and so also makes for an excellent sampling tool, as well as a small scale production device.

Figure 8-10 shows one of the latest developments in dry washing equipment available on todays market. It is a motor driven dry concentrating unit, which employs the use of static electricity and high frequency vibration to help with gold recovery. In taking an overall look at this machine, first of all, there is a high powered air fan, which pumps air through a discharge hose to the concentrator's recovery system. The air currents which pass through the recovery system are adjustable so that the proper amount of flow of lighter materials through the recovery system can be obtained — similar to a sluice. The purpose of the steady air flow is to "float off" the lighter materials through the box, whereas the heavier materials — gold especially, will have too much weight to be swept through the recovery system by the air-flows.

Fig. 8—10. Electrostatic concentrating. drywashing production plant, which uses high frequency vibration to improve recovery.

The bottom matting in this type of concentrator is made of a specialized material, which will set up an electrostatic charge as high velocity air is passed through it from the air discharge hose. Fine pieces of gold — while not magnetic, will attract to surfaces that have been electrostatically charged, similarly to the way magnetic particles attract to a magnet. So the bottom matting in this type of concentrator attracts the fine gold to itself and tends to hold them there. The hand operated dry washing plant shown in figure 8-9 also sets up an electrostatic charge when being operated and fine gold recovery is improved there too, but this motor driven unit keeps pumping all the time, so the electrostatic charge remains in full force all the time, and gold recovery is improved as a result.

This type of concentrator also uses a high frequency vibrating unit to keep the entire recovery system in continuous vibration while in operation. The purpose of this is similar to the purpose of tapping during dry panning, or shaking during wet panning. The way to get gold particles to settle quickly down through other lighter materials, is to put the materials into a state of suspension — either in water or in air, and then shake (vibrate), and that's the purpose of the vibrating unit on this concentrator. It vibrates the fine particles of gold down through the lighter materials that are being suspended by air.

This machine is excellent for the production demands of a one or two-man sized operation — it being able to process up to two tons of raw material per hour, which is the equivalent of what a medium sized wet sluicing operation can produce, and is about as much as one or two men can shovel into it at production speed when in streambed material. All that's necessary on the part of the operator is to set it up, start the engine, and to shovel into its classification unit. The concentrator does its own screening of materials and everything else automatically — which leaves the operator free to produce at his own confortable speed.

This vibrating electrostatic concentrator is one of the best gold recovering dry washing production plants that has ever been developed. Some large-scale professional dredging operations use the concentrator for their daily clean ups, and they seem to be very happy with the results.

Total weight is about 75-80 pounds, but the unit breaks down into separate pieces which can easily be carried by a single man. So the electrostatic concentrator can be carried to a hot spot if it's worth a few trips to do so. It also gets excellent gas mileage — about 3 hours to the gallon, and so can be used as an effective sampler if larger sized and more accurate samples are wanted.

DRY WASHING AND CLAY-LIKE MATERIALS

Again, material must be thoroughly dry to get the best results out of any dry washing plant. Sometimes, when out in the dry regions, you will run into moist clays — just like you will run into them sometimes in the wet streambed areas. Also, it's not too uncommon to find a pay layer along with the clay. Clays make dry washing procedure much more difficult, because they must be thoroughly dried out and crushed before being processed effectively by dry methods. Sometimes this means that the material needs to be set out in the sun to dry for a full day — or more,-before anything further can be done with it. Sometimes it's necessary to dig clay a couple days ahead of the processing stage, and alternate spending a day digging and laying out material to dry, and then a day processing dried material. This takes a bit longer and the procedure is more involved; but if a good paystreak is involved, you do what is necessary to recover the gold out of it. And if you are using a dry recovery process, it's necessary to dry the material out and fully break it up first.

Sometimes clay material will dry into very hard clumps; and to break it up and crush it down on any kind of a production scale, it is necessary to use rock crushing machinery -the same kind which is used in lode mining operations (See figure 9-5 in the following chapter).

The clean-up of concentrates from a dry washing-type plant is also best done by wet-panning. Usually, if you have room enough to haul around a dry washing plant in your vehicle, you'll also have room for enough water to pan off your final concentrates too. However, if for some reason water is not available to you, the clean-up of your dry concentrates can be done rather effectively by running them through your plant several times. The final clean-up steps, as laid out in Chapter 7, can then be done to separate the gold from the last bit of remaining waste material.

DESERT PLACER GEOLOGY

The chances of finding a hot-spot out in the desert, or in the other dry regions, are probably just as good — or better — as your chances of finding a hot-spot in the water sheds of the gold bearing mountainous areas. These chances are pretty good, providing that you are willing to spend the time, energy and study that is required to find such locations.

Probably your best bet is to start off with the **Where To Find Gold** books and studying the geological reports that apply. There has been a lot of small-time mining activity out in the dry regions — much of it lode mining, but some placer activity also. Much of this is recorded information today. It can be of great value to you to know where gold has already been found. It's almost a sure thing that the areas which were once worked for gold at a profit were not entirely worked out, and could be worked again with today's modern equipment at a profit. An area which has once proven to pay in gold values is a good generalized area in which to do some sampling activity to see if any new paydirt can be found. The desert areas were pretty much left alone by the large-scale mining activities of earlier times because of the accessibility problem. Often, there was not enough water to sustain life — much less to process gold bearing material. Winnowing, while effective, is rather limited in scope as a production activity. So those areas in the desert regions that once proved rich in gold values, probably still contain a lot of gold bearing material, and would become one likely direction to go when getting started. But the desert prospector should not limit himself to only the once proven areas, because most of the desert regions have gone pretty well untouched by any effective sampling activity — simply because of the accessibility problem, lack of water, and proper equipment to do the job up until recent years. So the desert rat has got a lot of ground at his disposal and very few competitors to worry about.

A single large rain or wind storm can change the entire face of the desert inside of just a few hours time. There is very little undergrowth in these areas to prevent a good sized rain storm from causing an incredible amount of erosion to occur. And so, you hear all the oldtimer's stories of finding bonanza sized gold deposits, marking their position, going out after tools and supplies, and then returning to find the desert entirely changed and the bonanza apparently gone. Undoubtedly, a percentage of these treasure stories are true. After all, many of those oldtimers had a good deal of gold to go along with their stories, and many of them spent the rest of their lives looking for their "lost mine," etc. All the indications point to the desert having the greatest placer deposits left on earth — other than the oceans. Many of the deserts were once the ocean floor, not to mention that a lot of ancient streambed still remains there — and the same streambed has proven to be extremely rich when it has been encountered in the mountainous areas.

All of the placer geology which applies to streambeds, as laid out in Chapter 2, also applies to desert placer deposits. The same remains true of eluvial deposits — which is the gold that has deteriorated from the lode and which has been swept some distance away by the forces of nature. Eluvial deposits in the deserts (called "Bajada placers") tend to spread out much more widely, and in different directions, because they are usually not eroding down the side of a steep mountainous slope. Because of this, they are sometimes a little more difficult to trace back to their original lodes, but it can be done — the answer being in doing lots of sampling.

When doing generalized sampling in the desert, concentrate much of your activities in the washed out areas, where natural erosion has cut through the other sediments and set up a concentration of heavier materials. Dry washes, dry streambeds and canyons are good for this. Get an eye for the terrain and in looking over the high points and the low points, you'll get an idea of where the water runs during the large storms. Areas in which the greatest amount of erosion has taken place are areas where a highest concentration of gold values are most likely to be located. Remember, that we're looking at millions of years of erosive effects — not hundreds. Most of these areas are untouched. In some low areas — like in canyons and dry washes, bedrock will be exposed, and these are ideal places for you to be able to get into the lowest strata of material — where the largest concentrations of values are most likely to be. Look over the various canyons, large and small alike. Often these have been formed by millions of years of erosion and so they are likely spots to find paying quantities of gold.

Streambed material can be recognized by the smooth water worn rocks. Where actual streambed material is present, it is a prime area to be sampling, because such material indicates that it has been exposed to a great deal of running water — which means a great deal of concentrating activity took place with those same materials. It's possible that the material was once washed out of an old ancient river and that a good sized gold deposit is present too, or near by.

Sometimes it's worthwile to do a little sampling in different stratas of desert material when they are present and exposed. Flood gold layers apply even more so in the desert because of the flash floods which can occur there.

Sometimes nice sized deposits are found just beneath boulders that lie on bedrock, or up in a layer above bedrock.

Sand dunes in the desert are not usually very productive, because they mainly consist of lighter weight sands that were deposited there by the wind. However, sometimes the wind can blow off the lighter weight sands, leaving the heavier materials behind and in an exposed state — similar to the gold beaches, and this is something that can be watched for.

DESERT SAFETY

The desert can be very dangerous if you go out into it unprepared for it's potential of extreme change. Those people who have spent a lot of time in the desert, respect it in a similar way that experienced seamen respect the mighty ways of the ocean. In the desert, the extreme heat during the day, and the bitter cold nights can be equally hazardous if you are there and unprepared for it.

Here are a few safety tips for you to take note of, if you should decide to venture out into the desert in your quest for gold and you are unfamiliar with desert ways.

1) Ensure that your vehicle is in good running condition with plenty of gas in the tank and water in the radiator.

2) Bring a lot of extra drinking water along — GALLONS, even if you don't plan to stay long. Also, some extra nutrition is a good idea. It's possible to get stranded, in which case you will get hungry and thirsty.

3) When traveling out on the desert trails and roads, keep track of your route and of where you are. You'd be surprised at how easy it is to get lost when you are wandering around out there. Mark your trail as necessary. Bring along a map of the area and a compass, and know how to use them to determine your exact location if necessary.

4) Bring along a snake bite kit, and know how to use it too. These are not expensive, and you never know; it could save your life. When walking around in snake country, watch where you step. Never step over a rock or log into its shadow. That's where the snakes take shelter from the hot sun. Avoid such places, or step up onto the rock and jump over the shadow area out of striking distance.

5) It's also not too difficult to get your vehicle stuck in the desert sand. Bring along a good sized piece of heavy rug or carpet. It will be a big help to get you some extra traction, should you somehow arrive in the position of needing it. Sometimes, you can let a little air out of your tires and get extra traction when stuck in the sand. However, be careful not to overdo it. A few pieces of 2 X 4 wood, about 3 or 4 feet long, can also be handy to have along when you get stuck. Ensure that your jack is in good operating condition before venturing out into the desert. Sometimes it can be your most useful tool in getting your vehicle out of the sand.

6) Always camp on high ground — and never down in the dry washes or arroyos, even it it's nicer down inside of one, because of a stream or scenic, etc. The reason is that when a good sized rain storm hits the desert, the various washes and erosive waterways flood very quickly. If you happen to be in one when the flood hits, it's goodbye to you and your gear. These floods can and have occurred just as readily from a rain storm which is happening elsewhere.

7) Bring extra warm clothes, even if you don't plan to stay the night — you never know. . .

8) And finally, don't over exert yourself when working in the heat. It's better to work steadily, and stop for a short rest when needed, if the heat starts getting to you. Have salt tablets on hand. Know the symptoms of heat exhaustion and know how to handle it, should you feel it coming on.

CHAPTER IX

LODE MINING BASICS

The prospecting and development of lode mines is a highly specialized field, that often requires a substantial investment and usually involves a very large and sophisticated technology, which is far in excess of the scope of this simple chapter. However, anyone engaged in the field of placer mining should have a general idea of what lode mining is and how lodes are found, and the basics of this I will attempt to outline for you in this chapter.

FINDING LODES

Probably the oldest and most often used methods of finding a lode is in looking for and tracing quartz float back to it's original source — the lode itself. "Float" (plural) are the large and small pieces of quartz that have deteriorated off the vein, and have been washed down the mountainside. (Eluvial deposit, as covered in chapter 2)

Quartz float is usually some shade of white in color, and so is often rather easy to see in contrast to the predominantly darker colors of the surrounding rock and debris.

A good pair of binoculars is always handy when looking for and tracing float deposits.

Gravity, and the other forces of nature tend to always move quartz float downward at an ever widening distance. The further such an eluvial deposit is moved from it's source, the wider and more dispersed that it usually becomes — much like in a triangle, as shown in figure 9-1.

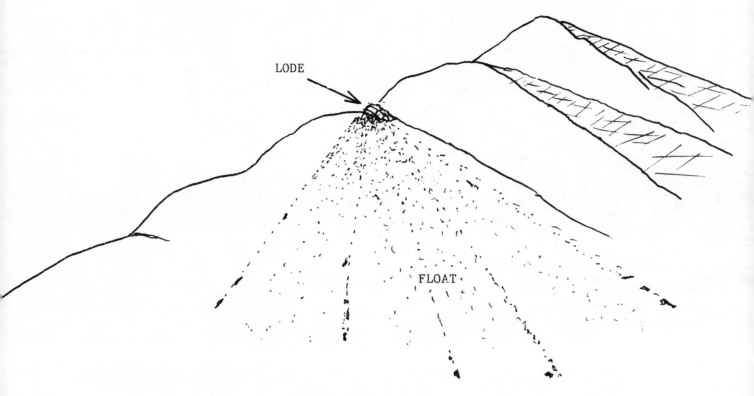

LODE

FLOAT

Fig. 9—1. Float usually becomes more widely dispersed, as it is swept further away from the lode.

When some promising looking float is located on a mountainside, the general direction to follow in order to find more of it, is upward.

In a stream of water, when a placer deposit is located in which all or most of the pieces of gold are very coarse and jagged and perhaps a good deal of quartz is still attached to some of the gold, it's a sign that the lode might be nearby, with the gold being swept into the streambed a short distance away. This is more apt to occur within the tributarys to the larger rivers, because the gold in most streams and creeks has been supplied by such lodes, that is unless they cross an area where an ancient river once ran. Many of the larger rivers have received much of their gold from the ancient river bed deposits. Regardless of the type of stream, if a placer deposit of very rough gold is located, it generally warrants an investigation of the banks in an upstream direction to see if any gold bearing quartz can be found.

Float, much like gold, tends to round out and acquire smoother edges as it is washed further away from the lode. So the roughness of a piece of quartz float is often an index of how far from the lode it has traveled.

How much work that should go into the searching for a lode, depends greatly upon the characteristics of the float which is being found. A piece of float showing visible signs of gold will prove to be a very rich specimen — and a very rich lode too, if it can be located. Prospectors have been known to search for years in an effort to find a single lode, from which they have located one or more pieces of promising looking float. In fact, many very rich mines were located in just this manner, after a long period of systematic searching done by a persistent prospector.

Float does not have to show visible signs of gold or silver content. The main indicator that shows the possibility of gold being present — and possibly in paying quantities — is a large amount of mineralization showing in the quartz itself. Mineralization in quartz float usually shows itself as a rusty red color. Any red spongy quartz float that is encountered should be followed to its lode if possible.

To find a single piece of promising float on a mountain side is encouraging, but it's not a sure index that the lode is nearby or that it will be easily found. There are many different ways that a single piece of gold bearing quartz could arrive at a specific location. Perhaps an Indian liked the looks of it and picked it up, only to discard it later. Maybe a bird picked it up because it was shiny and alluring; it's been known to happen. Or, perhaps a glacier once picked it up from somewhere else millions of years ago and helped to deposit it where you found it. Then again, it's possible that the single specimen once dropped out of some earlier prospector's back pack some years ago. Gold has a tendency to get lost as such . . .

Two pieces of similar quartz being found near each other, enormously increases the chances of a lode being present somewhere up above. Three pieces of similar float found in a near vicinity is even that much better, and so on.

Once a prospector has found some promising looking float, his aim is to trace it back to the lode by looking for more pieces and following their path upwards toward the source of the deposit.

When following the pieces of float up the side of a mountain, it sometimes occurs that you run across a larger sized piece of quartz which has also broken away (or has been blasted away) from the lode. Sometimes a very large piece can be half buried in the sediment and take on the look of an outcropping; you can be fooled into believing that it is the actual lode. If this is the case, you will usually find more float in evidence above — which is not likely to happen is the "false outcropping" where an actual lode — that is, unless there are additional outcroppings up above.

Sometimes, sediments have been washed down over the mountainside to cover the actual outcropping and much of its float. In this case it becomes more difficult to find the lode. Usually when this occurs, the only method of continuing is to dig sample holes to find the pieces of float, and continuing to move upward as long as you are finding traces of it. In that the float deposit becomes more widely dispersed as it descends downward, by looking at how wide a float deposit is, you can get a good idea of how much further up that load will be. The basic idea is to follow the float up the triangle to its apex in order to locate the lode. This can be done by using a systematic set of sample holes, when the float is buried by sedimentary material.

Abnormalties in bush terrain were always investigated by the old-time prospectors, because it signifys the possibility of a change in the hardness of the underlying rock, meaning a potential quartz vein. The exposed walls in canyons and gulches should always be carefully looked over. In their case, there is no sedimentary material to cover up any mineral lodes that might be present.

Any highly mineralized areas are worth the effort to check out, because many of the richest mines have been located in areas where the rock is highly mineralized. Such ground is indicated by quartz veins and threadlets being widely dispersed throughout the county rock.

One thing to keep in mind about lode prospecting, is that a good deal of erosion has taken place within the last hundred years or so, since the old-timers prospected the countryside. It's a good possibility that many outcroppings that were once buried by sediments have since been uncovered by the erosive effects on the countyside; and valuable lodes which were once hidden to view — or overlooked, might now be easier to locate.

RESEARCHING MINING RECORDS

There are several other ways of locating lode deposits and valuable mines, one of which is to talk with the locals and old-timers of the general area in which you are interested. They are usually a wealth of data, and will have plenty of interesting stories to tell about such matters.

Probably the best means of locating a well paying lode mine today, is by studying the various geological reports concerning the county — or counties — that you are interested in. Quite often, many of the notable lode mines within a county are listed in its various geological reports. Sometimes the reports contain all of the old production statistics for the mines in question — not to mention other valuable data which would be of interest (See figure 9-2 on next page).

By taking the information located within a geological report concerning the various hardrock mines within a county, and cross-referencing it to the data contained in the County Records Office, you can come-by the exact location of any mine that you are interested in, and find out whether or not the mine is presently owned by anyone — and if so, by whom. You can also often find out on what sized scale that the mine was being operated, the consistency and general make up of the ore, as well as exactly how it was being processed and how much it was yielding in gold and silver values. This is a means of prospecting for mines, which for the most part, have already proven themselves; and in which the hard work of finding them, and in their initial development, has already been done.

There are thousands upon thousands of abandoned lode mines in gold country that could be profitably worked at today's gold exchange market value. The majority of these were shut down and abandoned years ago when it became impossible to work them because of rising inflation and the fixed market exchange value for gold. Many such mines were shut down during the second world war and were never reopened afterwards.

GOLD, LODE—Continued

Map no.	Name of claim, mine, or group	Location	Owner (Name, address)	Geology	Remarks and references
	Armstrong	Sec. 6, T 37 N, R 12 W, MDB&M	Undetermined	9-in. quartz vein in quartz porphyry strikes NW, dips 20° NE.	About 13 mi. NE of Denny. Located in 1890 and developed by adit 210 ft. long; some high-grade ore was mined from surface workings. Idle. (Crawford 96:437; Brown 16:884.)
	Bailey	Sec. 15, 16, 21, T 35 N, R 10 W, MDB&M			No. 2 level of Globe Mine driven through mountain from Stuarts Fork side passed through this claim. Adit partly caved. (Miller 90:711-712; Averill 41:25.) See Globe also.
	Bateman and Mouldin	Sec. 14, 15, T 33 N, R 8 W, MDB&M	Undetermined	Quartz vein at contact of diorite porphyry and slate varies in width from a few inches to 5 ft.	Vein exposed in two old tunnels 100 ft. apart vertically. A small amalgamation plant was installed May 1932. Idle. (Averill 33:9.)
33	Bear Tooth (Fischer)	Sec. 33, T 7 N, R 7 E, HB&M		Quartz vein. Gold in oxidized sulfides of pyrrhotite, pyrite and chalcopyrite.	An old property. 70 tons of sorted sulfides shipped to Tacoma in 1947 yielded $55 per ton in gold, silver and copper. (Aubury 08:144; Averill 41:25; herein.)
	Bell				See Golden Chest.
34	Belli	Sec. 32, T 38 N, R 7 W, MDB&M		In gabbroic rock near contact with serpentine.	Old pocket mine 7 mi. N of Trinity Center. (MacDonald 13: Plate 1.)
	Bette				See Golden Chest.
	Big Chief	Sec. 16, T 8 N, R 8 E, HB&M	Undetermined	14-in. quartz vein in schist.	Two claims near Old Denny located in 1908. Tunnel on vein for 100 ft; ore assayed $15 to $60 per ton in gold. (Brown 16:884.)
	Bigelow	Sec. 15, 16, T 34 N, R 10 W, MDB&M	Undetermined	A short ore shoot in hornblende schist and granodiorite.	6 mi. NW of Weaverville. 70-ft. shaft. A little high-grade produced. Idle. (Brown 16:884.)
	Bismark	Sec. 12, 13, T 33 N, R 8 W, MDB&M			Patented quartz claim in Deadwood district 4 mi. E of Lewiston. Idle.
35	Black Cloud Group	Sec. 31, 32, T 34 N, R 9 W, MDB&M	Undetermined	Dark and light colored, fine grained, porphyritic dikes penetrate mica schist and interbedded siliceous slate and metavolcanic rock.	3 mi. NE of Lewiston. 9 unpatented claims prospected by shallow surface cuts; ore estimated to assay $4 to $6 per ton, based on 3 surface samples and 40-ton mill run. (Averill 41:26-27.)
	Black Diamond				See Mason and Thayer.
36	Blagrave	Sec. 10, T 37 N, R 7 W, MDB&M	Undetermined	Meta-andesite country rock	3 mi. NE of Carrville. No published description. (MacDonald 13: Plate 1.)
37	Blue Jacket	Sec. 17, 18, T 37 N, R 7 W, MDB&M	Undetermined	Ore shoot of low-grade quartz with rich spots, 2½ ft. wide, 200 ft. long. Strikes N 40° E, dips 40° SE; vein cuts granodiorite, aplite, and serpentine. Some free gold in aplite and granodiorite.	Near Carrville. Attempt was made to develop it on large tonnage basis; has adit 820 ft. long with drifts, raises, and stopes. Producer prior to 1896. (Crawford 96:439; MacDonald 13:25-27; Brown 16:884-885; Averill 31:29.)

Fig. 9–2. Here's a sample of a single page taken from the "Tabulation of Mines" section in a county geological report. Note: The monetary figures concerning the ore values from the mines are based on $35/ounce figures, so compute accordingly.

It takes a bit of time and study to locate these old mines in this way, and it's also necessary to go out and take samples for assay in order to see if the mine or mines are presently of value. Many of them are, and so it's an excellent way to find good gold mines; because you are studying records concerning mines that were once successfully operated. Actually, now is the time to be locating mines in this way, because very little has been done on this so far — but there is more and more interest all the time. When you consider the amount of work and expense that can be bypassed in locating good mines by this method, it's surprising that all the good ones have not already been snapped up — which they have not.

SAMPLING A LODE

Once a promising looking lode is found — whether it is an already developed mine or an outcropping that you have discovered, you will want to take samples so that you can have an assay done. An assay report will give you a good idea of how much gold and silver is contained within the ore which you are having tested. At this writing, assayers are not hard to find that will give you an accurate report on your hardrock samples. The going rate, per fire assay, is about $10 for gold and $12.50 for a report on both gold and silver. Some outfits charge a little more. Many of the more prominent assayers advertise their services in the monthly mining publications. Samples can be sent to them through the mail if necessary.

Most serious hardrock prospectors do not rely on a single assay report, but send their samples off to three different assayers and take the average for the final analysis. The reason for this is that the actual assay is done only on a fraction of the sample which you have taken, and its accuracy depends on the sample being crushed and thoroughly mixed first. Even with this competently done, once in awhile, the assay can be off. Also, there's a chance of a technician making a mistake. So in having three separate assays done — by different individuals, and discarding any one of the reports if it greatly contradicts the other two, and in taking the resulting average, a prospector is pretty well assured of getting a fairly accurate report on his samples. Some prospectors learn to do their own assays, it being faster and far less expensive to do so, (about 20c per assay) when a lot of testing is being done. "Do it yourself" assay kits are available, and are also advertised regularly in the monthly mining publications.

When testing for the valuable mineral content in an outcropping or a mine, even the most precisely done assay can only give you an accurate report as well as you have taken an accurate sample of the lode itself. To get an accurate sample of a lode for assay purposes, you don't just take samples of the best looking ore part of the lode. You want to get, as precisely as possible, a sample which shows the over-all average of the ore that you will be processing if you should decide to mine the lode.

The reason that you need the assay done in the first place, is so that you can have some idea of how much gold and silver values are contained within the average ore that you will process if you mine the lode. Taking samples of only the highest-grade parts of the entire ore body will give you a better report, but it's also misleading and won't give you an accurate report on the average ore that you will be processing. This is perhaps one of the most important things to know about hardrock prospecting. The assay reports resulting from the sample that you take from the face of the orebody will be used to determine if it is worthwhile to undergo any further activity or investment concerning that lode. So you want to do as good a job as possible in taking a sample which will show the over-all average of the ore that you would process if the mine were developed further. This is usually done by taking a number of smaller samples from different parts of the entire face of the lode, being careful to take equal proportions of both high and low-grade ore to the degree that they are present on the face of the orebody. This is sometimes done by systematically taking small samples at regular intervals across the face of the exposed orebody. These smaller samples are then all put in a single body, crushed down, and mixed together to form the overall sample which will be assayed. It's also worthy of note that unless you are planning to send the entire sample off to a single assayer, you should attempt to crush the sample down as finely as you can, and mix it together as thoroughly as possible before separating portions of it to be sent off. This will ensure that you get an accurate sample of your sample to each assayer.

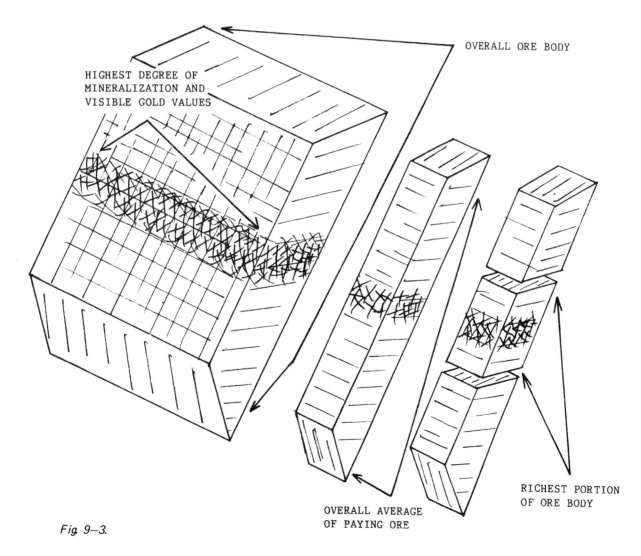

HIGHEST DEGREE OF
MINERALIZATION AND
VISIBLE GOLD VALUES

OVERALL ORE BODY

RICHEST PORTION
OF ORE BODY

OVERALL AVERAGE
OF PAYING ORE

Fig 9—3.

If there is a particularly rich portion of the lode that you would like to know about, there certainly is nothing wrong with having a sample of it assayed separately, just as long as it doesn't get mixed up with the over-all sample. It's interesting to know that one portion of the orebody is paying 10 ounces to the ton of ore, but it's more important to know what the over-all average of ore will pay. (See figure 9-4)

One thing to keep in mind is that you do not necessarily need to process all of the rock that you blast. Your tunnel may need to be five feet wide and seven feet tall in order for you to have working room, and your vein may only be 2½ feet wide. This means that you might be blasting away more than you are processing, which would need to be taken into consideration when figuring out the costs of operating the mine. The ideal scene is to have a vein that is wide enough, and pays consistently enough that all of the blasted rock is also processed. However, this is not always the case. It should be pointed out that the narrower a lode vein is, the richer that it will need to be in order to mine it at a profit, because there will be just that much more worthless rock ("gangue") which must be blasted out and hauled out of the way in order to get at the lesser amounts of high grade ore, as the vein gets narrower.

When taking samples for assay, don't disregard taking a portion of the "contact zone" which lies between the lode and the country rock. Sometimes the contact zone contains the most values.

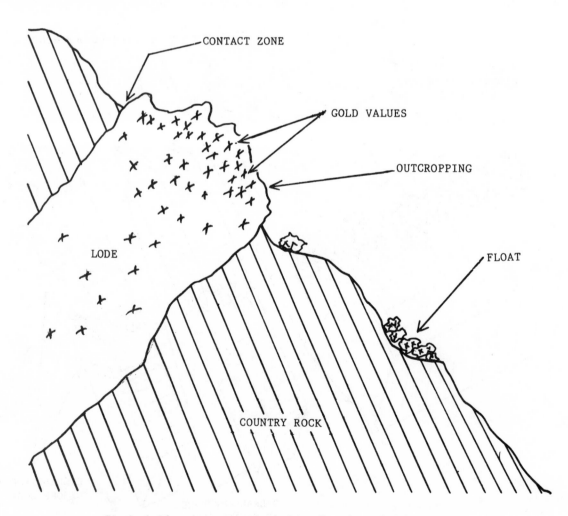

Fig. 9—4. Often the outcropping is richer than the underlying ore body.

When sampling an undeveloped lode, one thing to keep in mind is that the outcropping itself is often richer in mineral values than the underlying orebody, and can give a false picture of what the rest of the orebody contains in values. The reason for this is that years upon years of natural erosion often has caused the surface quartz to be washed off, leaving much of the mineral values behind to be absorbed into the remaining outcropping. This will make the outcropping itself richer in mineral content than the underlying orebody, as shown in figure 9-4.

So in order to get an accurate index of the mineral content in an undeveloped outcropping, it is well to get down into it as deeply as possible before taking samples. It is for these same reasons outlined above that quartz float sometimes assays out to have more mineral values than the lode from which it came.

An orebody does not need to have visible gold present in order to be rich in gold content. However, if visible gold is present, it is likely to be a very rich lode. Sometimes, pyrites can look a lot like gold when visible in hard rock form. The solution to this is to get an assay done, or try the hardness test to see if the golden material is brittle, or try nitric acid — before getting all excited about your find.

Most developed mines have no visible gold what so ever. An orebody can be so saturated with fine particles of gold that it can pay very well indeed, and yet you may never see any gold at all until after it's processed out of the ore. Some ores can pay as much as five or six ounces in gold to the ton of ore being processed — and more, and yet not show any visible sign of gold.

Probably the best index of whether or not gold is present in an orebody is how much mineralization that is in evidence, just like in the float. The presence of iron pyrites is often an index that gold will be there too. Iron pyrites will oxidize (rust) when exposed to air and moisture, which turns them into a rusty red-brown color. So the presence of a lot of rusty red and brown mineralization within the quartz rock of the lode is a pretty good indicator of potential gold too. Down into the orebody itself, where the minerals have not yet been exposed to the effects of oxygen and moisture, the minerals will take on a darker color, not a rusty red color like they do after being oxidized.

Mica, by itself is not the same as iron pyrites and is not an index that gold will possibly be present in the ore.

DEVELOPMENT

At today's market value of gold, and with the equipment that is readily available on the market, it would be reasonably safe to say that a small time hardrocking operation could be run at a profit in ore which is paying a half ounce or more in recoverable gold values to the ton of ore being processed. A cubic yard of hardrock ore weighs on the average of about 2 to 3 tons. There are other factors which can come into play and make it necessary for the ore to be of higher grade in order to run a viable operation. One example would be in having a narrow vein in which much more rock needs to be blasted than that which is being processed for its gold and silver values. Another example is in having ore which needs an involved and expensive processing procedure in order to release and recover the gold and silver values from the waste rock in the ore.

An assay report which says that there is a half ounce of gold to the ton of ore, is stating that there is a half ounce of gold present. However, it is not necessarily true that a half ounce of gold can be recovered out of the ore by using ordinary processing methods. Sometimes, you will run into rich orebodies in which a large percentage of gold is locked in so tightly with various sulfides, that it is all but impossible to recover most of the values without using the most advanced (and expensive) chemical extraction processes.

So after the fact of a favorable assay report on a lode, it's a good idea to take a larger sample — say a couple hundred pounds or a ton or two — if possible, of the average ore, and have a professional refinery or processing plant process the sample and do an analysis for you. In doing so, you can obtain an accurate report on the recoverable values, a flow chart on how to process your ore to recover the most values at the least expense, and a list of the equipment that you will need to use in order to do so. This is not an inexpensive process to have done; and if you are planning to enter operations on a small scale with portable equipment, perhaps it is not necessary. On the other hand, if you are planning to invest a substantial amount of money to open up a single mine, it is highly recommended that you have a large sample treated as such before you invest in a processing plant. In this way, you will find out the best possible way to recover the most values, and save a lot of money — and gold — in the long run.

One thing that should be mentioned at this point, is that it is always a good idea to keep quiet as to the exact location of the source of your samples during the initial testing stages, at least until you have obtained positive results and have filed the proper paperwork on the more valuable mines found.

Once you have an index of the recoverable values in the orebody that you have sampled, you can calculate that against the costs of operating a plant and of developing the mine, and determine if an operation within your limits can be run at a profit. Sometimes a road needs to be put into the area. This is another factor which would need to be entered into the initial investment figures. If you are considering refurbishing an already developed older mine, sometimes much of the shoring needs to be strengthened. That would be another factor to enter in.

How much initial investment it will take to start up a mine is largely determined by the size of the operation that you are planning on. A normal flow plan of a plant, from start to finish, would normally be something as follows: Breaking away the ore from the orebody — Transporting ore to the processing plant — Breaking large pieces of ore into medium sized pieces — Breaking medium sized pieces of ore down into small pieces — Crushing small pieces of ore down into fine powder — Concentrating the heaviest powder (contains gold and silver) — Amalgamating the gold and silver values out of the concentrates — Separating the mercury from the gold and silver by use of retort to give a final product that is ready for sale. This process can be done in a multitude of varying systems and sizes of operation.

A small operation might consist of breaking the ore away with the use of a pick, pounding it into powder with the use of hammers, panning the gold, and amalgamating as necessary. Many of the earlier mines were run in just this manner, and at a profit, too.

Fig. 9—5. Portable "Rock crusher — Rollermill."

On a larger scale, a portable impact hammer could be used to break away ore from the orebody and to break it down into medium sized pieces, which could then be placed into a portable "rock crusher," as shown in figure 9-4 above. This particular machine is a combination "rock crusher" and "roller mill," and so carries out two functions. First it takes medium sized pieces of ore — of about 4" to 6" size and quickly breaks them down into ¼" pieces. These then drop down into the second stage (roller mill), which crushes the ore down into fine powder of about 150 mesh. The machine is reported to be able to crush one ton of medium sized ore down to 150 mesh per hour, which is more than sufficient to meet the needs of a small hardrocking operation of this size. The powder from the mill can then be fed into a portable recirculating concentrating plant. The concentrates can then be amalgamated to recover the gold and silver values.

An operation of this size can be effectively run by one or two men and is able to process up to 4 or 5 tons of ore per day at little expense, under ideal conditions. This size of operation is becoming very popular today to the small time operator, because it doesn't require a huge investment to get set up with the equipment. Also, there are plenty of abandoned mines around that will make a small operation such as this pay well. And finally, the equipment is all portable. So it can easily be moved from site to site for sampling purposes, in an effort to locate richer lodes. Some prefer to use this scale of operation to sample out lodes with the idea of investing in the development of a good one once it is found.

A small professional operation, on a slightly larger scale, would probably employ the use of a portable power drill to make holes in the face of the orebody so that a few charges of dynamite can be set to blast out larger portions of ore. The ore could then be run through a series of rock crushers and a mill. The resulting powder could then perhaps be run over a professional concentrating table. The gold could then be amalgamated or extracted chemically. The entire setup would use conveyor belts so that the ore could be placed in the first rock crusher and end up as the final heavily concentrated material and gold, with little or no further attention from the operator of the plant.

An operation such as this could probably move about 10 tons of ore per day under favorable conditions, and could be effectively run by a three man team, one drilling, one shoveling ore into a cart ("mucking") and hauling it to the processing plant, and one man overlooking the plant's operation.

The larger that an operation is — meaning the more volume of ore that it is able to process, then the lesser grade of ore that it will usually be able to process at a profit.

Also, the larger the size of an operation, the larger the size of the initial investment and the operating costs.

If you are considering investing a large amount of money into the development of a single orebody, it's always a good idea to have the orebody "core drilled" beforehand to ensure that there is enough valuable ore present to warrant the size of your investment. A core drill will drill deep into the orebody and bring out samples from different depths. These samples can then be tested to see what kind of values that the ore contains as it stretches deeper into the earth.

There is always the possibility of an orebody crossing a fault zone and being sheared off so that the rich orebody suddenly ends, with the other section being somewhere else and not to be found. This is something that would be found out in having the ore body core drilled. Core drilling is a rather expensive procedure to have done, but so is the development of a lode mine on a professional scale, and if large amounts of capital are being invested, it's usually worthwhile to know that the orebody is large enough to warrant the expense.

Once the orebody has been sampled by core drilling, and it has been established that the values continue for hundreds of feet into the mountainside, and that you have lots and lots of ore to process, well, then you have got yourself a real goldmine and can be rather certain of good returns on your investment, providing of course that you have got a skilled manager to run the show and develop the mine.

Full development procedures are out of the scope of this single chapter on basics. If you have gone far enough along to be interested in developing a lode mine, I highly recommend that you acquire the technical manuals covering the subject and study them well. It's also a good idea to bring on a proven successful and competent mining consultant to help you get started.

CAUTION: Don't ever run an internal combustion engine inside a mine tunnel. Carbon momoxide poisoning can creep up on someone quite fast in such places; it can be very dangerous! If electric lighting is wanted in a tunnel, run the generator outside of the shaft and stretch an extention cord in to the work site. These should preferably be hung out of the way in a dry place.

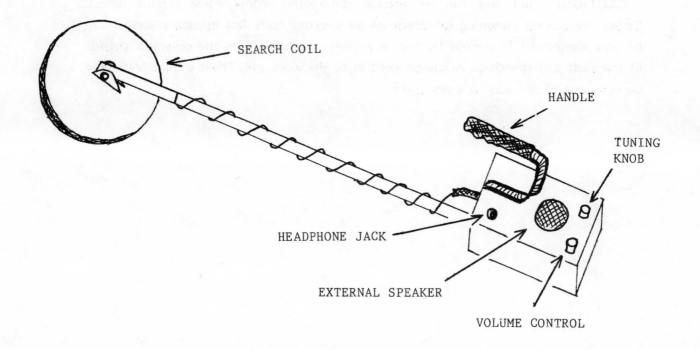

SEARCH COIL

HANDLE

TUNING KNOB

HEADPHONE JACK

EXTERNAL SPEAKER

VOLUME CONTROL

CHAPTER X

ELECTRONIC PROSPECTING

There are many different kinds and models of electronic metal/mineral detectors to be found on today's market. This chapter is set up as a guideline to give you the basic knowledge that you will need in order to choose the proper detector for your prospecting needs, and to show you how to use the one that you do choose as an effective prospecting tool.

The first point to remember is that the type of electronic detector that is used in the finding of gold and other precious minerals is not a "geiger counter." A geiger counter is an entirely different electronic tool, which is used to detect radioactive elements.

The type of electronic device which is used to prospect for gold is called a metal/mineral detector. Metal/mineral detectors are rather simple to use, and can be helpful in assisting a prospector in locating gold or silver deposits, once he or she has had a little experience in using one properly. While they are rather simple to use, it takes lots of practice with a metal/mineral detector before a person can use one proficiently in prospecting activities.

There are many different models being offered on today's market, most of which are of more use to the treasure hunter than to the gold prospector (two entirely different fields). Those detectors that are of most use to the gold and silver prospector generally fall under two separate catagories: The **Beat Frequency Oscillator** ("BFO"), and the **Very Low Frequency Transmitter Receiver** ("VLF – TR").

BEAT FREQUENCY OSCILLATOR

First we'll take up the BFO, which is the simpler of the two, but is just as important to the needs of some prospectors.

The BFO type detector usually has two main settings, which are "metal" and "mineral". As far as electronic detectors are concerned, the difference between the two is that "metals" are targets which are conductive of electricity — such as copper, gold, silver or iron; while "minerals" are targets which are magnetic non-conductive materials — such as magnetic black sands (FE_3O_4), which are also known to prospectors as "black sand concentrates". An iron object which has been in the earth for an expended period of time, and having thoroughly deteriorated, will often read out on an electronic detector as a mineral instead of a metal object — which it no longer is.

So the two basic settings on a BFO detector are "metal", electrically conductive targets (gold and silver), and "mineral" — non-conductive magnetic particles (magnetic black sands).

Different detectors have different ways of sounding out on reading targets. Some detectors have a light that will turn on and off. Some have a meter with a needle on a dial — which will also give you an idea of the intensity of the reading that is given off by the various targets. Other detector's have a tone that changes in volume when the detector is passed over a specified target. Probably the best type of metal/mineral detector for prospecting purposes is the type that has an audio tone in which the pitch changes when the search coil is passed over a reading target, and which also has a hook-up for an optional set of head phones.

The advantage to using head phones while prospecting is that the person can shut out all of the background noises from the surrounding environment and so can concentrate fully on any possible change in tone while scanning — and be able to watch where he is stepping and where he is scanning while doing so.

On most types of tone changing BFO detectors, the tone will not only raise in pitch when the search coil is passed over a target for which it is set to sound out on, but it will also lower in pitch when the search coil is passed over a target of the opposite setting. For example, if a BFO detector is on the metal setting and is passed over a large gold nugget, the detector's audio tone should raise in pitch. If the detector on the same metal setting is passed over top of a high concentration of magnetic black sand, the audio tone should lower in pitch. The same thing holds true in the opposite for the BFO detector which is adjusted to the mineral setting.

Unfortunately for the gold prospector, gold — as a metal, is generally not picked up very well by metal/mineral detectors. This is a comparative statement. Gold is not picked up on a metal/mineral detector nearly as well as — say steel or iron objects of the same size and shape. Some detectors will detect gold well enough that they will read out on nuggets or large deposits of smaller pieces of gold, and so can be used to hunt for gold in prospecting. But generally speaking, gold deposits will not read out on a metal/mineral detector nearly as well as many other metal objects will. This needs to be mentioned so that the prospector is aware that some detectors will just barely sound out on gold objects and some will not sound out at all.

I highly recommend that any person who is interested in buying a metal/mineral detector for the purpose of prospecting out deposits of gold, to bring some samples of natural gold along with him or her in order to test the various detectors before deciding which one to buy. This is to ensure that the one you do buy will sing out well when it is passed over gold objects. It is well to use natural gold samples — like nuggets or a sample bottle filled with gold flakes, when testing out the various detectors. This is better than using a gold ring or some other type of jewelry, because jewelry is usually made of gold which has been alloyed with other metals — that may read out on a metal/mineral detector better or worse than the natural gold objects will. To do otherwise than to use natural gold samples when testing a detector is not an accurate test and can give one a false idea of what feats that the various models are able to accomplish out in the field.

Manufacturer's claims are interesting, but not always entirely accurate for the prospector's needs under field conditions, and if you are going to use the detector for the purpose of locating gold deposits, it's best to test the different models for yourself — using real samples, and decide which one will actually give you the best results. In this way you are likely to find a great deal more gold.

The best detectors for finding gold are not necessarily the most expensive ones. The varying costs in detectors usually are in ratio to the amount of additional circuitry that is put into the detector for extra features — which usually have little or nothing to do with the operation of the detector for prospecting purposes.

Metal/mineral detectors read out on gold better as the pieces become larger. As an example, a detector might sound out very well when it's search coil is passed over an eighth ounce nugget, yet not sound out at all when passed over three times as much fine gold that is accumulated in a glass jar.

How tightly that a gold deposit is concentrated also makes a large difference as to how well that it will cause a metal/mineral detector to sound out. Whereas a quarter ounce of flake gold in a jar might sound out well on a detector, perhaps 2 ounces of the same flake gold which is spread out over a small area might not read out at all. This is one factor which is important for the gold prospector to realize, that any detector, BFO or otherwise, will read out on tighter concentrations of gold better than larger amounts of gold which are more widely dispersed, and that they will read out on nuggets — particularly the large ones, best of all.

Magnetic black sands (black sand concentrates) tend to read out very strongly on BFO type detectors as a mineral.

One other interesting fact about BFO type detectors is that they tend to read out on the most dominent element — either "metal" or "mineral" — whichever is most present in the ground that the detector is being passed over. For example, if you are passing the search coil over ground that contains gold, which would read out as a metal, yet there is a large amount of magnetic black sand in that same ground, it is likely that the BFO detector will read out on the black sands as a mineral and ignore the gold. Equal amounts of both metal and mineral elements in a section of ground — in any quantity, will prevent the BFO detector from sounding out on either element.

Because the BFO-type detectors read out so well on highly mineralized ground (magnetic black sands), the presence of highly mineralized ground tends to drown out any traces of gold which lies in or under. This is known as "interference" in the electronic detecting field.

So, a mineral response on a BFO detector does not mean that there is no gold present, only that there is heavily mineralized ground — which may be blocking out any gold readings.

In some places where nuggets hang up — as in a set of fast water rapids, the constant velocity of the flow of current might be too fast to allow a predominate amount of heavy black sands (which can cause interference on a BFO detector) to collect. It is for this reason that many electronic prospectors direct their activities towards areas having very shallow streambeds and exposed bedrock. Fast water areas are more likely to have less streambed covering the bedrock traps — where the larger sized gold nuggets are most likely to be.

DEPTH CAPABILITIES

How deep into the ground that a specific metal/mineral detector will pick up an object depends on various conditions. Surprising to many, how much a detector costs has little to do with its depth sounding capability. In fact, some of the less expensive models are able to probe deeper and pick up on gold better than some of the more expensive detectors. The Federal Communication Commission has put a maximum limit on the signal strength that can be used in metal/mineral detectors. So the idea that a more expensive model puts out a stronger signal to probe deeper is simply not true.

The type of object itself has much to do with how deep into the ground that it can be located with a metal/mineral detector. Different kinds of objects have varying amounts of magnetic and electrically conductive properties, and so affect electronic detectors differently. Also, some detectors will pick up some kinds of objects better than others. As mentioned earlier, gold is not one of the better reading metals, so cannot be picked up with a metal/mineral detector as deeply as say — an iron object of similar size and shape. This is the main reason why I stress so strongly that you should test the various detectors thoroughly before you buy one.

Another factor which determines how deep an object will be picked up by any detector is the size of the object itself. Whereas a 2 pennyweight nugget (1/10th ounce) might be picked up 3 inches deep into the ground with a certain metal dector, a 5 pennyweight nugget (1/4 ounce) might be picked up 6 inches deep into the same ground with the same detector.

How much an object has deteriorated and has been absorbed into the soil is another factor as to how deep the object will be picked up. Iron objects tend to oxidize and become slowly absorbed into the surrounding material. This causes the target to appear larger and read out more strongly. So it will be picked up at greater depth with a metal/mineral detector. Once such a target has thoroughly deteriorated as an object, it will stop reading as a metal and start reading as highly mineralized ground. As mentioned in Chapter 1, gold does not oxidize or deteriorate, so this factor does not apply to natural gold targets.

The size of a search coil on a metal/mineral detector is also a factor in how deeply that the detector will pick out objects. Larger sized coils usually are able to pick up objects at greater depth than smaller sized coils are able to, but they do not have as much sensitivity in being able to detect smaller sized objects. Smaller sized search coils haver greater sensitivity to small objects, yet do not have the depth probing capability that the large coils do. Medium sized coils, from 5 to 8 inches in diameter, usually combine the features of having both a reasonable amount of sensitivity for the smaller sized objects, and acceptable depth scanning ability. Many nugget hunters prefer to have the smaller sized search coils because they have the greatest small object sensitivity (gold nuggets) and because the smaller sized coils can get into tighter spots, like in and around tree roots and inside of exposed crevices, where nuggets are most likely to be found with a metal/mineral detector.

Almost all detectors are made so that various sized coils can be attached — depending on what they are to be used for. When testing a detector, don't make the mistake of assuming that if the device sounds out well on a gold sample when using a coil of one size, that it will also sound out well when using a coil of a different size. Your best bet is to test the detector with the various sized coils to see which size works best for your own needs.

Probably one of the most important factors which determines how deep that a metal/mineral detector will pick up a gold object is how much mineralization (interference) that is present in the ground which is being scanned. More minerals = less depth. This is especially true of the BFO type detectors. Because black sands are usually in evidence in the same streambeds where gold deposits are located, the BFO detectors are not usually used to directly detect gold in streambeds of any depth, but are more often used to scan places where there is a very shallow amount of streambed material present or none at all.

Probably the BFO is most often used amongst experienced prospectors for the purpose of locating black sand concentrations where gold deposits are most likely to be. Then the reading areas are sampled to see if gold is present. The BFO does this part of the job very well.

VERY LOW FREQUENCY — TRANSMITTER RECEIVERS

The VLF type detector is a more recent development in the field of electronic prospecting. These are designed with circuitry that will cancel out the effects that highly mineralized ground has on a BFO type detector. VLF detectors have the ability to look through or past highly mineralized ground and pick up metal objects (gold) that would not read out on the other type of metal/mineral detector.

The VLF, being able to cancel out the interference caused by mineralized ground is more suited for the finding of gold deposits and nuggets directly. However, it still remains true that nuggets will have to be a size large enough, or deposits will have to be tightly concentrated to be picked up on a VLF, just like with the BFO type detector. In fact, there are some VLF detectors which have difficulty in sounding out on gold samples at all, so this type of detector must be just as thoroughly tested, before buying.

The VLF type detector, being a mineralization cancelling device, sometimes does not have the ability to detect the heavy black sand concentrations as the BFO detector is able to. So usually the VLF is best suited in scanning directly for gold, whereas the BFO is best suited in helping the prospector to locate gold deposits in an indirect sort of way — by finding the highly mineralized ground in a gold bearing area.

Because of the discrimination adjustment on the VLF, sometimes a highly mineralized target will read out as a metal object — giving a false reading. All VLF detectors come with a set of manufacturers instructions which tell how to determine when this is happening, and show how to tell if the reading object is truly metalic or not.

The manufacturers instructions for the metal/mineral detector should be thoroughly studied, because you will be able to operate the detector only as well as you understand it, and you should practice with it. Whether you own a BFO or a VLF type detector, it takes lots of practice to become proficient with one in prospecting out gold deposits. Once you get out into the field and start working at it — if you haven't already, you'll see what I mean.

ELECTRONIC PROSPECTING DRILLS

The following is a set of drills which have been put together to give the new (or old) owner of a metal/mineral detector some practice with his tool and to allow him or her to get a good grasp of what it's gold finding capabilities are.

DRILL no.1: Take a file to a piece of iron or steel (like a nail), and allow the pieces of metal to fall into a container. Pour some filings onto a piece of paper and pour some glue over the filings to hold them intact. Pour more filings on top of the glue and then pour on more glue. Continue this until the conglomerate is giving off a strong mineral reading on your detector. Make three different such sheets of mineralization, one giving off a very mild mineral reading, one causing a medium sized signal, and one which gives off a strong signel.

If you are already an experienced gold miner and have some black sand concentrates laying around somewhere, use a magnet to collect some magnetic black sand and use these instead of iron filings, as shown above.

These different mineralized conglomerates will give you a good index of how your detector will react to different degrees of mineralized ground.

DRILL no.2: Acquire at least a half ounce of placer gold, preferably more, with a variety of fine, flake and nuggets so that a wide range of testing can be done.

Carefully place the gold in a pile on a clean sheet of paper in a location where there is no other metalic object reading on your detector. Scan the gold with your detector from varying distances to get an idea of your distance capabilities on a large compacted gold deposit.

Now spread the gold out over a slightly wider space on the paper and scan again to check distance. Continue to spread the gold out wider and wider until it no longer reads on your detector. This drill will give you a good idea of what sized accumulations of gold will read at what distances.

Pay particular attention to the type of sound readings that you get when scanning over gold targets. These drills should be done with headphones if they will be used out in the field — which is recommended. After awhile, you'll start to be able to tell the difference between gold and some other metalic readouts by the difference in the tone of the read. Usually stronger reading metals will give a sharper and louder change in tone, whereas gold tends to cause a softer and more indistinct read — especially when located in smaller amounts or at a distance. Do the drill and see for yourself, as it could be different on your metal/mineral detector.

Do this same drill while using various sized gold nuggets, if available. Check out the different readings caused by the assorted nuggets and accumulations from various distances.

After this drill, you will have a good idea of your detector's gold finding abilities and know the proper sound that your detector makes when it is reading out on a natural gold target.

DRILL no.3: Using the flake gold and nuggets in different accumulations, as shown in drill no. 2, place the different sheets of mineralization over top of the gold and note the responses on your metal/mineral detector. If you have a VLF, practice cancelling out the mineralized sheets, and test to see what sized accumulations of gold can be picked up while doing so. Try more and more mineralization, combining the sheets together if necessary to see how much mineralization that the VLF will look through and still have sensitivity to gold targets.

If you are doing these drills with a BFO type detector, try combining different amounts of mineralization with the various sized accumulations of gold, and determine for yourself on your own detector just how much mineralization that it takes to block out the different sized accumulations of natural gold.

I am certainly aware that sometimes it is difficult to come by a collection of gold flakes and nuggets if you don't already have a collection of your own. However, the time spent in locating one, or in talking a friend into lending you his collection — or in talking him into doing these drills with you, will be worth at least 20 times as much time spent out in the field with your detector. These drills will not teach you how to prospect out gold deposits — only practice and experience out in the field will do that. However, these drills thoroughly done, will quickly familiarize you with your detector and give you certainty on the use of it, and also give you the basics that you will need to learn to prospect with a detector. And these basics could take hundreds of hours to learn otherwise.

HELPFUL TIPS ON TUNING

Each model of detector has it's own set of operating and tuning instructions which you should follow, but here are a few pointers which have proven successful in the prospecting field which you should take note of.

Some manufacturers recommend that their volume changing reading type detectors be tuned to just below the hearing range. The purpose of this is so that the slightest reading will make a sound — which can be easily distinguished from the silence. For prospecting purposes, it works better if you tune these type of detectors so that the audio signal is always within hearing range. This will run down the batteries just a bit faster, but it's much better to be able to hear the signal at all times, because when looking for natural gold targets, the slightest change can mean a lot. Also the detector's audio signal will sometimes drift off to a lower volume range due to temperature changes or loss of battery voltage, and if the audio signal is tuned into the non-hearing zone and drifts into an even lower range, you might be scanning for several minutes without having the detector tuned properly and not even know of it. In the case of electronic prospecting, this can be an "unknown about" expensive lesson to learn.

The main cause for a detector's tuning to drift is loss of battery voltage, and when this occurs it's time to replace the batteries with a new set in order to get the best performance out of your detector — which is needed when hunting directly for gold.

It's always a good idea to bring along an extra set of batteries into the field when prospecting, because when they quit, you are finished until new batteries are installed.

When you are operating a metal detector, it's good practice to remove all rings, bracelets, watches and other jewelry from your hands and arms, because they can give a false read on the detector. This is especially true when you are testing a detector before buying, or when you are tuning your detector to sound out properly on a special metal target while passing it under the search coil with your hand.

One other tip on tuning is that you should remember, when using a VLF ground cancelling type metal/mineral detector, to periodically re-tune the detector as new areas are being scanned. A change in location usually changes the amount of mineralization in the ground. This is especially true when you are scanning from streambed to bedrock areas.

Also, when the angle of the search coil on the shaft is changed to fit a new set of conditions, the detector must always be re-tuned to correspond with the new relationship between the coil and the metal shaft.

OTHER IMPORTANT FACTORS TO CONSIDER WHEN BUYING . . .

If you are looking over a metal/mineral detector that you are interested in buying, test it to make sure that it's tuning does not drift on it's own. This test can be done by placing a good set of batteries into the device, turning it on, allowing it to warm up for a minute, tuning it in, and by allowing it to sit and run for 5 to 10 minutes. If the audio tone drifts during this time, you might want to look around for a similar detector that has greater stability.

Another thing, is to make sure that the batteries which are being used by the metal/mineral detector are readily available at the normal stores out in the field — not the kind that need to be special ordered.

If you are going to use your detector for prospecting purposes, you should acquire one that has a shielded, waterproof search coil. Shielded coils are built with a thin layer of air between the inner and outer plates — which keeps the outside surface rubbing noises from reading out on the detector. An unshielded coil, being used under moving water — as in a stream, will make so much interfering noise that the operator will have great difficulty in distinguishing the actual read outs which are given off by metalic objects.

The same thing holds true for waterproof search coils. "Gold nuggets" usually always means streamed material — which often indicates the presence of water. While you can use a plastic bag to protect a non-waterproof coil, it can be punctured easily while moving it around. If that occurs, part of your investment can be ruined and you'll be out of business until you replace it. Most metal/mineral detectors come with shielded, waterproof coils. It's only mentioned so that you are aware of what is best for the job so that you can make sure that you buy what you need.

CAUTION: Wetness and dampness are not good for the control box of any type of electronic detector. Be careful to avoid getting yours wet when working around water. If you intend to use a detector out in the field on a damp or rainy day, you can cover the control box with a clear, loose fitting plastic bag and secure it to the shaft of the detector. The bag should be loose enough so you can work the various control knobs without having to untie the bag and take it off in order to set-up or re-tune the detector.

PROSPECTING FOR PLACER DEPOSITS

When you are hunting around for gold nuggets and concentrated accumulations of placer gold with the use of a metal/mineral detector, it is always a good idea to bring along a sample of placer gold, so you can tune your detector to read out well on similar gold targets, and so you can be directly familiar with what a reading gold target sounds like.

All the rules of placer geology apply to nugget hunting, and your knowledge of such should be put to use in order to pinpoint where the larger sized deposits and gold nuggets are most likely to be found.

Particular attention should be paid to locations which have little or no streamed so the search coil can scan as closely to the bedrock as possible. Also, exposed tree roots along the edges of the present streams or rivers have proven successful many times in the past — especially on the smaller tributaries in the higher elevations of known gold country.

When dealing with streambeds, you generally do not find too many other reading metalic objects besides gold, unless the spot in which you are scanning is near an inhabited location — like a park or an old dump, etc. So it is reasonably safe to check out any target that gives off a metalic reading in a streambed. Once you have been scanning a particular area for awhile, you'll start to get the idea of how much "trash" (metalic objects of no value) is in the vicinity. Once you get good, you'll pretty well be able to distinguish the difference between most of the trash and those reads caused possibly by gold. Pay particular attention to the very faint readings, as is often the case with placer gold targets.

When you do have a reading target, it's exact position in the ground should be pin pointed by scanning over it in fore and aft and left to right motions, and by noting when the detector sounds out while doing so. Often a steel or iron object can be distinguished by noting the size and shape of the object while scanning in this manner, because sometimes these objects are of a large and lengthy size.

Once you have pin pointed the exact position of a reading target, carefully dig up that portion of ground, using a shovel, and place the material in your gold pan. Here's where a large sized plastic gold pan comes in real handy. Be careful not to cause any more disturbance or vibration of the streambed than is necessary while you are attempting to dig up a target. It's possible to miss the target on the first try and cause it to vibrate further down into the streambed because of it's superior weight and lose it, and not be able to locate it again with the detector.

Once you have dug up that section of material where the target was reading, place it in your plastic gold pan and scan it with your detector. If the contents of the pan do not make your detector sound out, scan the original target area over again. If you get a read in the original location, pour the contents of the pan neatly into a pile out of your way, pin point the reading target all over again, and make another try at getting the target into your gold pan. Continue this until you finally have the reading target in your pan. If you can't see the target, pan off the contents until the target is visible.

There is a good reason why you don't ever throw away any material from the target hole until after you know for certain exactly what the reading target is. If you are looking for placer gold deposits and it happens that your detector is sounding out on a gold nugget, the chances of additional gold being present in paying quantities within the material which has been dug out of the hole are pretty good — even if it makes no read out on your detector. Remember; it usually takes large sized pieces or heavy concentrations of gold to make a metal/mineral detector sound out, and so there could possibly be hundreds of dollars worth of gold in a single shovel full of material, and yet it might not be tightly concentrated enough to cause your detector to sound out. So wait until you have seen the reading target before you start throwing any material away.

If you dig for a target and then cannot get any further read on the detector from either the pan or in the original target area, the thing to do is quickly pan off the pan's contents. There is always a possibility of a concentrated gold deposit which is no longer concentrated enough to read out on your detector. In this case, you are most likely to have some of the gold deposit in your gold pan — which will be discovered when you pan off the contents.

Another procedure which is popular amongst some electronic prospectors, with a BFO detector on the mineral setting, is in scanning the lower stratas of dry streambed (bench deposits) which have been exposed by erosion, and attempting to locate the heavy concentrations of black sand along the bedrock. Once found, these deposits can be dug up and panned for gold. Then with the detector on metal setting, the bedrock area is scanned again with the intention of locating any gold that might be trapped in the bedrock cracks and crevices — which are no longer being blocked from the detector's view by the black sand interference.

PROSPECTING OLD MINING TAILINGS

It is usually possible to find piles and piles of old mining tailings extensively throughout most proven gold bearing country.

Many of the larger sized earlier gold mining operations, the ones that were set up to move large volumes of material, concentrated fully on recovering only the fine and medium sized values from the material that was processed. This meant that the larger sized material needed to be classified out so that the smaller sized material could be run over controlled slow moving recovery systems. Classification was usually done either by the use of mechanically vibrating classification screens, or with the use of a "trommel." A trommel is a large circular screening device which rotates and tumbles material through, and allows the smaller classification of materials to pass through the outer screen and into a channel which directs them to the recovery system, while the larger sized materials are passed down the inside of the trommel to be discarded out of it as waste.

In many of the larger sized operations, there was no means set up to recover any of the larger sized pieces of gold which were screened out along with the other large materials, and so the larger sized nuggets were often discarded along with the waste material as tailings.

Anywhere that you see very large tailings piles — especially near the present waterways, they are evidence of a large volume type of operation where it's possible that the larger nuggets were discarded with the waste and are likely to still be there. The result is that many of these large tailings piles still have large goodies inside of them — which sing out very nicely on the proper metal/mineral detectors. One way to distinguish the right kind of tailings pile to be looking through is that there should be a pretty wide range of material size in the tailings pile. Tailings piles which consist only of the larger sized rocks were most likely stacked there by hand during a smaller sized surface type operation.

Scanning tailings piles with the use of a metal/mineral detector has proven to be highly remunerative at times in the past, and should not be overlooked as a possibility for finding nice specimen sized gold nuggets. The VLF ground cancelling type detectors are best suited for this because the tailings usually also contain a large quantity of mineral content, which is likely to cause interference on a BFO type detector.

PROSPECTING OLD MINING SHAFTS

The first thing to mention about prospecting around in old mine shafts is that they are dangerous! There are different things that can go wrong when snooping around in such places, the main danger being that of a potential cave-in. The shoring in some of these old shafts have often become rotten and faulty over the years and it's always best to not lean up against or to bump any of the old wooden structures that are situated in any old mine shaft. Loud, sharp noises have also been known to "bring the roof down" in some old mines.

Shafts which extend down into the earth on a declining angle are particularly dangerous, because should the ladders or suspension systems be faulty and collapse while you are down inside, you may not have any way to get out again. It is for this reason that it is always a good idea to bring along a caving rope — and to use it, when exploring declining type old mine shafts. Caving rope is different than mountaineering type rope in that it is made not to stretch nearly as much.

It is noted that even the most experienced cave explorers shy away from entering declining type mine shafts because of the dangers that are involved.

Another potential danger involved with exploring old mine shafts is encountering poisonous or explosive gasses. Sometimes entire mines were shut down because of such gasses — even when they were good producing mines. These however, were usually caved in and closed off to prevent unsuspecting adventurists — like you and me, from entering at a latter date and getting into trouble.

Before you enter any old mine and start sorting through it's low grade ore piles or pecking away samples off the walls of the mine, it's always a good idea to make sure that nobody else presently owns the mine, and if somebody does, to get their permission first. There is probably nothing more dangerous in a mine shaft — cave ins and poisonous gases included, as some old cankankerous miner who catches you — uninvited, in his mine and thinks that you are stealing his gold!

There is probably more danger in prospecting old shafts than in any other gold prospecting activity.

After all that, just in case I have not succeeded in scaring you out of the idea of entering old mine shafts and such in your prospecting adventures, here are a few pointers on how and where you might find some rich ore deposits or rich ore specimens with the use of your metal/mineral detector.

But first, let me recommend that if you do go into such places, that you bring along a buddy and leave another one at the surface with explicit instructions not to enter the shaft under any circumstances, but to go get help in the event that you should get into trouble within. It's also a good idea to let a few others know where you are going, just in case your outside man doesn't follow orders and you all become trapped in some way.

There are two main sources of possible gold/silver in an old mine.

1) Highgrade ore specimens that may have been placed in the low grade ore piles and left as waste material, or . . .

2) High grade ore which has yet to be mined.

With exception of the largest production hardrock mines, there is always a certain amount of rock (ore) that has been blasted away from the wall of the tunnel that is not milled and processed — because it is of such low grade value that it is not worth the expense to do so. Sometimes the vein that was being followed into the mountainside was not as wide as the tunnel needed to be in order to progress into the mountain. Therefore that rock which was not part of the vein itself, or the contact zone, that looked to be of lower grade value was also discarded into the waste ore piles.

Crushing and milling ore is and always has been a timely and expensive process. For this reason, a good many times only processed what appeared to be the highest grade ore that was blasted away from the tunnel. The rest was usually piled in the shafts out of productions way.

In the smaller sized operations — the kind where the ore was crushed and milled by hand and then processed with a gold pan to recover the values, only the highest of high grade ores could be processed at a profit. The rest was usually laid aside out of the way.

The sorting of a higher-grade ore from lower-grade ore has always been a matter of judgement on the part of the individual who was doing that part of the job and until the more recent breakthroughs in electronic detecting equipment, the sorting needed to be done by eye, because there simply was no other way.

The interior of mine tunnels was most often poorly lit during earlier days by the use of miners candles, and the air inside the shaft was often extremely foul after the result of the powder explosions that were used to blast away the ore from the interior of the mountain. As a result, it is easy to invision that a great deal of higher-grade ore was probably discarded as waste material in many mines.

How rich that the ore was in a mine will have a lot of bearing on whether or not a present day prospector will find high-grade ore in the waste piles of that mine. The size of a mine does not necessarily have anything to do with how high-grade that it's ore was — although it will have a large bearing on how much waste ore will be available to test. County reports can be looked over to locate the numerous old mines within an area. Many of these reports also have data as to the grade of ore that was being extracted from some of the mines. (See figure 9-2 for example.)

When you are testing ore samples in a mine with a metal/mineral detector and you don't come up with any specimens, try a few different piles. If you still don't come up with any other specimens, it was probably not a high-grade mine. Try another.

Keep in mind that the floor of a mine shaft is likely to have a lot of iron objects lying on it that can cause your detector to read out falsely.

One of the fastest and most effective ways of thoroughly checking out samples with the use of a detector is to lay the detector down on the ground or on a make shift bench with the search coil pointing upward so that individual ore samples can be passed by the most sensitive portion of the coil. The 3 inch diameter search coils are probably best suited for this kind of work because of the increased amount of sensitivity and because there is no great need of increased depth sounding.

The most sensitive portion of the search coil is usually located near the center of the bottom edge. It can be easily pinpointed by passing a coin back and forth across the coil while the detector is in tune, and by finding where the coin causes the loudest and sharpest reading. The most sensitive area should be marked brightly with a magic marker so that it will be easier for you to move ore samples directly past it. In this way, the most accurate testing is possible.

It is a good idea to bring along a bucket, or a napsack so that you will have something in which to carry out your specimens as you find them.

Both the BFO and the VLF ground cancelling type metal/mineral detectors can be used to locate high-grade ore specimens successfully.

Being that the VLF type detectors phase out any mineralization and will pick up gold/silver when present in quantity, using this type of detector means that you will only be going after the very rich ore specimens. Just as in placer nugget hunting, larger sized and more compacted gold deposits are necessary in order to get a sample to read out on the detector. Yet, when dealing with hardrock samples, you are dealing with compacted material and it is not too uncommon to find rich ore specimens and some success is being made out in the field in this manner.

For the individual who is more interested in finding a wider range of high-grade ore specimens — which are rich enough to be worth milling on a small scale for the gold and silver values, perhaps the BFO is the better type of metal/mineral detector to be used for the job. The reason for this is that the BFO does exceptionally well at picking up highly mineralized ore, and when you are dealing with hardrock veins, high mineralization is a good index of gold being present, especially when you are working with the ore that was blasted out of a previously successful gold mine.   Ore which contains large amounts of locked in values or lots of fine gold that is thoroughly dispersed throughout the ore, is not likely to read out as a metalic on any kind of conventional metal/mineral detector, although the high degree of mineralization that usually goes along with such ore probably will sound out on a BFO detector as a mineral. So the BFO type detector is handy in finding rich ores which might otherwise be un-detectable.

By placing the BFO detector on it's mineral setting and keeping the specimens that cause it to sound out, a person can accummulate a lot of good paying ore. With the use of a BFO as such, entire ore piles can be scanned first in an effort to find one that has a great deal of mineralization present.

There are portable rock crushers and mills and processing plants which are available on the market — as covered in chapter 9, and perhaps by combining these with the use of a good BFO type detector to pick out the highly mineralized discarded ore, a small operation could be quite profitable without having to foot the costs of developing a lode mine.

LOCATING RICH ORE DEPOSITS

When prospecting around inside an old mine with a metal/mine detector, don't discount the idea of scanning the walls of the various shafts for the purpose of locating the rich ore deposits that might have been overlooked by those who originally developed the mine. With today's market value of gold and advanced milling techniques, a small scale mining operation can be run profitably in ore that is paying about ½ ounce to the ton in gold values — or even less, depending on the nature of the ore, as covered in the last chapter. Abandoned mines which will pay this well and even better are scattered all over the west by the thousands. If a person was really interested in locating a lode mine that he could work at a profit, one way would be with the use of a BFO type detector to prospect the various abandoned mines within the area of his or her interest. In using the BFO to scan the walls of such mines, highly mineralized ore deposits can be located, samples can be taken for assay purposes, and a person can rather effectively find the mines having the richer paying ore deposits. When prospecting like this, it's a good idea to bring a can of spray paint, a pen and paper, and some separate bags, so that the samples can be accurately marked as to where they came from, along with their respective deposits being marked with the spray paint.

If you are not interested in starting up a lode mine, but are just kicking around looking for a bonus, again, the VLF type detector is good for looking through mineralization and in detecting the richest type of deposits. If however, you do locate a reading metal inside the wall of a mine shaft with a VLF detector, and you have determined that it is not some falsely reading mineralization, then it's well worth your while to investigate further, because the chances are pretty good that you have located some bonanza paying type ore.

CHAPTER XI

GOLD MINING PROCEDURE

One of the first things to determine when getting started in a gold mining operation of any size is the general area in which you plan to operate. As mentioned in an earlier chapter, time and study that is spent in locating an area which is likely to pay in many many gold deposits, is time and study that will pay off very well in the end. If you intend to succeed in finding lots of good paying deposits, it's not enough to just go anywhere, because in that way should you find a deposit it will be strictly on the basis of chance or luck. It's been done this way before — but not consistently. It's OK to find a deposit of gold once in a while, but it's much better to be able to get into them one after the next. How well that you do in picking out your general operating area, will greatly determine how well that you will be able to stay into paying quantities of gold, so it's well to put a little extra effort into finding a good area in which to do your mining.

SAMPLING — IT'S PURPOSE

Pay attention to this, because I could never say it strong or loud enough, and I could never say it too many times. THE KEY TO SUCCESS IN GOLD MINING — ON ANY SIZED SCALE, IS IN DOING LOTS AND LOTS OF SAMPLING. (Some call it sniping.) The whole idea behind sampling is to keep moving around and testing out different spots until you find one that you can work effectively with the equipment which is at your disposal, where the gold silver and platinum values are enough to make the effort of working the ground worth your while.

Generally speaking, as mentioned earlier, placer deposits run in streaks (or "stringers"). These streaks are found in certain common locations — as outlined in earlier chapters of this manual. The idea behind sampling, is to locate a paystreak or some other kind of gold deposits BEFORE you start into any serious production mining activity.

There is another way to go about it. That is to start mining in any likely spot and *hope* that you will run into a deposit sooner or later. I have seen this procedure used over and over again by beginners — myself included, and have yet to see it pay off with any kind of consistency at all. I'm not too far off when I say that at least 99% — or more, of the long term successful mining operations of any size today, are using the sampling method of finding paying quantities of gold first, before a production operation is started. I, myself, have never seen ANYONE succeed for an extended period of time who did not know how to sample well, and who was not willing to sample energetically in an effort to locate gold in paying quantities.

When sampling, if you test a specific location and don't find an acceptable quantity of gold in the material, move to another likely spot and try there. This procedure is simply continued until you find an acceptable paying deposit.

You usually do not recover a lot of gold when sampling. You are not trying to. You can gauge how well a production operation is doing by how much gold is being recovered. A sampling activity is different. Probably the only way that a sampling operation can be gauged is by looking at how much ground has been covered by effective sampling. It's easy to lose a bit of morale when you are sampling, because you are not seeing the gold adding up in your poke (collection of gold). This is especially true when you have just finished cleaning out a good paying streak, and you are now back into sampling again. However, you can't let it get you down that you are not recovering lots of gold while sampling. If you are not covering lots of areas with effective testing, you can let that get you down a bit; and some evaluation will be in order to find out what you are doing wrong. If you test out an area effectively, and there is not enough gold there to start up a production operation, that's fine — great! Now you know that there isn't enough gold in that spot. That's all you were trying to find out — and you've succeeded. There is no reason in the world to feel bad about it. Often, when you find out where the paying deposits are not located, it will help you a great deal in determining where they are more likely to be. So each sample hole, effectively done, gets you that much closer to a paying deposit. Get the idea?

Once you have been at it awhile, you'll discover for yourself that finding the deposits is a sure thing if you take on sampling in a very serious and systematic manner.

Gold mining is the kind of activity where you are making nothing today (sampling) and are making thousands tomorrow (production). How many sample holes on the average that it will take you to find paying deposits, depends on your ability to sample, and on how good the general gold bearing area is that you are operating within.

Your sampling ability depends upon how serious you are about finding gold, and in doing it right. If you persist, and study like mad, and work at it, you'll get better as you gain experience. My present average is a pay streak every 1¼ holes. That's 4 out of 5. This is true — believe it or not; but I've put myself into a reasonably good area. I've been here long enough to know the area well, I've been at it hot and heavy in this area — full time, for a few years, and I've received instruction from a few of the best prospectors in the business. But I'm not withholding any information from you. As a matter of fact, I'm giving you much more than was ever given to me — so there's no reason why you shouldn't be able to do as well or better than I do.

In a sampling operation, testing can be done with the use of a gold pan, a sluice box, a dredge, a drywashing plant, a hydraulic concentrator, or any combination of these — whichever you have at your disposal to use that will do the most effective job of sampling in the areas that you are interested in.

The gold pan, as mentioned earlier, is the most versatile sampler in existence. However it is limited in it's production ability. If you are way out in the field on a sampling expedition, the gold pan is probably your best tool for the job. The same holds true if you want to move quickly through an area and just do a fast — but not necessarily thorough, job of it.

If you want to test out the dry streambed material alongside of a swift moving creek, stream or river, perhaps a small sluice box can be brought along for the job. It takes a little more effort to carry one in with you and to set it up at each location, but it's not that much more difficult and it will save you lots of time and energy in the long run, because thoroughly sampling an area with a sluice box can be done so much faster than it can be done with a gold pan. Plus, larger sized samples can be taken and so more accurate testing will be possible.

The hydraulic concentrator is an excellent combination sampling/production machine, because it is not too heavy that it cannot be packed into a wide range of areas. Yet, it can be quickly set up to produce or sample — with excellent recovery, in any area in which water is located nearby. Figure 11-1 shows another version of the same hydraulic concentrator that was covered earlier in chapter 5, but this one contains the additional feature of a 2½ inch dredge suction hose system, which can be attached to the concentrator. This rig is excellent for testing out those smaller sized creeks and streams that run through gold bearing areas. The advantage to using this kind of machine to sample out small streams is that it can be used to accomplish many tasks. First of all, the engine/pump unit is totally separate from the sluicing unit, and the sluicing unit doesn't float — but sits on a short stand. So set up is just a matter of laying the engine unit down in a stable level position, setting up the sluicing unit in a similar way, and then starting the engine. This is a lot easier than having to dig a hole to float a dredge of similar size. Also, the dredging unit runs off a nozzle jet type system, so you can work the suction nozzle in and out of the water without worry of losing the prime in your suction hose. This is a big feature because it means that you can work in very shallow streambeds effectively, and that you can pick up and move to other positions without having to keep the nozzle under the water at all times, like you have to when using the power jet type system. If you are a two man team and

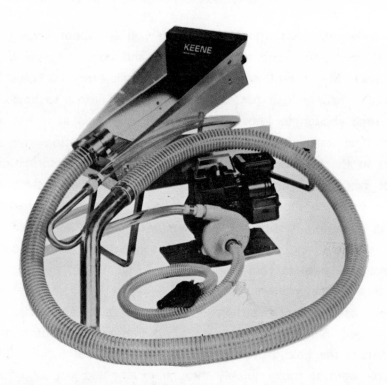

Fig. 11—1. A nifty combination hydraulic concentrator — 2 1/2 inch suction dredging unit, which has a very wide range of operation ability.

want to get more work done, one man can dredge into the concentrator, and one man can shovel into it, both at the same time. Or you can unhook the power hose from the dredge system and attach it to the concentrating unit if you just want to shovel. You can also unhook the pressure hose from either component and use it to wash streambeded material that is lying above the water into the stream (hydraulicing) and then dredge that material out of the stream into the concentrator — if it's faster and more effective to do so. (You will want to look into the local laws before doing this as sometimes it's "not allowed.") Another thing that can be done with this nifty machine is to use it to pump water up into a small hole which you have dug. Once the hole is filled with water, you can dredge in your man made water filled hole with the dredging unit pumping into the concentrator. The concentrator can be positioned so that the water runs off its sluice box a short distance away and flows into the hole. This way you will only have to re-fill your hole with water every once in awhile. This is quite a machine, and you can get quite a lot done with one — either in a sampling or production activity. I know a guy who has one of these and does very well with it. He uses a wheelbarrow to haul it around the countryside — along with his gas and clean-up gear. I know another guy who works small creeks with the use of a gold pan and a small shovel — and is doing an average of 2-3 pennyweight a day and sometimes he hits nice sized pockets. I just can't imagine how well he would do with one of these dredge/concentrating units. I'm trying to get the two together, to find out.

As mentioned earlier, the electrostatic type dry concentrating unit makes a very effective sampling machine in the dry areas where you don't have to haul it very far. Otherwise the lighter weight dry washing plants can be used to sample with good results; or winnowing and dry panning can be done if necessary, and can be made to work.

Electronic detectors are usually not used by themselves as samplers, but usually in conjunction with other sampling gear. Nugget hunting and sampling are actually two separate activities. Sampling is simply testing out different areas to see how much gold is present in the material there, with the intention of finding acceptable paying deposits to be worked on a production scale. Nugget hunting is an activity of strictly going after the larger pieces or accumulations of gold. The VLF type detector is most often used as a nugget hunting device, whereas the BFO type detector is most commonly used in sampling activity, to help the prospector to determine what material to test out for it's gold values. An example of the use of a BFO in a sampling activity would be as follows: search out the general area which you have chosen for a likely spot where some rough type of bedrock is exposed. Tune the detector in on the mineral setting and scan the area until the highest reading mineralized zone is found. Get some bottom strata samples from that area — just above bedrock if possible. If there's not enough gold in that spot, continue to scan and sample the immediate area for additional highly mineralized zones until the gold deposit is located or until you have determined that an acceptable deposit is not present. This is probably the best use of a metal/mineral detector for placer prospecting purposes. Some miners perfer the use of them and some don't.

When engaging in a sampling activity, it is always best, if possible, to test the same type of ground that you intend to work on a production scale, should you find a pay streak. For example, if you are planning to dredge, then the most effective sampling would be beneath the water's surface. Some results can be obtained by sampling the shoreline by surface methods in an effort to locate new dredging ground — but it is never a sure thing that because you are finding gold up on the banks, that you will also find a good deposit in the stream when you bring on your gold dredge. The only sure way to find out if a body of water will have an acceptable paying gold deposit is to test that body of water. Mini dredges work well as samplers where the material is relatively shallow — and they are relatively light, and easy to carry around.

CREVICING

One other popular means of sampling underwater locations is with the use of a mask, snorkle and screwdriver. The method is called "crevicing" or "fanning," and is usually done in the streams and creeks that are located in the high country of gold bearing areas, where the water moves too fast during the winter months to allow any streambed to form in many areas. This leaves the various bedrock crevices and other irregularities open to observation during the slow water periods of the year.

By floating down these streams and carefully looking over the gold traps in the bedrock, a person can locate gold nuggets, flakes, and sometimes entire pockets of coarse type gold. Often the individual pieces are found wedged into the various bedrock traps and need to be wedged out with a strong screwdriver.

This activity is best done during the late summer months, while the water is running at it's lowest and slowest and warmest — which allows you to look over more of the streambed.

Sometimes it is necessary to sweep off small deposits of sand or light gravel, which tends to collect in some of the bedrock irregularities once the water has slowed down. This can be done by waving your hand back and forth over the light deposit to "fan" the material aside.

One thing about these higher tributary channels is that the water usually rushes through them in a torrent during the winter storms and spring run-offs, sometimes causing a large amount of new re-deposited gold to be washed over the continuously exposed traps in the bedrock. If you find a good spot, it's probably worthwhile to keep quiet about it and check it out over and over again on a yearly basis.

MOSSING

The moss which is located on the edges of gold bearing streams rivers and creeks has a tremendous gold trapping ability. Sometimes gold can even be recovered out of the moss that is up on the stream banks, well away from the water. Often, paying quantities of gold can be recovered by an activity which is being directed solely at the moss from the river banks.

One of the better methods of "mossing" is by filling up a large bucket or wash tub with the moss taken from the banks of a gold bearing stream. The moss is then thoroughly broken up and pulled apart inside the bucket — which is filled with water. Once this is done, the contents of the tub are panned off and the gold is recovered out of the resulting concentrates. This activity, done consistently over the period of a day, can bring in a surprising amount of gold in some areas.

Sampling of the moss should be done ahead of time to see which areas carry the greatest amount of values.

Care should be taken when you are removing the moss from it's original bedrock location to avoid shaking it unnecessarily, because quick movements tend to shake gold loose from the moss, especially while underwater.

Some prospectors go so far as to save the moss pieces after it is torn apart in the tub. Then take it back to camp, dry it out, burn it inside a container, and pan off the ashes. You would be surprised at how much additional gold that can be recovered by doing this to the moss saved from a consistent type of mossing operation.

A FEW MORE TIPS ABOUT PROCEDURE

One thing to keep in mind about the general area that you have chosen to mine, is that your sampling activities may show either where the gold deposits are located, or the lack of them in that general area. If sampling has shown you that the area does not have very many deposits, it's well to have in mind a second choice of general location in which to go.

How well that an area has to pay in order for you to work for it's gold content largely depends on the size of your production operation — meaning how much volume of streambed material that your equipment can process effectively. For example, a hydraulic concentrator is able to process a great deal more volume of material than a gold pan can. So a gold panning production operation will need to have richer paying ground to process if a profit is to be made. When sampling, a person should have a good idea of the capabilities of his production equipment. This way he can compare the gold content in the ground that he tests to the amount of material which he feels that he can comfortably and consistently process on a production scale, and figure out whether or not the ground that he samples should be mined or not.

The kind of gold that a prospector finds in a location can also designate which type of equipment that would be best used for recovering the gold. Paying quantities of fine gold, for example, would be recovered in the best way with the use of a wet type of slow moving recovery system in which the materials are thoroughly classified down to size before being processed. A pay streak containing medium and coarse sized values can be effectively worked by dry concentrating equipment when set up properly, if water is not available.

Sometimes you can run into old bench deposits in which the bottom stratum of streambed is paying well, but is so compacted that it must be thoroughly broken up before being run through any recovery system. This is common in some of the ancient channel beds and also in some of the more recently formed benches — usually the ones that have had a lot of material resting on top of them. When this type of gravel is encountered, care should be taken to thoroughly break up the material before running it into your processing plant. Otherwise the gold is likely to be washed right through the recovery system along with the compacted material which it is attached to. Sometimes, in the case of compacted material, when an operation wants to process volume amounts, it is necessary to employ the use of rock crushing equipment — as covered in chapter 9, in order to break up the material enough to release the gold so that it can be recovered.

Clay type material must also be thoroughly broken up and dissolved before being run through a recovery system. Otherwise, not only is it likely to be washed through your recovery system along with the gold that is inside of the clay, but the clay is also likely to grab onto further pieces of gold which are already trapped in your recovery system, and take them along too, as it is washed through.

Directly beside or below where a tributary enters a larger sized waterway is usually not a good location in which to find a good sized placer deposit — simply because of the increased amount of force which flows at that point.

If a tributary is showing a good amount of coarse type gold, start sampling in an upstream direction until you can no longer find traces of that kind of deposit. Then drop back and find where the gold has entered the tributary. It's likely that if the gold enters in the immediate area, that high-grade type float will be present in or on the stream bank. If so and you find it, your search will probably then take you up the mountainside towards the lode itself.

While kicking around in the hills and on the river banks during your placering activities, it's always well to keep your eyes open for high-grade quartz float. Since you are moving about in gold country, and are in the business anyway, well who knows — you just might get lucky.

Once you have found a pay streak, you can get down to the business of mining it out thoroughly. While mining the material, it's always best to stack the larger sized rocks and boulders neatly out of the way — preferably on top of already worked ground, so that they will not have to be moved by you again. A pick can be used to break open the cracks, crevices and other bedrock irregularities in order to get all of the gold out of them. A whisk broom and wire brush can be a big help to you in thoroughly cleaning up the bedrock. The larger sized rocks that are taken from the paying strata of streambed materials, which will not be run through the recovery system, should be thoroughly cleaned of gold bearing material before they are stacked on the tailings pile. In this way, an operation will get the most return out of the amount of effort being expended.

When producing with just a gold pan, it's probably best to direct your activities towards places where there is little or no overburden sitting on top of the pay layer. Otherwise you will find yourself shoveling lots of material that you will not be processing. Places where some erosion has cut it's path through an old bench, leaving the lowest strata exposed, are excellent locations for a panning type operation, as are places where exposed bedrock irregularities are present — with streambed materials inside.

A streambed, having material a total of 3 feet deep — with the lower stratum paying well, is probably within the range of a pick and shovel sluicing or hydraulic concentrating type operation. Anything much larger than that is starting to get outside the range of a hand operated mining venture — that is unless the upper stratums are paying, or the lower stratum is extremely rich. The reason for this is that all of the upper material will be needed to be removed in order to get at the lower stratum of the streambed materials. And when you are talking about 3 or 4 feet of material — or more, you are talking about moving a lot of material by hand. Anything more than that is getting into the range of earth moving equipment type operations. That is — unless you are planning to drift mine.

DRIFT MINING

Many of the old benches contain an extremely rich lower stratum of streambed material; and yet, have a great deal of overburden lying on top, which places this kind of streambed out of bounds for the small mining operations, because there is simply too much material to be moved by hand when using the conventional methods.

There is another way to mine these old streambeds, which was extensively used in the earlier mining days. It consists of tunneling along at the bottom of the steambed and processing the lower stratum of material which is removed as the tunnel is moved forward.

There are different ways to go about a drift mining operation, with the most common method being to start off with a tunnel that extends at a right angle to the direction which the old streambed once flowed. The tunnel is extended across the width of the streambed along the bedrock, with the lower stratum of materials being tested as progress is made. This first tunnel is called a "cross cut." The cross cut is continued until the pay streak is discovered, and it's outside boundaries are determined. The entire width of the pay streak is then mined by moving the tunnel forward and backwards along the bottom stratum of material. This is called "drifting."

Shoreing was most commonly always done in this type of mining — meaning that wood beams are cut, shaped and installed inside the tunnel to prevent the roof from caving in. Needless to say, this kind of operation can also be rather dangerous to the miners who work in the drift or cross cut — where even a small amount of streambed material can drop from the ceiling and give you a good knock on the head. Hard hats are a must! (And life insurance.)

The cutting of the tunnels in drift mining is not normally done by explosives, because blasting tends to weaken the streambed structure and increase the chances of a cave-in. Most often, it was the pick and shovel method of digging that was used by the early timers to move their tunnels along.

The means of starting a cross cut into the lower stratum can be done in several different ways, depending on the situation of the streambed. Often it was necessary to sink a vertical shaft down through the streambed to bedrock, where the cross cut could be started, as shown in figure 11-2. In this case it is necessary to hoist all of

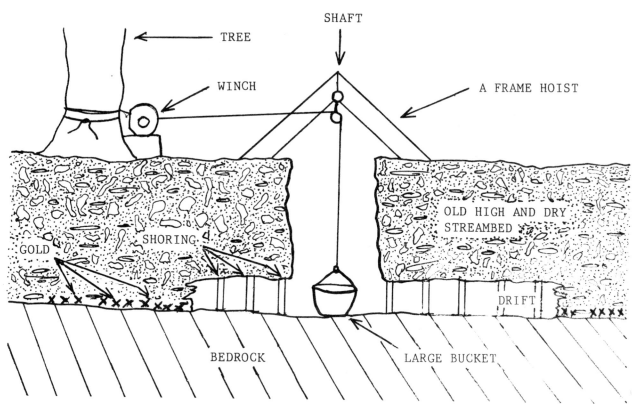

Fig. 11–2 Vertical shaft type of drift operation.

the tunnel material up through the shaft in order to get it out of the drift and the cross cut. The material is then processed at the surface. The oldtimers used a hand operated windlass to hoist the material up to the surface of the streambed, whereas todays miner has the use of electric or gasoline powered winches to do the job and speed up the process.

In another situation, where the side of an old bench is exposed, the cross cut can be made directly into the side of the streambed, as shown in figure 11-3. In this case, material from the lower stratum can be carted directly out of the drift to be processed, and so less work is required than in the situation where it's necessary to hoist the material up to the surface by way of a vertical shaft.

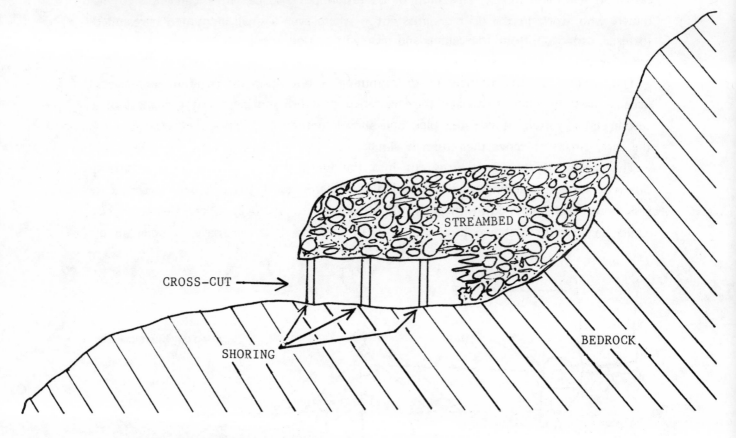

Fig. 11—3. Drift mining with a cross-cut started from the side of a bench.

Sometimes the early timers preferred to blast a cross cut into the hardrock just below the lowest stratum of streambed material. They would test the bottom of the bench materials which were located at the ceiling of the hardrock tunnel as it was moved forward. In this way, blasting could be used to make the original cross cut in an effort to find out if a pay streak was present. (See figure 11-4 on next page).

Once a pay streak was located in this manner, and it's boundaries were determined, the drift could be started from the lower tunnel. The advantage to a cross cut of this nature was that the pay dirt could be shoveled down into the lower cross cut — where a cart would be waiting. This was far easier than in shoveling the material up into a cart — which is more difficult when inside of the tight fitting space of a drift mine. It also provided a place for water to drain out of the drift if it was present.

When water was encountered in a cross cut, drifting was usually done only in the upstream or uphill direction, which allowed the water to flow down hill into the cross cut, where it would run out, or in the case of having to start with a vertical shaft, a water pump at the surface would pump the water out of the cross cut.

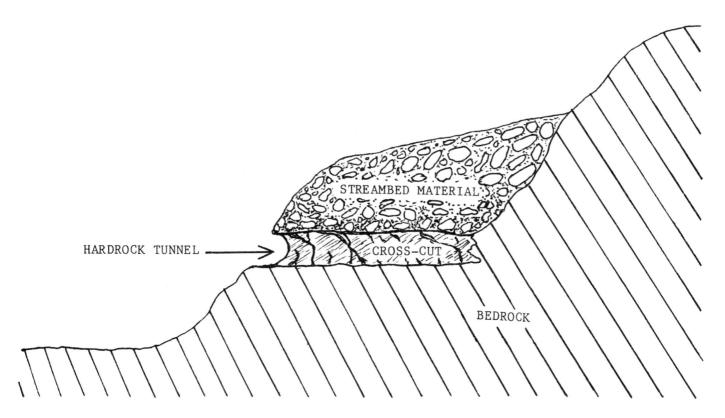

FIG. 11—4. Making the original cross-cut tunnel through the hardrock, just beneath the streambed materials. materials.

When water was not a problem, drifting was usually done in both directions from the cross cut and continued as long as the pay streak did.

Because the pick and shovel method of removing material in a drift mine was rather slow — resulting in a very low volume of material which could be processed during the early days, the material which was being mined had to pay on the average of an ounce in gold to the cubic yard of material. Needless to say, that is some fairly rich placer ground, yet there is evidence of drift mining having occurred all over gold country in the Western United States. So the lower stratums of many of the old streambeds must be indeed rich — at least in many places.

Perhaps today, with the exchange value of gold being what it is, and with the use of a portable type electric or air powered impact hammer, a small drifting operation could move much more material than was possible during the earlier days, and so could be run at a nice profit.

GLOSSARY

ALLOY: When two or more metals are fused together they form an alloy.

AMALGAM: Mercury (Hg) has a tremendous affinity for gold, silver and many other metals. When mercury is mixed with one or more of these other metals, the resulting mass is called "amalgam."

AMALGAMATION: Is the process of using mercury to separate gold, silver, platinum and or other metals from a larger volume of useless materials. Amalgamation is one of the oldest and most effective processes used by the every day miner to collect the fine particles of gold out of a set of concentrates.

ANCIENT STREAMBEDS: See TERTIARY CHANNELS

ASSAY: An analysis of an ore sample or a gold sample to determine the proportions of gold, silver, platinum and or other valuable metals to the amount of waste material included in the sample.

BASADA: A desert eluvial deposit.

BAKED POTATO RETORTING: A method of separating the mercury from the gold or other metals that have been collected during an amalgamation process, in which an uncooked potato is used to save most of the mercury during separation. See chapter 7 for details.

BATEA: One of the earliest types of gold pans, made of wood and used a great deal amongst the Indians of the Western United States. The Spaniards still use them.

BAR: Deposits of sand, rocks, gravel and sometimes gold, located in streambeds where the force of water lets up, such as at the inside of the curves where the stream or river changes direction.

BEDROCK: The solid rock surface which underlies the sediments in a streambed. Also known as the earth's outer crust or "country rock."

BENCHES: Also known as "terrace placers." Sections of old streambed which have been left high and dry by the present stream of water are referred to as "benches." Many benches still contain large paying quantities of gold.

BLACK SANDS: Are a mixture of the heaviest (darkest) streambed materials, which tend to collect in any type of recovery system. They are usually composed mostly of minerals of the iron family. Black sands, because of their superior weight over that of most of the other materials in a streambed, are usually also found along with gold in placer deposits.

BLEEDING OFF: Natural erosion of bench gravels into a present stream or river.

BLOCK TYPE RIFFLES: Semi modern type of riffles, which are still being used in many of today's homemade recovery systems to good result. Covered in chapter 5.

BLUE LEAD: Bottom stratum of ancient riverbed gravels were often called the "blue lead," because of their color and the fact that they were "followed" by the early timers wherever they led. The blue lead gravels were often incredibly rich.

BONANZA: A very rich gold deposit — whether it be a lode or placer, is often referred to as a "bonanza."

BULLION: Gold or silver which has been cast into bars or ingots form.

BURNING A PAN: After repeated use, gold pans tend to accumulate a certain amount of grease or oils on them, which can adversely affect gold recovery. These can be removed from a steel pan by heating it over an open fire until it reaches a dull red glow and then by dropping the pan into cool water. See chapter 4 for details.

CARAT: A single unit of weight often used by jewelers to measure gold and precious stones. 24 carats would be pure gold. 12 carats would be 50% gold, and so on.

CEMENTED GRAVEL: Hard packed streambed material, which can be found on top of bedrock or up in a layer above bedrock. Cemented gravels often contain gold in paying quantities, but not always.

CHAMOIS: A thin sheet of soft leather that is used to squeeze amalgam to separate any excess mercury out of it before retorting is begun. Covered in chapter 7.

CINNABAR: A red colored ore from which mercury is extracted.

CLAIM: See MINING CLAIM.

CLAIM JUMPER: Someone who commences mining activities without permission on a section of land in which the mineral rights are legally owned by another.

CLASSIFICATION: The process of screening out the larger sized materials from a body of ore, streambed gravels, or a set of concentrates. Classification is usually done with the use of one or more sizes of mesh screening.

CLASSIFIED MATERIALS: Those materials which have been screened through a certain size of classification screen.

CLASSIFIER: A screening device itself is often referred to as a "classifier." There is a classifier commonly found at the head of most sluice boxes on gold dredges today.

CLASSIFY: See CLASSIFICATION.

CLAY: Sometimes a streambed will contain a layer of clay, which should be thoroughly broken up before being run through a sluice box, or the sticky substance is likely to grab at least some of the gold out of the sluice as it is being washed through.

COUNTRY ROCK: Is the earth's crust and that rock which surrounds a specialized ore body — like a quartz vein.

COARSE GOLD: Has two meanings: 1) Rough and sharp edged pieces of gold that have not yet been pounded smooth by traveling some distance from the original lode. 2) Larger pieces of gold (nuggets), ranging in size from 10 mesh and larger is sometimes referred to as "coarse gold."

COYOTING: Same as DRIFT MINING.

CREVICE: A split, crack, split or open fissure in the bedrock's surface. Those crevices that are located at the bottom of a streambed are likely to trap gold out of the material as it is passed over during a large storm.

CREVICING: The prospecting activity of searching exposed bedrock areas to find and extract gold from the various gold traps. See chapter 11 for details.

CROSS-CUT: Drift mining is usually started with a tunnel that is made at a right angle to the direction which the old dry streambed used to flow, along it's bottom edge. Sampling is done as the tunnel is progressed, in an effort to locate a pay streak. This first tunnel is called a "cross-cut."

CRUST: The outer hard layer of rock which surrounds the earth.

DIKE: A narrow section of igneous rock which extends upwards out of the country rock. Dikes which extend up through the foundation of a streambed can make excellent gold traps. Details in chapter 2.

DIRECTOR: See WATER DIRECTOR.

DREDGE: See SUCTION DREDGE.

DRIFT: In drift mining, once the cross-cut has been made and the outside boundaries of the pay streak have been determined, the tunnel is moved forward and or backwards along the pay streak in order to recover the gold out of the lower stratum. This tunnel is called the "drift."

DRIFT MINING: A method of mining dry bench deposits in which tunnels are made along the lower stratum of material so that the gold can be processed out of those gravels. The lowest gravels in such deposits are usually by far the richest. See chapter 11 for more details on this procedure.

DRY PANNING: A technique of recovering gold with the use of a gold pan without water. Procedure covered thoroughly in chapter 8.

DRY PLACER: Placer deposit of gold, silver or other valuable stones or minerals that are located in a dry area.

DRY WASHER: A piece of gold mining equipment designed to process dry placer materials without the use of water. Such equipment usually employs the use of air currents to separate the lighter worthless materials from the heavier and more valuable minerals.

DUCTILITY: Quality of being able to be pounded flat or drawn out into thin wire-like forms without becoming brittle and breaking up. Gold is a very ductile metal.

DUST: Extremely fine particles of gold are referred to as "gold dust." A good recovery system, being used in some areas will recover a considerable quantity of "dust" — often enough to pay all of the operating expenses, sometimes more. In the earlier days of mining, a pinch of gold dust was worth a dollar. Today, the same pinch is worth about 20-25 dollars.

ELECTRO STATIC CHARGE: Static electricity tends to act as a magnet towards gold and helps to trap the finer sized pieces, and so is used in some of the more sophisticated dry washing machinery.

ELECTRO STATIC CONCENTRATOR: A dry washing plant which employs the use of static electricity to assist in the recovery of the fine particles of gold.

ELECTRUM: Any alloy of gold and silver in which the silver content exceeds 20% is labeled "electrum."

ELUVIAL DEPOSIT: A deposit of gold and other lode materials that have been swept away from the original lode, but have not yet reached a running stream of water.

EXPANDED METAL RIFFLES: The "turned up kind" of expanded metal makes an excellent recovering riffle system as long as too much water force and materials are not directed over it at once. See chapter 5 for details.

FALSE BEDROCK: Sometimes an extremely hard packed layer of sediment in a streambed will act as a "false bedrock," and even give the impression of being the bedrock itself. Placer gold deposits can often be located both above and below such layers.

FANNING: Sweeping light sands out of the bedrock irregularities while crevicing in shallow water.

FINE GOLD: Those particles of gold that are small enough to pass through 40 mesh screen are known as "fine gold."

FINENESS: A system which is used to indicate the purity of a gold sample or specimen. A specimen having a fineness of .900 would be 90% gold. A fineness of .650 would be equivalent to 65% gold, and so on.

FIRE ASSAY: A means of doing an analysis on a sample, in which all of the gold and silver is extracted, then separated, weighed, and measured in proportion to the original sample to determine how much gold and silver is present.

FLAKE GOLD: Flat-like chips of gold — most of which are probably pounded flat and smooth during their travel down along the streambed. Most placer gold is found in flake form.

FLOAT: (Eluvial deposit) Loose pieces of quartz rock or some other kind of gold bearing rock which has traveled down and away from it's original source. Float is usually what is followed by the prospector in his effort to locate a lode deposit. Covered thoroughly in chapter 9.

FLOTATION PROCESS: One method of recovering fine particles of gold with the use of chemicals, that causes the particles of gold to attach themselves to air bubbles and "float" to the surface, where they can be skimmed off, to be refined further.

FLOOD GOLD: That gold which has been washed down in a storm to rest on top of a layer that was deposited at an earlier time. Flood gold is that gold which is resting in a flood layer up off the bedrock.

FLOOD LAYERS: Sometimes a streambed will have different layers of material that were laid down during different storms at different periods of time. Sometimes each separate layer contains it's own gold in varying amounts. These different layers are called "flood layers."

FLOUR GOLD: Same as GOLD DUST.

FLUME: A man-made water ditch, often made out of wood or by digging a trough into the hillside, for transporting water to mining sights during the earlier days of mining.

FOOLS GOLD: See PYRITES.

FREE MILLING GOLD: Those particles of gold that are not chemically locked in with the other elements in an ore.

GANGUE: The non-valuable rock and waste materials that are associated with the valuable minerals in a lode deposit.

GEIGER COUNTER: An electronic device which is used to detect radio active elements.

GEOLOGICAL MAPS: Specialized maps that show the location of the various geological rock formations within a specified area.

GLORY HOLE: Term used to express an exceptionally rich placer deposit.

GOLD: An exceptionally heavy, ductile, malleable, yellow, precious metal. Covered thoroughly in chapter 1 of this manual.

GOLD CATCH: A location in which gold has been trapped.

GOLD FEVER: An adverse condition that affects some people when they are confronted with riches — either in real or abstract form. See chapter 1 for details.

GOLD NUGGETS: Those pieces of gold that are too large to pass through 10 mesh screen are referred to as "nuggets."

GOLD PAN: One of the earliest devices ever developed to help separate particles of gold from the worthless materials contained in a streambed. The gold pan is widely in use today — it's uses and the various techniques covered in chapters 4 and 8 of this volume.

GOLD RUSH: A wild scurry of miners who are hurrying to mine the gold out of a newly found gold bearing location.

GOLD SNIFTER: A small hand operated suction device that is used to extract the gold out of the bottom of crevices and other bedrock irregularities.

GOLD TRAP: Any location where gold has or is likely to become trapped.

GRADIENT: The downward slope of a streambed or a sluicebox.

GRAIN: A term used to label small particles of gold, and also as a unit of weight in the troy system of measurement, in which 24 grains equals 1 pennyweight. One grain also equals 64.8 milligrams.

GRIZZLY: A classification device that is used to prevent boulders and larger sized rocks from being dropped into a sluicebox along with the smaller sized materials.

GROUND SLUICING: An earlier type of sluicing method in which a channel is dug down to the bedrock for water to be passed through. Gold bearing material is then shoveled into the channel where it is washed through by the running water, and the gold becomes trapped in the bedrock irregularities. See chapter 5 for picture and further details.

GRUBSTAKE: The practice of a storekeeper extending credit — or another person putting up money for the purpose of outfitting a prospector and keeping him supplied until he makes a strike. In exchange, that person then receives an agreed upon percentage of the find.

HAIRLINE CRACKS: The minute sized cracks which are located in the bedrock's surface upon the bottom edge of a streambed can sometimes yield a surprising amount of gold.

HARDROCK MINING: Same as LODE MINING.

HEAD OF BOX: The upper end of a sluice box, where the streambed materials are shoveled into.

HEADER BOX: The forward most section of the sluicebox upon most suction gold dredges today is designed to slow the materials down and spread them out evenly over a classifier as they enter. This upper section is referred to as the "header box." Pictures and further details contained in chapter 6.

HEMATITE: An iron ore (Fe_2O_3) which is of a reddish brown color. Hematite is one of the main non-magnetic minerals that comprises black sand concentrates.

HIGH-GRADE: The richer ore samples of a lode mine, usually those that show a significant amount of visible gold.

HIGHGRADING: Is when a person is stealing the higher-grade ore samples or gold specimens from the mining operation — whether that person is an employee, a partner or an outsider. Highgrading has been a problem since the earliest days of gold mining.

HOOKA AIR SYSTEM: Air breathing system used on most gold dredges, in which the air is pumped down to the divers through an extended air line.

HOT SPOT: Any location that contains acceptable paying quantities of gold or other valuable minerals.

HUNGARIAN RIFFLES: Modern day concentrating type riffles which are commonly found in many of todays dredge and sluice boxes. Details covered in chapter 5.

HYDRAULIC CONCENTRATOR: A very efficient sluicing device which can be used effectively as either a production or sampling machine. The hydraulic concentrator has a very wide range of variety in it's ability to process streambed material, and is an excellent piece of placering equipment for the one or two man sized operation. Details in chapters 5 and 11.

HUDRAULIC MINING: A method of gold mining in which a large volume of water is directed at gold bearing streambed so that its materials can be washed down through sluice boxes, where the gold can be recovered.

IMPURITIES: Very seldom does natural gold come in 100% pure form. Usually in it's natural form, gold is alloyed with various other metals — including silver, copper and platinum. These other metals are known as impurities, simply because they subtract from the purity of the gold itself. Also, sometimes the small amount of waste materials that are contained in a final set of concentrates are referred to as "impurities."

INTERFERENCE: When prospecting with the use of a metal/mineral detector (electronics), sometimes the magnetic black sands are enough in evidence that they will block out any reading that a metallic object would give if it were present. This is called "interference."

IRIDIUM: Is one of the metals from the platinum group. Iridium has a specific gravity of 22.6 as opposed to gold's specific gravity of 19.3, so it's heavier substance.

IRON PYRITES: (Fools gold) Iron pyrites are the glittery, brassy yellow colored compounds that are often mistaken to be gold by beginning gold miners.

JET: Is that component on a suction dredge that water is pumped into, and which creates a suction up through the suction hose. The jet is designed so that streambed material can be pumped directly to the recovery system without having to be run through the water pump. Details covered in chapter 6.

LOCKED IN VALUES: Valuable minerals (gold) which are chemically locked in with other elements within an ore, requiring more involved methods of processing so that the values can be released and recovered.

LODE: Veins that contain valuable minerals are referred to as "lodes." Gold, in hardrock form, (lode) is commonly associated with quartz veins that protrude through the general country rock which makes up the earth's crust. Lodes are the original source of placer gold deposits.

LOW-GRADE: Ore deposits which contain valuable minerals, but not enough of them that they can be mined at a profit, unless mined by a very large scale of operation.

LUTE: Is a sealing compound that is used around the upper edge of the gold chamber on a retort to prevent any leakage of mercury vapors during the retorting process. See chapter 7 for full details.

MAGMA: Molten material which lies beneath the earths outer crust.

MAGNETITE: Fe_3O_4 The heavy black sands (iron) that are found in the heavy concentrates that are collected in a recovery system. Magnetite is what the BFO type metal/mineral detectors sound out on when turned in on the "mineral" setting.

MALLEABLE: That quality of being able to be hammered or extended into various shapes and forms without being broken in the process.

MATERIAL: "Material" is a term that is used to indicate all of the rocks, sand, gravel, mud, clay and silt which makes up a streambed.

MERCURY: ("Quick silver") A heavy, silvery colored, liquid type of metal which has a tremendous affinity for gold, silver and many other metals. Mercury is often used amongst gold miners to collect the fine gold values out of a set of heavy concentrates that have been taken from a recovery system. The procedure is called "amalgamation," and is covered thoroughly in chapter 7.

MESH: Signifies the number of openings that are contained in a lineal inch of screening. For example, 10 mesh screen will have 10 openings per lineal inch and 100 openings per square inch.

METALIC: (Electronic detecting) A metalic target consists of an object which conducts electricity "metalic" and "mineral" are the two main settings on a BFO type metal detector. Details in chapter 10.

MILLING: The process of crushing or pounding an ore down into a very fine powder so that the valuable minerals can be released — to be recovered by a later mechanical or chemical process.

MINERALIZATION: Is the condition of an ore or streambed material having a high degree of minerals present in the rock or the material. In electronic prospecting, "mineralization" specifically means the presence of magnetite (Fe_3o_4). In lode mining, a high degree of mineralization is often a good index of the presence of gold in some amount. In placer mining, a large amount of mineralization (heavy black sands) in a specific location is an indication of where a gold deposit might be found if it traveled through that area.

MINERAL: Any natural, non-living substance that is mined out of the earth can be classified as a "mineral." Gold, silver and platinum are all metal minerals. Also, (electronic prospecting) magnetic black sands sound out on a metal/mineral detector when it is tuned in on the "mineral" setting.

MINING: The entire process of extracting and processing the valuable minerals out of raw ore or sedimentry material.

MINING CLAIM: A section of land on which the mineral rights have been legally "claimed" for a certain period of time by an individual or group so that the gold or other valuable minerals can be mined without interference from other private parties.

MOSS: A class of small green or brown plants that grow in very close association with one another, forming clumps of carpet-like growth; which thrives in moist areas — as on the banks of rivers and streams. Moss has a tendency to trap large amounts of fine particles of gold.

MOSSING: A gold mining activity in which the moss along a stream of water is collected and thoroughly broken up in a container from which the contents are then panned in order to recover the gold. Full procedure covered in chapter 11.

NATURAL RIFFLES: The natural bedrock foundation of a riverbed contains numerous different kinds of irregularities which act as gold traps. These can be small — such as a crack or crevice, or can be a major change in the bedrock's slope or shape.

NITRIC ACID: A clear, fuming, highly corrosive liquid, that is often used to clean gold of various impurities.

NUGGET: See GOLD NUGGET.

OLD CHANNEL: ("Ancient streambed") See TERTIARY CHANNELS.

ORE: Any deposit of rock from which a valuable mineral/metal can be profitably extracted.

ORE BODY: Same as LODE.

OUTCROPPING: That end of a lode which extends outward from within the earth and is exposed to view, is called an "outcropping".

OVERBURDEN: Is the lower-grade streambed material that lies on top of a placer paystreak. Usually, the overburden must be removed first, before processing of the paystreak is possible.

PAN: See GOLD PAN.

PANNING: A method of separating the gold out of streambed materials with a gold pan. Procedures covered in Chapter 4 and 8.

PAY: How much gold that a lode or streambed is yielding to a mining activity, is often expressed as to how much that it is "paying."

PAY DIRT: Streambed material which contains acceptable paying quantities of gold values is sometimes called "pay dirt."

PAYSTREAK: See STREAK

PENNYWEIGHT: A unit of the troy system of weight measurement. One pennyweight equals 24 grains, or a twentieth of a troy ounce.

PLACER DEPOSIT: Free gold that has eroded away from its original lode, and which has been swept into a stream of running water, will tend to accumulate in certain common locations. These accumulations are called "placer deposit" (Thoroughly covered in Chapters 2 and 3 of this volume).

PLATINUM: Is a family of 6 rare and valuable metals which are usually silvery white in color. Because platinum is sometimes recovered along with gold, it's well for the placer miner to know what it looks like, so that he does not discard it along with the waste materials from his recovery system.

PLAYED-OUT: All gold deposits — whether placer or lode, will run out sooner or later. When all of the known about paying quantities of gold or other valuable minerals have been mined out of such a lode, it is said to have "played-out."

PLEISTOCENE CHANNELS: The remnants of the earliest river and stream channels that started during the present Quaternary geological time period. Many of these earlier streambeds are in evidence today — left high and dry, and sometimes quite some distance away from the present streams and rivers. Many of the pleistocene channels (benches) remain untouched by earlier mining activities, and still contain large and consistently paying gold deposits.

PLUGGER POLE: A long thin rod — made of metal or PVC piping, that is used to tap the plug-ups out of the jet on a dredge, from the surface, when they occur.

POKE: A miner's container of gold. In the earlier days of mining, a small leather bag was often used to hold a miner's collection (poke) of gold. Today, plastic and glass jars are most commonly used for this.

POLE RIFFLES: An early form of riffle system, in which round poles — usually made out of wood, were laid close together in either a lengthwise or crosswise direction in the sluice box for the purpose of trapping the gold. Pictures and further details in chapter 5.

POTATO RETORTING: See BAKED POTATO RETORTING.

POT HOLE: Holes or cavaties in the bedrock surface which act as gold traps. Some pot holes trap gold well and some do not, depending on the nature of the hole and the water action which flows over top of them. Details in chapter 2.

PRIMER: That device on a suction dredge which connects the water pump to the water, which is also designed to be manually filled with water, so that the pump can be easily primed from the surface. See figure 6-3 for picture.

PROSPECTING: The activity of attempting to find a deposit of gold or some other valuable mineral. Prospecting usually involves lots of moving around and taking numerous samples until an acceptable deposit is located — at which time mining activities can begin.

PUNCHING HOLES: See SAMPLING.

PYRITES: See IRON PYRITES.

QUARTZ: Consists mainly of silica — which had a tendency to trap gold and the other heavy minerals as they were pushed upward through cracks and fissures by the superheated steam from the earths molten interior, millions of years ago. The vast majority of hardrock gold mining has been directed at quartz veins — which protrude through the general country rock that forms the earths crust.

QUATERNARY PERIOD: Is the present geological time period that started about 2 million years ago, and came just after the Tertiary time period — both periods, which belong to the "Cenozoic era." (geological time) The Quaternary period breaks down into two separate epochs — the "Pleistocene," which was the first, and the "Recent," which is the present epoch.

QUICK SILVER: See MERCURY.

RAW ORE: Ore as it comes directly out of a lode.

RAIL RIFFLES: A semi-primative early development in riffle systems, in which railroad irons were used right side up, upside down, lengthwise, and in crosswide driections in sluice boxes. NOTE: Rail riffles are still widely used amongst some of the medium sized surface bench operations that are operating in the Yukon during the time of this writing. See figure 5-6 for picture.

READ: (Electronic detecting.) When a metal/mineral detector sounds out on a target, or indicates it's presence in some other way, it is sometimes referred to as a "read" on the detector.

RECENT BENCHES: Those high and dry streambed gravels that have been formed since the passing of the Pleistocene epoch. (Within the past 11,000 years.)

RECOVERY: The ability to trap gold values out of streambed material or out of an ore material. Also, the ability to separate the gold values from a set of concentrated material which was taken from a recovery system — often done with the use of mercury, see AMALGAMATION.

RECOVERY SYSTEM: Is that component part, or set of components, designed to recover the gold or other valuable minerals out of the material that is being processed. In placer mining, the recovery system usually consists of a sluicing device and/or a gold pan. In hardrock mining the recovery system can consist of any number of machines — such as a vibrating concentrating table, or chemical vats or amalgam plants, or any combination of these and others.

RESIDUAL DEPOSIT: Is a deposit of gold and float that has dropped from its original lode, but has not yet been swept away by the various forces of nature.

RETORT: Is a device that is used to separate mercury from gold or other metals once the amalgamation process has been completed. A retort saves the mercury so that it can be used once again in later amalgamation processes.

RICH: Streambed material — or a lode, which contains acceptable paying quantities of gold — or better, is often said to be "rich."

RIFFLES: Are the various types of baffles and obstructions that lie at the bottom edge of any sluicing device for the purpose of trapping the gold out of the materials which are washed through. There are many different kinds of riffles, including hungarian type, right angle type, expanded metal type, block, zig zag, rail, pole, stone riffles, and many more — covered in chapter 5.

RIGHT ANGLE RIFFLES: Are usually made of 90 degree angle iron, always pointed in a downstream direction, and sometimes tilted forward slightly to obtain the best result. These are concentrating type rifles which have tremendous strength. See figures 5-9 and 5-10 for pictures and further details.

SALTING: Introducing gold from an outside source to a gold mine — either placer or hardrock, to make it appear to be richer than it actually is. Another form of salting is to take only the highest-grade ore samples for assay, leaving the lesser-grade samples that make up the bulk of the ore body. This will make a mine appear to be richer than it actually is, and is misleading to any prospective buyers, investors or grubstakers.

SAMPLING: Basically consists of exploratory testing in an effort to locate acceptable paying ground prior to starting a production mining operation. This is usually done by digging sample holes in the likely spots to find gold deposits, should they be present within that general area. The material from each sample hole is tested to check the gold content. The prospector continues to make sample holes until a sufficient pay streak or deposit is located, at which time mining activities are begun with the intention of recovering the gold out of the deposit. Full procedures covered in chapter 11.

SCUBA: Self Contained Underwater Breathing Apparatus (scuba tanks, etc.) was used during the earlier days of suction dredging but has since yielded to the hooka air breathing systems — which are more efficient for todays dredging activities.

SEDIMENTS: Earth, rocks and other materials that have been deposited by gravity, wind, water, ice and the other forces of nature.

SHORING: Reinforcing the walls and ceiling of a tunnel with the use of wood beams to help prevent cave-ins.

SILVER: A shiny metalic element that is usually found in close association with gold to some degree. Silver is also considered to be a precious metal and is superior to any other metal in it's ability to conduct electricity and heat.

SLOPE: Is a term which is commonly used to express the downward gradient of a sluice box or streambed.

SLUICE BOX: Is a trough-like device that water and streambed materials are washed through, which also has a series of baffles or obstructions (riffles) lying along its bottom edge for the purpose of trapping the gold out of the material as it passes through. See chapter 5 for complete description, plus pictures.

SLUICING: The activity of shoveling or directing streambed material into and through a sluice box in order to recover the gold out of the material. Sluicing can be done on any scale — from one man shoveling into a small sluice, to a large scale of heavy earth moving type of operation.

SNIPING: See SAMPLING.

SPARK ARRESTOR: Is a device that attaches to the muffler on an internal combustion engine. It prevents any sparks from being emitted that could possibly start a fire. Spark arrestors are required when operating any gasoline engine powered mining equipment inside the National Forests of California, and in other states.

SPECIFIC GRAVITY: Is the ratio of the weight of a volume or mass of any substance, as compared to the weight of an equal volume of water. The specific gravity of gold is 19.3, which means that any sized mass of pure gold will be found to weigh 19.3 times as much as an equal volume of pure water.

SPECIMEN GOLD: Larger sized pieces of gold, having individualistic characteristics are classified as "specimen gold," and will generally bring in a larger monetary exchange than an equal weight of fine sized gold.

SPREADER: See WATER SPREADER.

STREAK: Often a deposit of gold will follow a narrow path down a streambed. This usually occurs where there has been some kind of major change in the flow of water in the streambed — such as towards the inside of a bend, or where there is a major change in slope. Streaks (or "stringers") almost always are found to have specific boundaries — which if you stay to the inside of them, you will be into gold and if you move to the outside, you will no longer get paid as well — if at all.

STRIKE: A term that is used to express when a deposit of gold is found. Good strikes are made usually after a thorough sampling activity has been done.

STRINGER: See STREAK.

SUCTION DREDGE: Machine designed to suck up submerged streambed materials and wash them through a floating or suspended sluice box at/or from the water's surface. The gold rush of the 80's is largely due to suction dredges, because they can process so much more material with far less effort than most other methods of gold mining. Details and pictures contained in chapter 6.

TAILINGS: Once the streambed or hardrock materials have been processed for their valuable mineral content, they are discarded as waste material and referred to as "tailings."

TARGET: Any object or material that causes a metal/mineral detector to sound out is referred to as a "target."

TERRACE DEPOSIT: See BENCHES.

TERTIARY CHANNELS: (Ancient rivers.) Are the old dried up rivers that ran in a southerly direction during the Tertiary time period — that geological time period which went prior to our present Quaternary period and which ended about 2 million years ago. It was during the Tertiary period that most of the extremely rich surface lodes were eroded and their gold was washed down into these ancient rivers. Much of the gold in todays river system was once washed out of the Tertiary channels at an earlier time.

TOPOGRAPHICAL MAP: A specialized map that shows the positions of streams, rivers, mountains and hills of a given area, and the general lay of the land and its various natural objects along with their relative elevations above or below sea level. See figures 3-5 and 3-6 for examples.

TRIBUTARY: A smaller sized stream of water that flows into and contributes to a larger stream of water.

TRIPLE SLUICE DREDGES: Are one of the latest developments in dredging equipment, providing the best recovery that is presently available on those dredges that employ the use of hydraulic type of recovery systems. Pictures and further details covered in chapters 5 and 6.

TROY WEIGHT: Is a system of weight measurements that is commonly used amongst miners and gold dealers.

$$24 \text{ grains} \ldots \ldots \ldots = 1 \text{ penny weight}$$
$$20 \text{ penny weight} \ldots \ldots = 1 \text{ troy ounce}$$
$$12 \text{ troy ounces} \ldots \ldots = 1 \text{ troy pound}$$

See the conversation chart at the back of this book for conversions to the gram system of measurement.

VALUES: Those minerals that are contained in an ore body or in streambed materials that are of value to the prospector or miner.

VEIN: A hardrock deposit of ore or rock that is dissimilar to the surrounding country rock, which more or less, has a uniform development as to its length, width, and depth.

WATER DIRECTOR: Is a "do it yourself" water barrier that is set up in a streambed to direct more water through a sluice box.

WATER SPREADER: Is a "do it yourself" device that is used to spread out water evenly as it enters a sluice box, when being pumped from an exterior source through a hose or water pipe.

WET PLACER: A placer deposit that is located beneath the water's surface.

WINNOWING: An old — but effective, method of mining or prospecting dry placer material by which the material is tossed up into the air with the use of a wool blanket. The process is best done when there is a slight wind to help blow off the lighter waste materials. Procedure and picture covered in chapter 8.

WIRE GOLD: Gold that is thinly dispersed through it's hardrock matrix — taking on the form of thin wire.

ZIG-ZAG RIFFLES: An earlier type of riffle system in which block type riffles were made to extend part way across the sluice box and alternately placed down it's length to cause the water and material to flow around the riffles instead of over the top. Picture shown in figure 5-6.

MINERS REFERRAL

Miners Referal is a business whose purpose is to bridge the various communication gaps amongst the mining profession.

Our purpose is to bridge the communication gap between individual miners and the various proven mining locations, gold buyers, equipment dealers, and the claim owners who wish to sell or lease their claims or make them available on some other type of deals. We also have other types of specialized information: such as the availability of claim brokers, investors, mining consultants, legal assistance, mining groups, mining related government offices, and jobs available or wanted in any specific or general area. All of our data is now on computer and is indexed by STATE and COUNTY.

When requesting information -- or giving us information -- about any specific or general area, please remember to include the STATE and the COUNTIES which are involved. In Alaska, since there are no counties, please include the DISTRICTS involved or the nearest towns. We will be of much more help to you if you do so.

When requesting a referral, we ask that you send us a self-addressed, stamped envelope and $10 for each specific referral that you ask of us. A specific referral is defined as the standard data for one STATE and COUNTY. Our standard referral response is to send you the information we have listed in that COUNTY on claims for sale, claims for lease, claims available on some other type of deal -- like percentage basis or joint venture. We also send you a list of gold buyers and mining equipment shops for that specific COUNTY, and we conclude with a list of the adjoining COUNTIES (in the main Western States) and tell you how many claims that we have on file in each of them.

If you want a referral on other specialized information, we ask that you send us a self-addressed, stamped envelope and $10 for each specialized referral that you ask of us. It is necessary for you to tell us what type of information that you want, and also what area that you want the information for. Specialized information is listed in the paragraph above. All of it is indexed by COUNTY, and also by STATE or any portion of a STATE -- meaning North, South, East, West or Central. For example: "Please give me a list of mining related government offices in Northern California." Or: "Give me a list of the investors who are interested in mining ventures in Oregon."

Our standard referral information is also listed by different categories, such as: lode, placer, bench, dredging, dry placer. It is also sorted so that we can tell you if the property is for sale, lease, available on percentage deal or joint venture. So there are other ways that you can ask for specialized referrals. For example: "Please give me a list of all lode claims available for sale in Northern California." Or: "Give me a list of all dredging claims available on a percentage basis in Southern Oregon."

Now that we are on computer, the different ways in which you can request information are limited only by your own imagination. Just look over the different sorts and categories of data and decide what you want to know for the area of your choice. We do require that you be reasonable, however. Do not request too broad of a data category for too broad of an area. For example, "Give me a list of all claims available for sale and lease in the State of California," is an unreasonable request; it would take a book to print this information out! Specialized requests should be limited to one category of information for one specific or generalized area. For example: "Give me a list of all bench-type placer claims available for sale in Northern California."

We guarantee only to give you the information that we have on file. It may, or it may not, be of value to you. We are constantly expanding our data so that we can provide more and better service to you. If we do not have helpful information for you today, you should try us again in a few months; because we are continously pouring a steady flow of new data into out files.

We also urge you to feed us information about any of the specific areas that you have had experience in -- especially the areas that we have referred you to. This is one of the ways that we are able to correct and improve our information so as to give you more accurate referrals. We list our data exactly as it is given to us; you are the ones who go and check it out. Let us know how it goes! Information about the various gold buyers and other specialized categories is extremely valuable to us; send it in!

Miners Referral is not responsible for any actions or disputes which may occur between the miner, claim owner, investor, or claim broker, etc. We are simply a referral service; we get people together. What they do once they connect up is their business and responsibility. However, we do want to hear of any problem you have with someone we have referred you to. If we receive repeated reports of unethical dealings by any single miner, claim owner, investor or broker, etc., we will take that person out of our files. This is in an effort to provide the best possible service to our clients.

If you have claims for sale, lease or want to make them available to others on some other type of deal, and if you want us to list the information in our files; or if you buy gold, have an equipment shop, if you are an investor, mining consultant, or if you want data listed under any of the other special categories, write us and we will send you a form to fill out so that we can get complete data into our files.

MINERS REFERAL
P.O. Box 1932
Weaverville, CA 96093

FEEL FREE TO WRITE THE AUTHOR

I am very interesting in hearing from you regarding this book, mining in general, or about anything else that you would like to communicate.

Once in a while, I teach classes or have some other activity going -- which I will let you know about, if you write and let me know you are interested.

Sometimes, I also do consulting work -- or joint ventures. Let me know if I can be of assistance.

All mail sent to the below address will be received by me, and answered by me directly.

Dave McCracken
P.O. Box 702
Big Bar, CA 96010

WEIGHT CONVERSION TABLE

1 Troy Pound . . . .= 12 Troy Ounces . . . .= 373.241 Grams

1 Troy Ounce . . . .= 20 Pennyweight . . . .= 31.104 Grams

1 Pennyweight . . . .= 24 Grains . . . . . .= 1.552 Grams

1 Grain . . . .= 64.8 Milligrams